# THIS UNIQUE BOOK

*has been designed to reward the casual reader and the language student alike.*

*When you open it, your eye will light upon two different languages. On the left-hand page you will find the authentic German text of a great short story by a representative master of the literature; on the right you will read a faithful English translation, so designed that each paragraph of the German text faces its English rendition.*

*Readers fascinated by the short story in general will find here many interesting and exciting examples. For those who wish to study the development of the form in German, the stories are arranged chronologically, so that the growth of the art may be followed, as well as enjoyed. Those who wish to practice German will find an excellent, working German-English vocabulary, and valuable notes on background material and unusual idioms.*

*learn the literature through the language, the language through the literature*

**Bantam Dual-Language Books**

# GERMAN STORIES | DEUTSCHE
# STORIES | NOVELLEN
## A BANTAM DUAL-LANGUAGE BOOK

Stories in the Original German

Edited by
**Harry Steinhauer**
**Antioch College**

With translations, critical introductions,
notes and vocabulary
by the Editor

Published by Bantam Books, Inc.

GERMAN STORIES

A BANTAM DUAL-LANGUAGE BOOK
*published January 1961*
*2nd printing.....November 1961*
*3rd printing........October 1962*
*4th printing........August 1964*
*5th printing*
*6th printing*
*7th printing*
*8th printing*
*9th printing*

*"Ein Landarzt" by Franz Kafka. Reprinted from* ERZAEHLUNGEN, *by Franz Kafka, by permission of Schocken Books, Inc. Copyright, 1935, by Schocken Verlag, Berlin. Copyright, 1946, by Schocken Books, Inc., New York.*

*"Schwere Stunde" by Thomas Mann. By permission of Frau Thomas Mann. All rights reserved. The translation of "Schwere Stunde," by Thomas Mann, which appears in this volume was specially prepared by Professor Steinhauer for use only in* GERMAN STORIES: A BANTAM DUAL-LANGUAGE BOOK. *It appears with the permission of Alfred A. Knopf, Inc., publishers of the volume* STORIES OF THREE DECADES, *by Thomas Mann, in which the authorized English translation by H. T. Lowe-Porter may be found.*

*"Seegeister" by Ilse Aichinger. From:* DER GEFESSELTE © *1953 by S. Fischer Verlag. English translation by permission of Noonday Press and Joan Daves on behalf of S. Fischer Verlag.*

*"Die drei dunklen Könige" by Wolfgang Borchert. Permission granted through Sanford Jerome Greenburger on behalf of Rowohlt Verlag. English translation, by permission of Sanford Jerome Greenburger on behalf of Rowohlt Verlag. The translation of "Die drei dunklen Könige," by Wolfgang Borchert, which appears in this volume was specially prepared by Professor Steinhauer for use only in* GERMAN STORIES: A BANTAM DUAL-LANGUAGE BOOK. *It appears with the permission of New Directions, publisher of the volume* THE MAN OUTSIDE: THE COMPLETE PROSE WORKS OF WOLFGANG BORCHERT, *with an introduction by Stephen Spender, in which the authorized translation by David Porter may be found.*

*"Der blinde Geronimo und sein Bruder" by Arthur Schnitzler. Copyright, 1905, by S. Fischer Verlag. Permission granted through Franz J. Horch Associates on behalf of S. Fischer Verlag and Henry Schnitzler. English translation by permission of Franz J. Horch Associates on behalf of Henry Schnitzler.*

*"Der Dichter," by Hermann Hesse. From Hermann Hesse,* MAERCHEN, *copyright, 1955, by Suhrkamp Verlag, Berlin. All rights reserved.*

# CONTENTS

For those who are interested in this book for language study, it is suggested that the stories be read in the following order of difficulty: Hesse, Schnitzler, Goethe, Aichinger, Stifter, Kafka, Borchert, Keller, Hoffmann, Mann.

# Foreword

THE TWO literary genres in which the Germans have achieved special distinction are the lyric and the novella. In the latter field they are latecomers; German literature has no Boccaccio, no Chaucer, no Cervantes, no Marguerite de Navarre. The *exempla* of the Middle Ages, the *Kalendergeschichten* and other collections of shorter fiction are not self-conscious art in the sense that the work of the above-mentioned writers is. But, just as Germany's political development in modern times was late but rapid, so the artistic novella sprang into being suddenly and almost immediately attained great heights of excellence. The most distinguished writers of German novellas in the nineteenth and twentieth centuries are Goethe, Kleist, Tieck, Hoffmann, Stifter, Storm, Keller, Meyer, Raabe, Hauptmann, Schnitzler, Hermann Hesse, Thomas Mann, Paul Ernst, Wilhelm Schäfer, Ricarda Huch, Hans Franck, Kafka, Werner Bergengruen; and this catalogue is anything but exhaustive.

It is an irony of history that Goethe, who was the least pedantic of men, should have given rise to a tradition of pedantic criticism centered about the nature and scope of the novella. In the framework to his own collection of tales *Unterhaltungen deutscher Ausgewanderter* (Conversations of German Émigrés), the characteristics of the novella are formulated and developed. The brothers Schlegel continued the speculation on this subject; they were followed by Tieck, Mundt, Laube, Spielhagen, Heyse and the numerous lesser lights who have multiplied distinctions and invented critical straitjackets for the genre.

We are told that the novella must have an "unheard-of event"; it must have one or more "turning points," a "silhouette," a "falcon." It cannot show development of character; it cannot even deal with character. It must confine itself to one event. It must be realistic; it must not be realistic. When we arrive at Johannes Klein's recent monumental study of the German novella, we find the most ingenious differentiations between the novella, tale, narrative, fairy tale, sketch, anecdote, short story. But how much of this theorizing is justified by what writers of undisputed merit create? For instance, one of the most palatable generalizations made about the novella—and it has been made over and over again—is that it must confine itself to one central event. Yet this is patently not so. Flaubert's

famous novella *Un Coeur simple* describes a whole life, not a single event; so does Stifter's *Abdias*, Thomas Mann's *Tonio Kröger*, Henry James' *Daisy Miller*; so does Heinrich Mann's eight-page short story *Der Sohn*. The novella is too short to deal adequately with character? Isn't Kleist's *Anekdote aus dem Preußischen Kriege* a superb character study on one page? The polemic could be carried on at length.

Historically, the development of shorter fiction conforms broadly to the development of European literature in general, from classicism to romanticism, to realism, to naturalism, to symbolism (called neoromanticism in Germany), to expressionism and back to neo-realism. And the genre becomes more artistic all the time. That is, writers become more conscious of formal matters. The air of negligence and carelessness that pervades earlier storytelling yields to the creation of subtle atmosphere and deliberate effects. The dramatic power of Kleist's work cannot conceal a certain amount of carelessness in craftsmanship; later writers of much smaller stature learn to form more tautly, with far greater virtuosity.

The stories which make up this collection were chosen primarily to help students of German learn German. Accordingly, the basic principle of selection was linguistic ease or rather a gradation from the very easy to the more difficult. But the Bantam slogan of learning "literature through language and language through literature" introduced a second criterion for inclusion in the book: literary excellence. It is hoped that this ideal has been realized both in the authors represented and in the selection made from their writings.

But from the outset still another principle of selection was present in the editor's mind: to provide a *representative* collection of novellas. Those who are interested in making a study of shorter German fiction as a genre will discover that every major current is represented in this collection. It is perhaps worth pointing out, too, that the term "German" is used in its wider cultural sense to include Austrian, Swiss and German-Czech writers.

The translations have been made as literal as was consonant with smooth, readable English; for it was felt that, if the translations were to help the reader to interpret the German texts, they must not depart too far from the structure of the original. For this reason, there is no story in the book by Heinrich von Kleist, the greatest German master in the genre. Kleist's intricate sentences cannot be rendered into twentieth-century English without breaking them up into three or four shorter sentences and changing the sequence of his statements. This would have defeated the purpose of the book.

A word of thanks must be registered here to Mr. Donald Reis of Bantam Books for being an ideal editor.

HARRY STEINHAUER

# German Stories

# Johann Wolfgang von Goethe

## (1749–1832)

It is futile to attempt an introductory note on Goethe in the space of a page or two. The mere chronology of the principal events of his life would burst the limits at our disposal. It is therefore preferable to assume that the reader will go to an encyclopedia and read about Goethe there, and to devote this page to a note on Goethe's relation to the German novella.

Goethe is usually regarded as the founder of this genre in German literature. Not that there was a dearth of shorter fiction in German letters before him; but such writing was not counted as serious art—it was thought of as mere entertainment. Goethe was the first writer in Germany to recognize that prose fiction could and should be created according to the laws of good taste. In 1793 he adapted one of the stories from the anonymous French collection *Cent Nouvelles nouvelles* and offered it to Schiller for his periodical *Die Horen,* where it ultimately appeared. This is our tale of the virtuous attorney. He went on to adapt further tales, and to create others from his own imagination. Taking his cue from Boccaccio, he framed these stories in a social setting which gave them an outer unity and allowed him to interject a running commentary on the theme of each story and on the nature of the novella as a literary genre. The whole collection appeared in 1795 under the title *Unterhaltungen deutscher Ausgewanderten* (Conversations of German Émigrés).

No two of these novellas are alike, and one is tempted to say that the body of Goethe's work in this genre anticipates

the main development in shorter German fiction that was to take place in the next century. The story of the virtuous attorney may be described as the earliest form of fiction: the moral tale or apologue which we find in antiquity in the fables of Aesop and others, in the parables of the Bible, the haggada of the Talmud and in the medieval *exempla*. But in the same collection Goethe included psychological and sociological tales, and a purely romantic fairy tale which he called *Das Märchen*, but which is really an allegory. His later novellas, incorporated into the novels *Wilhelm Meister* and *Die Wahlverwandtschaften* (The Elective Affinities), are also varied in type, with perhaps a predilection for the moral tale.

The later Goethe was a "classicist"; that is, he abandoned his early impulse to freedom in content and form for the classical aesthetic principle of limitation and control. The story of the virtuous attorney is a typical example of "classicism." The material with which Goethe worked was not of his invention although he did transform the material of his source. The characters in the story are so little individualized that they have no names. The interest in psychology is definitely subordinated to that of theme, in accordance with the hierarchy of values laid down in Aristotle's *Poetics*. Nor is there any concern for local color, milieu or the sociological factors governing the behavior of the principals in the action. In fact, so intently is Goethe's gaze fixed on the main business at hand—which is the moral lesson the young woman learns—that he makes no use of the difference in age between husband and wife as a motive for explaining her behavior. The structure of the plot is equally simple. There is no playing with artistry, no subtle imagery, no hidden symbolism, such as the literature of the novella was to develop later, and which Goethe himself used in other stories. The tone or atmosphere is serious, without being solemn; it might easily have been infected with the scurrility which prevails in Goethe's source *Cent Nouvelles nouvelles*.

For anyone interested in studying the development of the German novella as an art form, Goethe's tale of the virtuous attorney is an excellent starting point.

# DER PROKURATOR

## von Johann Wolfgang von Goethe

IN EINER italienischen Seestadt lebte vorzeiten ein Handelsmann, der sich von Jugend auf durch Tätigkeit und Klugheit
auszeichnete. Er war dabei ein guter Seemann und hatte
große Reichtümer erworben, indem [1] er selbst nach Alexandria [2] zu schiffen, kostbare Waren zu erkaufen oder ein-
zutauschen pflegte, die er alsdann zu Hause wieder abzusetzen
oder in die nördlichen Gegenden Europas zu versenden
wußte.[3] Sein Vermögen wuchs von Jahr zu Jahr um so mehr,[4]
als er in seiner Geschäftigkeit selbst das größte Vergnügen
fand und ihm keine Zeit zu kostspieligen Zerstreuungen
übrigblieb.

Bis in sein fünfzigstes Jahr hatte er sich auf diese Weise
emsig fortbeschäftigt und ihm war von den geselligen Ver-
gnügungen wenig bekannt worden, mit welchen ruhige Bürger
ihr Leben zu würzen verstehen; ebensowenig hatte das schöne
Geschlecht, bei allen Vorzügen seiner Landsmänninnen, seine
Aufmerksamkeit weiter erregt, als insofern er ihre Begierde
nach Schmuck und Kostbarkeiten sehr wohl kannte und sie
gelegentlich zu nutzen wußte.

Wie wenig versah er sich daher auf die Veränderung, die in
seinem Gemüte vorgehen sollte, als eines Tages sein reich
beladen [5] Schiff in den Hafen seiner Vaterstadt einlief, eben
an einem jährlichen Feste, das besonders der Kinder wegen [6]
gefeiert wurde. Knaben und Mädchen pflegten nach dem
Gottesdienste in allerlei Verkleidungen sich zu zeigen, bald
in Prozessionen, bald [7] in Scharen durch die Stadt zu scherzen

# THE ATTORNEY
## by Johann Wolfgang von Goethe

A LONG time ago, in an Italian seacoast town, there lived a merchant who had distinguished himself since his youth by industry and prudence. He was at the same time a good seaman and had acquired great wealth by taking trips to Alexandria to buy or exchange precious wares which he was then able to sell at home or to send on to the northern regions of Europe. His fortune increased from year to year, all the more since he found his greatest pleasure in his business and had no time left for costly amusements.

In this way he had busily occupied himself till his fiftieth year and had come to know little of the social pleasures with which sedate citizens manage to spice their lives. Nor had the fair sex, despite all the advantages enjoyed by his country-women, aroused his attention, except insofar as he knew very well its desire for jewelry and precious things and on occasion was able to make use of the knowledge.

How little, then, did he foresee the change that was to occur in his heart when, one day, his richly laden ship landed in the harbor of his native city—on the very day of an annual festival that was celebrated especially for children. Boys and girls showed themselves in all sorts of costumes after church service, sporting through the city now in processions, now in bands, then playing all kinds of games in the field on a

und sodann im Felde auf einem großen freien Platz allerhand
Spiele zu treiben, Kunststücke und Geschicklichkeiten zu
zeigen und in artigem Wettstreit ausgesetzte kleine Preise zu
gewinnen.

Anfangs wohnte unser Seemann dieser Feier mit Vergnügen
bei; als er aber die Lebenslust der Kinder und die Freude der
Eltern daran lange betrachtet und so viele Menschen im
Genuß einer gegenwärtigen Freude und der angenehmsten
aller Hoffnungen gefunden hatte, mußte ihm bei einer Rück-
kehr auf sich selbst sein einsamer Zustand äußerst auffallen.
Sein leeres Haus fing zum erstenmal an, ihm ängstlich zu
werden, und er klagte sich selbst in seinen Gedanken an:

„O ich Unglückseliger! warum gehn mir so spät die Augen
auf? Warum erkenne ich erst im Alter jene Güter, die allein
den Menschen glücklich machen? Soviel Mühe! soviel Gefahren! Was haben sie mir verschafft? Sind gleich [8] meine
Gewölbe voll Waren, meine Kisten voll edler Metalle und
meine Schränke voll Schmuck und Kleinodien, so können
doch diese Güter mein Gemüt weder erheitern noch befriedigen. Je mehr ich sie aufhäufe, desto mehr Gesellen
scheinen sie zu verlangen; ein Kleinod fordert das andere, ein
Goldstück das andere. Sie erkennen mich nicht für den
Hausherrn; sie rufen mir ungestüm zu: ‚Geh und eile, schaffe
noch mehr unsersgleichen herbei! Gold erfreut sich nur des
Goldes, das Kleinod des Kleinodes.‘ So gebieten sie mir schon
die ganze Zeit meines Lebens, und erst spät fühle ich, daß
mir in allem diesem kein Genuß bereitet ist. Leider jetzt, da
die Jahre kommen, fange ich an zu denken und sage zu mir:
‚Du genießest diese Schätze nicht, und niemand wird sie nach
dir genießen! Hast du jemals eine geliebte Frau damit ge-
schmückt? Hast du eine Tochter damit ausgestattet? Hast du
einen Sohn in den Stand gesetzt, sich die Neigung eines
guten Mädchens zu gewinnen und zu befestigen? Niemals!
Von allen deinen Besitztümern hast du, hat niemand der
Deinigen [9] etwas besessen, und was du mühsam zusammenge-
bracht hast, wird nach deinem Tode ein Fremder leichtfertig
verprassen.‘

„O wie anders werden heute abend jene glücklichen Eltern
ihre Kinder um den Tisch versammeln, ihre Geschicklichkeit
preisen und sie zu guten Taten aufmuntern! Welche Lust

large, open square, performing stunts and feats of skill and winning small prizes offered in a friendly competition.

At first our seaman watched this celebration with pleasure. But when he had observed the high spirits of the children and the joy of the parents for a long time, and had found so many people savoring an immediate happiness and the most pleasant of all hopes, he was bound to be struck by his lonely state when he returned to himself. His empty house began, for the first time, to become a source of anxiety to him and he accused himself in his thoughts:

"Oh, unhappy man that I am! Why are my eyes opened so late? Why do I recognize only in my old age those good things which alone make man happy? So much effort! So much danger! What have they brought me? Though my storehouses are full of goods, my chests full of precious metals and my cabinets full of trinkets and jewels, these possessions can neither cheer nor satisfy my spirit. The more I amass them, the more companions they seem to demand; one jewel demands another, one gold coin another. They do not recognize me as master of the house; they call to me impetuously: 'Go and hurry, procure more like us! Gold is only happy with gold, and a jewel with another jewel.' So they have been commanding me all my life, and only of late do I feel that in all this there is no enjoyment for me. Unfortunately only now, when age is approaching, am I beginning to think and say to myself: 'You are not enjoying these treasures and no one will enjoy them after you! Have you ever adorned a beloved woman with them? Have you used them as a trousseau for a daughter? Did you put a son into the position of winning and holding the affection of a good girl? Never! Neither you nor anyone belonging to you has ever possessed any of your possessions, and what you have laboriously brought together a stranger will frivolously squander.'

"Oh, how differently will those happy parents gather their children about the table tonight, praise their skill and encourage them to do good deeds! What pleasure shone from

glänzte aus ihren Augen, und welche Hoffnung schien aus
dem Gegenwärtigen zu entspringen! Solltest du denn aber
selbst gar keine Hoffnung fassen können? Bist du denn schon
ein Greis? Ist es nicht genug, die Versäumnis einzusehen,
jetzt, da noch nicht aller Tage Abend [10] gekommen ist? Nein,
in deinem Alter ist es noch nicht töricht, ans Freien zu
denken, mit deinen Gütern wirst du ein braves Weib erwerben
und glücklich machen, und siehst du [11] noch Kinder in deinem
Hause, so werden dir diese spätern Früchte den größten Genuß
geben, anstatt daß sie oft denen, die sie zu früh vom Himmel
erhalten, zur Last werden und zur Verwirrung gereichen."

Als er durch dieses Selbstgespräch seinen Vorsatz bei sich
befestigt hatte, rief er zwei Schiffsgesellen zu sich und er-
öffnete ihnen seine Gedanken. Sie, die gewohnt waren, in
allen Fällen willig und bereit zu sein, fehlten auch diesmal
nicht und eilten, sich in der Stadt nach den jüngsten und
schönsten Mädchen zu erkundigen; denn ihr Patron, da er
einmal nach dieser Ware lüstern ward,[12] sollte auch die beste
finden und besitzen.

Er selbst feierte so wenig als seine Abgesandten. Er ging,
fragte, sah und hörte und fand bald, was er suchte, in einem
Frauenzimmer,[13] das in diesem Augenblick das schönste der
ganzen Stadt genannt zu werden verdiente, ungefähr sechzehn
Jahr alt, wohlgebildet und gut erzogen, deren Gestalt und
Wesen das Angenehmste zeigte und das Beste versprach.

Nach einer kurzen Unterhandlung, durch welche der vor-
teilhafteste Zustand sowohl bei Lebzeiten als nach dem Tode
des Mannes der Schönen versichert ward, vollzog man die
Heirat mit großer Pracht und Lust, und von diesem Tage
an fühlte sich unser Handelsmann zum erstenmal im wirklichen Besitz und Genuß seiner Reichtümer. Nun verwandte
er mit Freuden die schönsten und reichsten Stoffe zur Be-
kleidung des schönen Körpers, die Juwelen glänzten ganz
anders an der Brust und in den Haaren seiner Geliebten als
ehemals im Schmuckkästchen, und die Ringe erhielten einen
unendlichen Wert von der Hand, die sie trug.

So fühlte er sich nicht allein so reich, sondern reicher als
bisher, indem seine Güter sich durch Teilnehmung und
Anwendung zu vermehren schienen. Auf diese Weise lebte
das Paar fast ein Jahr lang in der größten Zufriedenheit, und

their eyes, and what hope seemed to spring from the present! But can you yourself not grasp at any hope? Are you an old man yet? Is it not enough to realize your neglect, now when the evening of your life has not come yet? No, at your age it is not yet foolish to think of courting; with your property you will acquire a good wife and make her happy; and if you live to see children in your home, these late fruits will afford you the greatest enjoyment, instead of becoming a burden and a source of confusion, as they often do to those who have received them too early from heaven."

When he had confirmed this plan in his own mind through this conversation with himself, he summoned two shipmates and revealed his thoughts to them. They, who were accustomed to be willing and ready in all situations, did not fail this time either but hastened into the city to inquire after the youngest and most beautiful girls; for their employer, having now become covetous of this type of goods, was to find and possess the best.

He himself was no more idle than his emissaries. He went, asked, saw and heard and soon found what he was looking for in a woman who, at this time, deserved to be called the most beautiful in the whole city—about sixteen years old, of fine culture and good upbringing, whose form and whole being revealed the most pleasant prospects and promised the best.

After brief negotiations, by which the most advantageous conditions were secured for the beauty both during the life of her husband and after his death, the marriage was celebrated with great splendor and joy; and from this day on, our merchant for the first time felt that he was really possessing and enjoying his wealth. Now he joyfully employed the most beautiful and richest materials for clothing the beautiful body of his beloved; the jewels glittered very differently on her breast and in her hair than they had formerly done in the jewel box, and the rings received an infinite value from the hand which wore them.

So he felt not only as rich as, but richer than before, inasmuch as his property seemed to increase through sharing and use. In this way the couple lived for almost a year in the greatest contentment, and he seemed to have wholly ex-

er schien seine Liebe zu einem tätigen und herumstreifenden Leben gegen das Gefühl häuslicher Glückseligkeit gänzlich vertauscht zu haben. Aber eine alte Gewohnheit legt sich so leicht nicht ab, und eine Richtung, die wir früh genommen, kann wohl einige Zeit abgelenkt, aber nie ganz unterbrochen werden.

So hatte auch unser Handelsmann oft, wenn er andere sich einschiffen oder glücklich in den Hafen zurückkehren sah, wieder die Regungen seiner alten Leidenschaft gefühlt, ja er hatte selbst in seinem Hause an der Seite seiner Gattin manchmal Unruhe und Unzufriedenheit empfunden. Dieses Verlangen vermehrte sich mit der Zeit und verwandelte sich zuletzt in eine solche Sehnsucht, daß er sich äußerst unglücklich fühlen mußte und zuletzt wirklich krank ward.

„Was soll nun aus dir werden?" sagte er zu sich selbst. „Du erfährst nun, wie töricht es ist, in späten Jahren eine alte Lebensweise gegen eine neue zu vertauschen. Wie sollen wir das, was wir immer getrieben und gesucht haben, aus unsern Gedanken, ja aus unsern Gliedern wieder herausbringen? Und wie geht es mir nun, der ich bisher wie ein Fisch das Wasser, wie ein Vogel die freie Luft geliebt, da ich mich in einem Gebäude bei allen Schätzen und bei der Blume aller Reichtümer, bei einer schönen jungen Frau eingesperrt habe? Anstatt daß ich dadurch hoffte, Zufriedenheit zu gewinnen und meiner Güter zu genießen, so scheint es mir, daß ich alles verliere, indem ich nichts weiter erwerbe. Mit Unrecht hält man die Menschen für Toren, welche in rastloser Tätigkeit Güter auf Güter zu häufen suchen; denn die Tätigkeit ist das Glück, und für den, der die Freuden eines ununterbrochenen Bestrebens empfinden kann, ist der erworbene Reichtum ohne Bedeutung. Aus Mangel an Beschäftigung werde ich elend, aus Mangel an Bewegung krank, und wenn ich keinen andern Entschluß fasse,[14] so bin ich in kurzer Zeit dem Tode nahe.

„Freilich ist es ein gewagtes Unternehmen, sich von einer jungen, liebenswürdigen Frau zu entfernen. Ist es billig, um ein reizendes und reizbares Mädchen zu freien und sie nach einer kurzen Zeit sich selbst, der Langenweile,[15] ihren Empfindungen und Begierden zu überlassen? Spazieren diese jungen, seidnen Herrn nicht schon jetzt vor meinen Fenstern

changed his love of an active and roaming life for the feeling of domestic bliss. But an old habit is not so easily discarded, and a direction we have assumed early in life can be diverted for a time, no doubt, but never wholly interrupted.

And so our merchant, too, when he saw others boarding ship or returning safely to harbor, had once more felt the stirrings of his old passion; indeed he had even sometimes felt uneasiness and dissatisfaction in his own home at the side of his wife. This desire increased with time and was finally transformed into such longing that he was bound to feel extremely unhappy and at last became really ill.

"What is to become of you now?" he said to himself. "Now you learn how foolish it is to exchange an old way of life for a new one in later years. How can we banish from our thoughts, indeed from our limbs, what we have always done and sought? And what is my condition now—I who have until now loved the water like a fish and the free air like a bird —when I've locked myself up in a building with all my treasures and the flower of all wealth, a beautiful young wife? Instead of what I had hoped for—to gain contentment from it and to enjoy my estates—it seems to me that I'm losing everything, since I'm acquiring nothing more. It is wrong to regard those people who seek to pile up property on property in restless activity as fools; for activity is happiness; and for the man who can feel the joy of an uninterrupted effort, the wealth which he has acquired is without meaning. I'm becoming wretched from a lack of activity, sick from a lack of movement, and unless I alter my course I shall be near death in a short time.

"Of course, it is a risky undertaking to separate oneself from a young, attractive wife. Is it right to court a charming and susceptible girl and, after a short time, abandon her to herself, to boredom, to her emotions and desires? Aren't these young gentlemen in silk even now parading up and down in front of my windows? Aren't they already seeking to attract my

auf und ab? Suchen sie nicht schon jetzt in der Kirche und
in Gärten die Aufmerksamkeit meines Weibchens an sich zu
ziehen? Und was wird erst [16] geschehen, wenn ich weg bin?
Soll ich glauben, daß mein Weib durch ein Wunder gerettet
werden könnte? Nein, in ihrem Alter, bei ihrer Konstitution
wäre es töricht zu hoffen, daß sie sich der Freuden der Liebe
enthalten könnte. Entfernst du dich, so wirst du bei deiner
Rückkunft die Neigung deines Weibes und ihre Treue
zugleich mit der Ehre deines Hauses verloren haben."

Diese Betrachtungen und Zweifel, mit denen er sich eine
Zeitlang quälte, verschlimmerten den Zustand, in dem er
sich befand, aufs äußerste. Seine Frau, seine Verwandten und
Freunde betrübten sich um ihn, ohne daß sie die Ursache
seiner Krankheit hätten entdecken können. Endlich ging er
nochmals bei sich zu Rate [17] und rief nach einiger Überlegung
aus: „Törichter Mensch! du lässest es dir so sauer werden,[18]
ein Weib zu bewahren, das du doch bald, wenn dein Übel
fortdauert, sterbend hinter dir und einem andern lassen mußt.
Ist es nicht wenigstens klüger und besser, du suchst das Leben
zu erhalten, wenn du gleich in Gefahr kommst, an ihr
dasjenige zu verlieren, was als das höchste Gut der Frauen
geschätzt wird? Wie mancher Mann kann durch seine Gegenwart den Verlust dieses Schatzes nicht hindern und vermißt
geduldig, was er nicht erhalten kann! Warum solltest du nicht
Mut haben, dich eines solchen Gutes zu entschlagen, da von
diesem Entschlusse dein Leben abhängt?"

Mit diesen Worten ermannte er sich und ließ seine Schiffsgesellen rufen. Er trug ihnen auf, nach gewohnter Weise ein
Fahrzeug zu befrachten und alles bereit zu halten, daß sie
bei dem ersten günstigen Winde auslaufen könnten. Darauf
erklärte er sich gegen seine Frau folgendermaßen:

„Laß dich nicht befremden, wenn du in dem Hause eine
Bewegung siehst, woraus du schließen kannst, daß ich mich
zu einer Abreise anschicke! Betrübe dich nicht, wenn ich dir
gestehe, daß ich abermals eine Seefahrt zu unternehmen
gedenke! Meine Liebe zu dir ist noch immer dieselbe, und
sie wird es gewiß in meinem ganzen Leben bleiben. Ich
erkenne den Wert des Glücks, das ich bisher an deiner Seite
genoß, und würde ihn noch reiner fühlen, wenn ich mir nicht
oft Vorwürfe der Untätigkeit und Nachlässigkeit im stillen

wife's attention in church and in the gardens? And what will happen once I'm away? Am I to believe that my wife could be saved by a miracle? No; at her age, with her constitution, it would be foolish to hope that she could abstain from the joys of love. If you go away, you will, upon returning, have lost your wife's affection and her fidelity together with the honor of your house."

These reflections and doubts with which he tormented himself for a while, aggravated the condition in which he found himself to an extreme. His wife, his relatives and friends were concerned about him without being able to discover the cause of his illness. Finally he consulted his inner mind once more and after some deliberation cried out: "Foolish man! You are taking so many pains to preserve a wife whom, if your sickness continues and you die, you will have to leave behind for another man. Isn't it wiser and better that you should at least seek to preserve your life even though you run the risk of losing in her what is treasured as woman's highest good? How many a man is there who cannot prevent the loss of this treasure even by his presence and who patiently does without that which he cannot preserve. Why shouldn't you have the courage to give up such a treasure when your very life depends on this decision?"

With these words he took heart, and sent for his shipmates. He charged them to load a vessel with cargo in the usual way and to be ready to sail at the first favorable wind. Then he explained the situation to his wife in the following words:

"Don't be alarmed if you see activity in the house from which you may conclude that I'm preparing for a journey. And don't feel sad if I confess to you that I'm thinking of undertaking a sea voyage again. My love for you is still the same as ever and will certainly remain so all my life. I recognize the value of the happiness which I've enjoyed at your side till now; these feelings would be even purer if I did not often have to reproach myself privately for my inactivity and negligence. My old inclination is awakening again and my old

machen müßte. Meine alte Neigung wacht wieder auf, und meine alte Gewohnheit zieht mich wieder an. Erlaube mir, daß ich den Markt von Alexandrien wiedersehe, den ich jetzt mit größerem Eifer besuchen werde, weil ich dort die köstlichsten Stoffe und die edelsten Kostbarkeiten für dich zu gewinnen denke. Ich lasse dich im Besitz aller meiner Güter und meines ganzen Vermögens; bediene dich dessen und vergnüge dich mit deinen Eltern und Verwandten! Die Zeit der Abwesenheit geht auch vorüber, und mit vielfacher Freude werden wir uns wiedersehen."

Nicht ohne Tränen machte ihm die liebenswürdige Frau die zärtlichsten Vorwürfe, versicherte, daß sie ohne ihn keine fröhliche Stunde hinbringen werde, und bat ihn nur, da sie ihn weder halten könne noch einschränken wolle, daß er ihrer auch in der Abwesenheit zum besten gedenken möge.

Nachdem er darauf verschiedenes mit ihr über einige Geschäfte und häusliche Angelegenheiten gesprochen, sagte er nach einer kleinen Pause: „Ich habe nun noch etwas auf dem Herzen, davon [19] du mir frei zu reden erlauben mußt; nur bitte ich dich aufs herzlichste, nicht zu mißdeuten, was ich sage, sondern auch selbst in dieser Besorgnis meine Liebe zu erkennen."

„Ich kann es erraten", versetzte die Schöne darauf; „du bist meinetwegen besorgt, indem du nach Art der Männer unser Geschlecht ein für allemal [20] für schwach hältst. Du hast mich bisher jung und froh gekannt, und nun glaubst du, daß ich in deiner Abwesenheit leichtsinnig und verführbar sein werde. Ich schelte diese Sinnesart nicht, denn sie ist bei euch Männern gewöhnlich; aber wie ich mein Herz kenne, darf ich dir versichern, daß nichts so leicht Eindruck auf mich machen und kein möglicher Eindruck so tief wirken soll, um mich von dem Wege abzuleiten, auf dem ich bisher an der Hand der Liebe und Pflicht hinwandelte. Sei ohne Sorgen; du sollst deine Frau so zärtlich und treu bei deiner Rückkunft wiederfinden, als du sie abends fandest, wenn du nach einer kleinen Abwesenheit in meine Arme zurückkehrtest."

„Diese Gesinnungen traue ich dir zu", versetzte der Gemahl, „und bitte dich, darin zu verharren. Laß uns aber an die äußersten Fälle denken; warum soll man sich nicht auch darauf vorsehen? Du weißt, wie sehr deine schöne und rei-

habit is attracting me once more. Permit me to see the market of Alexandria again; I shall now visit it with greater eagerness because I expect to gain there the most precious stuffs and the noblest treasures for you. I leave you in possession of all my goods and of my entire fortune; make use of it and enjoy yourself with your parents and relatives. The time of my absence will also pass, and we will see each other again with much joy."


Not without tears did his charming wife cast the most tender reproaches at him, assuring him that without him she would not spend one single happy hour. Since she could not hold him back and did not want to curb him, she merely begged him to think the best of her during his absence.

After he had discussed various matters concerning certain business and domestic affairs with her, he said after a brief pause: "I still have something on my mind about which you must permit me to talk freely; but I beg you most sincerely not to misinterpret what I am saying, but to recognize my love even in this anxiety of mine."

"I can guess it," the beautiful woman replied, "you are concerned about me since, like all men, you consider our sex to be basically weak. Until now you have known me as young and happy; now you believe that, in your absence, I'll be frivolous and easily seduced. I don't condemn this line of thought, for it is usual with you men. But as I know my heart, I may assure you that nothing can make such an easy impression on me, and that no possible impression can affect me so deeply as to lead me astray from the road on which I have walked hitherto, guided by the hand of love and duty. Don't worry; when you return you shall find your wife as tender and faithful as you found her each evening when you returned to my arms after a brief absence."

"I believe you are capable of this conviction," her husband replied, "and beg you to persevere in it. But let us think of an extreme situation; why shouldn't we be prepared for that too? You know how much your beautiful and charming person

zende Gestalt die Augen unserer jungen Mitbürger auf sich
zieht; sie werden sich in meiner Abwesenheit noch mehr als
bisher um dich bemühen, sie werden sich dir auf alle Weise
zu nähern, ja zu gefallen suchen. Nicht immer wird das Bild
deines Gemahls, wie jetzt seine Gegenwart, sie von deiner
Türe und deinem Herzen verscheuchen. Du bist ein edles und
gutes Kind, aber die Forderungen der Natur sind rechtmäßig
und gewaltsam; sie stehen mit unserer Vernunft beständig im
Streite und tragen gewöhnlich den Sieg davon. Unterbrich
mich nicht! Du wirst gewiß in meiner Abwesenheit, selbst bei
dem pflichtmäßigen Andenken an mich, das Verlangen
empfinden, wodurch das Weib den Mann anzieht und von
ihm angezogen wird. Ich werde eine Zeitlang der Gegenstand deiner Wünsche sein; aber wer weiß, was für Umstände
zusammentreffen, was für Gelegenheiten sich finden, und ein
anderer wird in der Wirklichkeit ernten, was die Einbildungskraft mir zugedacht hatte. Werde nicht ungeduldig, ich bitte
dich, höre mich aus!

„Sollte der Fall kommen, dessen Möglichkeit du leugnest
und den ich auch nicht zu beschleunigen wünsche, daß du
ohne die Gesellschaft eines Mannes nicht länger bleiben, die
Freuden der Liebe nicht wohl entbehren könntest, so versprich
mir nur, an meine Stelle keinen von den leichtsinnigen
Knaben zu wählen, die, so artig sie auch aussehen mögen, der
Ehre noch mehr als der Tugend einer Frau gefährlich sind.
Mehr durch Eitelkeit als durch Begierde beherrscht, bemühen
sie sich um eine jede und finden nichts natürlicher, als eine
der andern aufzuopfern. Fühlst du dich geneigt, dich nach
einem Freunde umzusehen, so forsche nach einem, der
diesen Namen verdient, der bescheiden und verschwiegen die
Freuden der Liebe noch durch die Wohltat des Geheimnisses
zu erheben weiß."

Hier verbarg die schöne Frau ihren Schmerz nicht länger,
und die Tränen, die sie bisher zurückgehalten hatte, stürzten
reichlich aus ihren Augen. „Was du auch von mir denken
magst", rief sie nach einer leidenschaftlichen Umarmung aus,
„so ist doch nichts entfernter von mir als das Verbrechen,
das du gewissermaßen für unvermeidlich hältst. Möge, wenn
jemals auch nur ein solcher Gedanke in mir entsteht, die
Erde sich auftun und mich verschlingen, und möge alle

attracts the eyes of our young fellow citizens. In my absence they will pay you even more attention than till now; they will seek to approach you in every possible way, and indeed to please you. The image of your husband will not always banish them from your door and heart as his presence does now. You are a noble and good child, but the demands of nature are legitimate and powerful; they are in constant conflict with our reason and usually gain the victory. Don't interrupt me! During my absence, even while you are dutifully thinking of me, you will certainly feel the desire by which a woman attracts a man and is attracted by him. For a time I shall be the object of your wishes; but who knows what sort of conditions will occur, what opportunities will arise, and another man will reap in reality what your imagination had intended for me. Don't become impatient, I beg you, listen till I'm through.

"Should the case arise—although you deny this possibility and I don't wish to precipitate it—that you could no longer live without the company of a man nor easily forego the pleasures of love, promise me only this: not to choose in my place any of those frivolous boys who, however polite they may look, are even more dangerous to a woman's honor than to her virtue. Dominated more by vanity than by desire, they go after every woman and find nothing more natural than to sacrifice one for another. If you feel inclined to look about for a friend, then look for one who deserves this name, who, by his modesty and discretion, can enhance the joys of love with the virtue of secrecy."

At this point the beautiful woman no longer concealed her pain, and the tears which she had until now repressed fell plentifully from her eyes. "Whatever you may think of me," she exclaimed after a passionate embrace, "nothing is further from my mind than the crime which you in a sense consider to be inevitable. If ever such a thought is born in my mind may the earth open and swallow me, and may I be deprived of all hope of that happiness which promises us such a

Hoffnung der Seligkeit mir entrissen werden, die uns eine so reizende Fortdauer unsers Daseins verspricht. Entferne das Mißtrauen aus deiner Brust [21] und laß mir die ganze reine Hoffnung, dich bald wieder in meinen Armen zu sehen!"

Nachdem er auf alle Weise seine Gattin zu beruhigen gesucht, schiffte er sich den andern [22] Morgen ein; seine Fahrt war glücklich, und er gelangte bald nach Alexandrien.

Indessen lebte seine Gattin in dem ruhigen Besitz eines großen Vermögens nach aller Lust und Bequemlichkeit, jedoch eingezogen, und pflegte außer ihren Eltern und Verwandten niemand zu sehen, und indem die Geschäfte ihres Mannes durch getreue Diener fortgeführt wurden, bewohnte sie ein großes Haus, in dessen prächtigen Zimmern sie mit Vergnügen täglich das Andenken ihres Gemahls erneuerte.

So sehr sie aber auch sich stille hielt und eingezogen lebte, waren doch die jungen Leute der Stadt nicht untätig geblieben. Sie versäumten nicht, häufig vor ihrem Fenster vorbeizugehen, und suchten des Abends durch Musik und Gesänge ihre Aufmerksamkeit auf sich zu ziehen. Die schöne Einsame fand anfangs diese Bemühungen unbequem und lästig, doch gewöhnte sie sich bald daran und ließ an den langen Abenden, ohne sich zu bekümmern, woher sie kämen, die Serenaden als eine angenehme Unterhaltung sich gefallen [23] und konnte dabei manchen Seufzer, der ihrem Abwesenden galt, nicht zurückhalten.

Anstatt daß ihre unbekannten Verehrer, wie sie hoffte, nach und nach müde geworden wären, schienen sich ihre Bemühungen noch zu vermehren und zu einer beständigen Dauer anzulassen. Sie konnte nun die wiederkehrenden Instrumente und Stimmen, die wiederholten Melodien schon unterscheiden und bald sich die Neugierde nicht mehr versagen zu wissen, wer die Unbekannten und besonders wer die Beharrlichen sein möchten. Sie durfte sich zum Zeitvertreib eine solche Teilnahme wohl erlauben.

Sie fing daher an, von Zeit zu Zeit durch ihre Vorhänge und Halbläden [24] nach der Straße zu sehen, auf die Vorbeigehenden zu merken und besonders die Männer zu unterscheiden, die ihre Fenster am längsten im Auge behielten. Es waren meist schöne, wohlgekleidete junge Leute, die aber freilich in Gebärden sowohl als in ihrem ganzen Äußern

charming continuation of our life. Remove the distrust from your heart and leave with me the whole, pure hope of soon seeing you in my arms again!"

After trying to calm his wife in every possible way, he took ship the following morning. His voyage was successful and he soon reached Alexandria.

Meanwhile his wife lived quietly in the enjoyment and comfort which the undisturbed possession of a great fortune afforded her. Apart from her parents and relatives she was in the habit of seeing no one. While her husband's affairs were carried on by loyal servants, she lived in a large house, and in its splendid rooms she joyfully renewed every day the memory of her husband.

Yet, however quiet and withdrawn a life she led, the young men of the town had not been idle. They did not fail to pass frequently under her window and in the evenings sought to attract her attention with music and songs. The beautiful recluse at first found these endeavors inconvenient and annoying but soon became used to them, and during the long evenings she accepted the serenades as a pleasant entertainment, without caring where they came from. At such times she could not repress many a sigh that was meant for her absent husband.

She had hoped that her unknown admirers would gradually grow tired; instead, their efforts merely increased and took on a quality of permanence. She was already able to distinguish between the recurring instruments and voices and the repeated melodies and could soon no longer deny her curiosity to know who the unknown, and especially the persistent men might be. She might well permit herself such an interest as a mere pastime.

She therefore began to look down into the street through her drapes and half-shutters from time to time, to observe the passers-by and especially to distinguish the men who kept their eyes on her windows the longest. They were mostly handsome, well-dressed young men, who revealed, however, frivolity and vanity both in their gestures and in their whole physical

ebensoviel Leichtsinn als Eitelkeit sehen ließen. Sie schienen mehr durch ihre Aufmerksamkeit auf das Haus der Schönen sich merkwürdig machen als jener eine Art von Verehrung beweisen zu wollen.

„Wahrlich", sagte die Dame manchmal scherzend zu sich selbst, „mein Mann hat einen klugen Einfall gehabt! Durch die Bedingung, unter der er mir einen Liebhaber zugesteht, schließt er alle diejenigen aus, die sich um mich bemühen und die mir allenfalls gefallen könnten. Er weiß wohl, daß Klugheit, Bescheidenheit und Verschwiegenheit Eigenschaften eines ruhigen Alters sind, die zwar unser Verstand schätzt, die aber unsre Einbildungskraft keinesweges aufzuregen noch unsre Neigung anzureizen imstande sind. Vor diesen, die mein Haus mit ihren Artigkeiten belagern, bin ich sicher, daß sie kein Vertrauen erwecken, und die, denen ich mein Vertrauen schenken könnte, finde ich nicht im mindesten liebenswürdig."

In der Sicherheit dieser Gedanken erlaubte sie sich immer mehr, dem Vergnügen an der Musik und an der Gestalt der vorbeigehenden Jünglinge nachzuhängen, und ohne daß sie es merkte, wuchs nach und nach ein unruhiges Verlangen in ihrem Busen, dem sie nur zu spät zu widerstreben gedachte. Die Einsamkeit und der Müßiggang, das bequeme, gute und reichliche Leben waren ein Element, in welchem sich eine unregelmäßige Begierde früher, als das gute Kind dachte, entwickeln mußte.

Sie fing nun an, jedoch mit stillen Seufzern, unter den Vorzügen ihres Gemahls auch seine Welt- und Menschenkenntnis, besonders die Kenntnis des weiblichen Herzens zu bewundern. „So war es also doch möglich, was ich ihm so lebhaft abstritt", sagte sie zu sich selbst, „und so war es also doch nötig, in einem solchen Falle mir Vorsicht und Klugheit anzuraten! Doch was können Vorsicht und Klugheit da, wo der unbarmherzige Zufall nur mit einem unbestimmten Verlangen zu spielen scheint! Wie soll ich den wählen, den ich nicht kenne? Und bleibt bei näherer Bekanntschaft noch eine Wahl übrig?"

Mit solchen und hundert andern Gedanken vermehrte die schöne Frau das Übel, das bei ihr schon weit genug um sich gegriffen hatte.[25] Vergebens suchte sie sich zu zerstreuen; jeder

appearance. They seemed to be more intent on calling attention to themselves by the attentions they paid to the beautiful woman's house than on demonstrating a kind of reverence to the beautiful woman herself.

"Really," the lady said jokingly to herself at times, "my husband had a clever idea. Through the condition under which he grants me a lover, he excludes all those who are paying me attention and who could possibly please me. He knows well that prudence, modesty and discretion are the characteristics of mature age, which our reason certainly values but which are unable to stir our imagination in any way or to stimulate our affection. I am certain that these men who are besieging my house with their attentions cannot awaken my confidence, and those to whom I could give my confidence I don't find in the least attractive."

In the security of these thoughts she permitted herself more and more to linger over the pleasures offered her by the music and the figures of the passing youths. Without her noticing it there gradually grew in her breast a restless desire which she thought of resisting only too late. The loneliness and the idleness, the comfortable, good and plentiful life were elements in which an illicit desire was bound to develop earlier than the good child thought.

She now began, though with quiet sighs, to admire among her husband's good points also his knowledge of the world and of people, particularly of the female heart. "So it was really possible—what I so vigorously contested," she said to herself, "and it was really necessary to advise caution and prudence in such an eventuality! But what power have caution and prudence where merciless chance seems to be merely playing with a vague desire? How am I to choose the man whom I don't know? And will there still be a choice upon closer acquaintance?"

With these and a hundred other thoughts the beautiful woman increased the evil which had already affected her enough. In vain she sought to distract herself; every pleasant

angenehme Gegenstand machte ihre Empfindung rege, und
ihre Empfindung brachte, auch in der tiefsten Einsamkeit,
angenehme Bilder in ihrer Einbildungskraft hervor.

In solchem Zustande befand sie sich, als sie unter andern
Stadtneuigkeiten von ihren Verwandten vernahm, es sei ein
junger Rechtsgelehrter, der zu Bologna [26] studiert habe, soeben
in seine Vaterstadt zurückgekommen. Man wußte nicht genug
zu seinem Lobe zu sagen. Bei außerordentlichen Kenntnissen
zeigte er eine Klugheit und Gewandtheit, die sonst Jünglingen
nicht eigen ist, und bei einer sehr reizenden Gestalt die größte
Bescheidenheit. Als Prokurator hatte er bald das Zutrauen der
Bürger und die Achtung der Richter gewonnen. Täglich fand
er sich auf dem Rathause ein, um daselbst seine Geschäfte
zu besorgen und zu betreiben.

Die Schöne hörte die Schilderung eines so vollkommenen
Mannes nicht ohne Verlangen, ihn näher kennenzulernen,
und nicht ohne stillen Wunsch, in ihm denjenigen zu finden,
dem sie ihr Herz, selbst nach der Vorschrift ihres Mannes,
übergeben könnte. Wie aufmerksam ward sie daher, als sie
vernahm, daß er täglich vor ihrem Hause vorbeigehe; wie
sorgfältig beobachtete sie die Stunde, in der man auf dem
Rathause sich zu versammeln pflegte! Nicht ohne Bewegung
sah sie ihn endlich vorbeigehen, und wenn seine schöne
Gestalt und seine Jugend für sie notwendig reizend sein
mußten, so war seine Bescheidenheit von der andern Seite
dasjenige, was sie in Sorgen versetzte.

Einige Tage hatte sie ihn heimlich beobachtet und konnte
nun dem Wunsche nicht länger widerstehen, seine Aufmerksamkeit auf sich zu ziehen. Sie kleidete sich mit Sorgfalt, trat
auf den Balkon, und das Herz schlug ihr, als sie ihn die Straße
herkommen sah. Allein wie betrübt, ja beschämt war sie, als
er wie gewöhnlich mit bedächtigen Schritten, in sich gekehrt
und mit niedergeschlagenen Augen, ohne sie auch nur zu
bemerken, auf das zierlichste seines Weges vorbeiging.

Vergebens versuchte sie mehrere Tage hintereinander auf
ebendiese Weise, von ihm bemerkt zu werden. Immer ging
er seinen gewöhnlichen Schritt, ohne die Augen aufzuschlagen
oder da- und dorthin zu wenden. Je mehr sie ihn aber ansah,
desto mehr schien er ihr derjenige zu sein, dessen sie so sehr
bedurfte. Ihre Neigung ward täglich lebhafter und, da sie ihr

object stirred her emotion into life and her emotion provoked pleasant images in her imagination, even in her deepest solitude.

This is the state she was in when she heard from her relatives, among other items of city news, that a young lawyer had just returned to his native town from his studies in Bologna. They could not say enough in his praise. Along with an extraordinary knowledge, he demonstrated cleverness and adroitness which were not common to youth and he possessed the greatest modesty together with a handsome appearance. He had soon gained the confidence of the citizenry and the respect of the judges as a lawyer. He went daily to the town hall to look after and transact his affairs.

The beautiful lady did not hear the description of such a perfect man without desiring to get to know him better and not without the secret wish that she might find in him the man to whom she could give her heart, even in conformity with her husband's prescription. How attentive did she therefore become when she heard that he went past her house daily; how carefully did she observe the hour when meetings in the city hall took place. Not without emotion, she finally saw him pass by, and if his handsome figure and his youth were bound to charm her, his modesty was, on the other hand, what caused her anxiety.

She had secretly observed him for some days and could no longer resist the wish to attract his attention. She dressed carefully, stepped on the balcony, and her heart beat fast as she saw him coming down the street. But how sad, indeed how ashamed was she, when he walked by, most gracefully, as usual with measured steps, absorbed in thought, his eyes downcast without even noticing her.

In vain she sought for several days in succession to be noticed by him by the same method. He always walked with his usual step, without raising his eyes or turning them in this or that direction. But the more she looked at him, the more he seemed to her to be the man whom she needed so badly. Her interest grew more lively with every day and, since

nicht widerstand, endlich ganz und gar gewaltsam. „Wie!"
sagte sie zu sich selbst, „nachdem dein edler, verständiger
Mann den Zustand vorausgesehen, in dem du dich in seiner
Abwesenheit befinden würdest, da seine Weissagung eintrifft,
daß du ohne Freund und Günstling nicht leben kannst, sollst
du dich nun verzehren und abhärmen zu der Zeit, da dir das
Glück einen Jüngling zeigt, völlig nach deinem Sinne, nach
dem Sinne deines Gatten, einen Jüngling, mit dem du die
Freuden der Liebe in einem undurchdringlichen Geheimnis
genießen kannst? Töricht, wer die Gelegenheit versäumt,
töricht, wer der gewaltsamen Liebe widerstehen will!" Mit
solchen und vielen andern Gedanken suchte sich die schöne
Frau in ihrem Vorsatze zu stärken, und nur kurze Zeit ward
sie noch von Ungewißheit hin und her getrieben. Endlich
aber, wie es begegnet, daß eine Leidenschaft, welcher wir lange
widerstehen, uns zuletzt auf einmal dahinreißt und unser
Gemüt dergestalt erhöht, daß wir auf Besorgnis und Furcht,
Zurückhaltung und Scham, Verhältnisse [27] und Pflichten mit
Verachtung als auf kleinliche Hindernisse zurücksehen, so
faßte sie auf einmal den raschen Entschluß, ein junges
Mädchen, das ihr diente, zu dem geliebten Manne zu schicken
und, es koste nun, was es wolle, zu seinem Besitze zu gelangen.

Das Mädchen eilte und fand ihn, als er eben mit vielen
Freunden zu Tische saß, und richtete ihren Gruß, den ihre
Frau sie gelehrt hatte, pünktlich aus. Der junge Prokurator
wunderte sich nicht über diese Botschaft; er hatte den
Handelsmann in seiner Jugend gekannt, er wußte, daß er
gegenwärtig abwesend war, und ob er gleich von seiner Heirat
nur von weitem gehört hatte, vermutete er doch, daß die
zurückgelasssene Frau in der Abwesenheit ihres Mannes
wahrscheinlich in einer wichtigen Sache seines rechtlichen
Beistandes bedürfe. Er antwortete deswegen dem Mädchen
auf das verbindlichste und versicherte, daß er, sobald man
von der Tafel aufgestanden, nicht säumen würde, ihrer Ge-
bieterin aufzuwarten. Mit unaussprechlicher Freude vernahm
die schöne Frau, daß sie den Geliebten nun bald sehen und
sprechen sollte. Sie eilte, sich aufs beste anzuziehen, und ließ
geschwind ihr Haus und ihre Zimmer auf das reinlichste
ausputzen. Orangenblätter und Blumen wurden gestreut,
der [28] Sofa mit den köstlichsten Teppichen bedeckt. So ging [29]

she did not resist it, it finally became very powerful indeed. "What!" she said to herself. "Since your noble, understanding husband has foreseen the condition in which you would find yourself in his absence, when his prophecy that you can't live without a friend and favorite has come true, are you to waste and pine away at a time when fortune shows you a youth wholly after your own heart and your husband's, a youth with whom you may enjoy the pleasures of love in impenetrable secrecy? Anyone who misses the opportunity is foolish, as is he who wants to resist the power of love!" With these and many other thoughts the beautiful woman sought to strengthen herself in her resolution and for only a short time longer was she driven hither and thither by uncertainty. But finally, as it happens that a passion which we resist for a long time at last carries us away suddenly and elevates our soul in such a way that we look back with contempt on anxiety and fear, self-restraint and shame, realities and duties as trivial hindrances, she suddenly formed the swift resolve to send a young girl in her service to the beloved man and to possess him at whatever cost.

The girl hurried and found him sitting at dinner with many friends; she conveyed to him her mistress's greeting precisely as it had been given her. The young advocate was not astonished at this message. He had known the merchant in his youth, he knew that he was away now; and although he had heard of his marriage only in a vague way, he surmised that the wife he had left behind probably needed legal help on some important matter during her husband's absence. He therefore gave the girl a most courteous answer and assured her that he would not fail to call on her mistress as soon as the dinner was over. With inexpressible joy the beautiful woman heard that she was soon to see and speak to the man she loved. She hurried to put on her best dress and swiftly had her house and her rooms cleaned most thoroughly. Orange leaves and flowers were strewn about, the sofa was covered with the most precious carpets. Thus the short span of time till he came, which would otherwise have become insufferably long for her, passed busily.

die kurze Zeit, die er ausblieb, beschäftigt hin, die ihr sonst unerträglich lang geworden wäre.

Mit welcher Bewegung ging sie ihm entgegen, als er endlich ankam, mit welcher Verwirrung hieß sie ihn, indem sie sich auf das Ruhebett niederließ, auf ein Taburett sitzen, das zunächst dabeistand! Sie verstummte in seiner so erwünschten Nähe, sie hatte nicht bedacht, was sie ihm sagen wollte; auch er war still und saß bescheiden vor ihr. Endlich ermannte sie sich und sagte nicht ohne Sorge und Beklommenheit:

„Sie sind noch nicht lange in Ihrer Vaterstadt wiederangekommen, mein Herr, und schon sind Sie allenthalben für einen talentreichen und zuverlässigen Mann bekannt. Auch ich setze mein Vertrauen auf Sie in einer wichtigen und sonderbaren Angelegenheit, die, wenn ich es recht bedenke, eher für den Beichtvater als für den Sachwalter gehört. Seit einem Jahre bin ich an einen würdigen und reichen Mann verheiratet, der, solange wir zusammenlebten, die größte Aufmerksamkeit für mich hatte und über den ich mich nicht beklagen würde, wenn nicht ein unruhiges Verlangen zu reisen und zu handeln ihn seit einiger Zeit aus meinen Armen gerissen hätte.

„Als ein verständiger und gerechter Mann fühlte er wohl das Unrecht, das er mir durch seine Entfernung antat. Er begriff, daß ein junges Weib nicht wie Juwelen und Perlen verwahrt werden könne; er wußte, daß sie vielmehr einem Garten voll schöner Früchte gleicht, die für jedermann so wie für den Herrn verloren wären, wenn er eigensinnig die Türe auf einige Jahre verschließen wollte. Er sprach mir daher vor seiner Abreise sehr ernstlich zu, er versicherte mir, daß ich ohne Freund nicht würde leben können, er gab mir dazu nicht allein die Erlaubnis, sondern er drang in mich und nötigte mir gleichsam das Versprechen ab, daß ich der Neigung, die sich in meinem Herzen finden würde, frei und ohne Anstand folgen wollte."

Sie hielt einen Augenblick inne, aber bald gab ihr ein vielversprechender Blick des jungen Mannes Mut genug, in ihrem Bekenntnis fortzufahren:

„Eine einzige Bedingung fügte mein Gemahl zu seiner übrigens so nachsichtigen Erlaubnis. Er empfahl mir die äußerste Vorsicht und verlangte ausdrücklich, daß ich mir

When he finally came, with what emotion did she go to meet him; when she sank down on the couch, with what confusion did she bid him sit on the stool close by! She fell silent in his presence, which was so desirable to her; she had not reflected on what she wanted to say to him; he, too, was silent and sat modestly before her. Finally she summoned her courage and, not without anxiety and embarrassment, said:

"You haven't been back in your native city for any length of time yet, sir, but you are already known everywhere as a richly talented and trustworthy man. I too am putting my confidence in you in an important and strange matter which, when I think about it, is more suitable for a father confessor than for an attorney. For one year I have been married to a worthy and rich man who was most attentive to me as long as we lived together and about whom I would not complain if a restless desire to travel and to trade had not torn him from my arms some time ago.

"As an intelligent and just man he probably felt the injustice he was doing me through his absence. He realized that a young wife could not be stored like jewels and pearls; he knew that she rather resembles a garden full of beautiful fruits which would be lost for everyone as well as for the owner if he were to lock the gate stubbornly for some years. He therefore spoke very earnestly to me before his departure, he assured me that I would not be able to live without a friend, he not only gave me his permission to find one but urged me and, so to speak, made me promise that I would freely and without hesitation follow the inclinations that would arise in my heart."

She stopped for a moment, but soon a very promising look from the young man gave her enough courage to continue with her confession:

"My husband added one single condition to his otherwise so tolerant permission. He recommended the greatest caution to me and requested expressly that I should choose a sedate,

einen gesetzten, zuverlässigen, klugen und verschwiegenen Freund wählen sollte. Ersparen Sie mir, das übrige zu sagen, mein Herr, ersparen Sie mir die Verwirrung, mit der ich Ihnen bekennen würde, wie sehr ich für Sie eingenommen bin, und erraten Sie aus diesem Zutrauen meine Hoffnungen und meine Wünsche."

Nach einer kurzen Pause versetzte der junge, liebenswürdige Mann mit gutem Bedachte: „Wie sehr bin ich Ihnen für das Vertrauen verbunden, durch welches Sie mich in einem so hohen Grade ehren und glücklich machen! Ich wünsche nur lebhaft, Sie zu überzeugen, daß Sie sich an keinen Unwürdigen gewendet haben. Lassen Sie mich Ihnen zuerst als Rechtsgelehrter antworten; und als ein solcher gesteh ich Ihnen, daß ich Ihren Gemahl bewundere, der sein Unrecht so deutlich gefühlt und eingesehen hat, denn es ist gewiß, daß einer, der ein junges Weib zurückläßt, um ferne Weltgegenden zu besuchen, als ein solcher anzusehen ist, der irgendein anderes Besitztum völlig derelinquiert und durch die deutlichste Handlung auf alles Recht daran Verzicht tut. Wie es nun dem ersten besten [30] erlaubt ist, eine solche völlig ins Freie [31] gefallene Sache wieder zu ergreifen, so muß ich es um so mehr für natürlich und billig halten, daß eine junge Frau, die sich in diesem Zustande befindet, ihre Neigung abermals verschenke und sich einem Freunde, der ihr angenehm und zuverlässig scheint, ohne Bedenken überlasse.

„Tritt nun aber gar wie hier der Fall ein, daß der Ehemann selbst, seines Unrechts sich bewußt, mit ausdrücklichen Worten seiner hinterlassenen Frau dasjenige erlaubt, was er ihr nicht verbieten kann, so bleibt gar kein Zweifel übrig, um so mehr, da demjenigen kein Unrecht geschieht, der es willig zu ertragen erklärt hat.

„Wenn Sie mich nun", fuhr der junge Mann mit ganz andern Blicken und dem lebhaftesten Ausdrucke fort, indem er die schöne Freundin bei der Hand nahm, „wenn Sie mich zu Ihrem Diener erwählen, so machen Sie mich mit einer Glückseligkeit bekannt, von der ich bisher keinen Begriff hatte. Seien Sie versichert", rief er aus, indem er die Hand küßte, „daß Sie keinen ergebnern, zärtlichern, treuern und verschwiegnern Diener hätten finden können!"

Wie beruhigt fühlte sich nach dieser Erklärung die schöne

reliable, clever and discreet friend. Spare me the need to say the rest, sir, spare me the confusion with which I would confess to you how very much I am taken by you and surmise from this confidence my hopes and my wishes."

After a brief pause the young, charming man replied with mature reflection: "How deeply obliged I am to you for the confidence by which you honor me and make me happy to so high a degree! I wish so much to convince you that you have not turned to an unworthy man. Let me reply to you first as a lawyer; as such I confess to you that I admire your husband for having felt and realized his injustice so clearly; for it is certain that anyone who leaves a young wife behind to visit distant parts of the world is to be regarded exactly like the man who abandons any other possession and by this most unequivocal action gives up all rights to it. Now, just as it is permitted to any man who comes along to take possession of such a fully liberated object, I must consider it all the more natural and proper that a young wife who finds herself in this situation should once again bestow her affection and give herself without hesitation to a friend who appears to her to be pleasant and trustworthy.

"But when, as is the case here, the husband himself, conscious of his injustice, in explicit words, permits the wife he left behind him what he cannot forbid her, there is no doubt left in the matter, all the more as no injustice is done to the man who has declared himself willing to bear it.

"If you now choose me as your servant," the young man continued with a totally different look in his eyes and the most animated expression, taking his beautiful friend by the hand, "you introduce me to a happiness of which until now I had no conception. Be assured," he exclaimed, kissing her hand, "that you could not have found a more devoted, more tender, more loyal and discreet servant."

How soothed the beautiful woman felt after this declara-

Frau. Sie scheute sich nicht, ihm ihre Zärtlichkeit aufs leb-
hafteste zu zeigen; sie drückte seine Hände, drängte sich
näher an ihn und legte ihr Haupt auf seine Schulter. Nicht
lange blieben sie in dieser Lage, als er sich auf eine sanfte
Weise von ihr zu entfernen suchte und nicht ohne Betrübnis
zu reden begann: „Kann sich wohl ein Mensch in einem
seltsamern Verhältnisse befinden? Ich bin gezwungen, mich
von Ihnen zu entfernen und mir die größte Gewalt anzutun
in einem Augenblicke, da ich mich den süßesten Gefühlen
überlassen sollte. Ich darf mir das Glück, das mich in Ihren
Armen erwartet, gegenwärtig nicht zueignen. Ach! wenn nur
der Aufschub mich nicht um meine schönsten Hoffnungen
betrügt!"

Die Schöne fragte ängstlich nach der Ursache dieser sonderbaren Äußerung.

„Eben als ich in Bologna", versetzte er, „am Ende meiner
Studien war und mich aufs äußerste angriff, mich zu meiner
künftigen Bestimmung geschickt zu machen, verfiel ich in
eine schwere Krankheit, die, wo nicht mein Leben zu zerstören, doch meine körperlichen und Geisteskräfte zu zerrütten drohte. In der größten Not und unter den heftigsten
Schmerzen tat ich der Mutter Gottes ein Gelübde, daß ich,
wenn sie mich genesen ließe, ein Jahr lang in strengem Fasten
zubringen und mich alles Genusses, von welcher Art er auch
sei, enthalten wolle. Schon zehn Monate habe ich mein
Gelübde auf das treulichste erfüllt, und sie sind mir in
Betrachtung der großen Wohltat, die ich erhalten, keinesweges
lang [32] geworden, da es mir nicht beschwerlich ward, manches
gewohnte und bekannte Gute zu entbehren. Aber zu welcher
Ewigkeit werden mir nun zwei Monate, die noch übrig sind,
da mir erst nach Verlauf derselben ein Glück zuteil werden
kann, welches alle Begriffe übersteigt! Lassen Sie sich die Zeit
nicht lang werden und entziehen Sie mir Ihre Gunst nicht,
die Sie mir so freiwillig zugedacht haben!"

Die Schöne, mit dieser Erklärung nicht sonderlich zufrieden, faßte doch wieder bessern Mut, als der Freund nach
einigem Nachdenken zu reden fortfuhr: „Ich wagte [33] kaum,
Ihnen einen Vorschlag zu tun und das Mittel anzuzeigen,
wodurch ich früher von meinem Gelübde entbunden werden
kann. Wenn ich jemand fände, der so streng und sicher wie

tion. She did not hesitate to show him her tenderness in the most ardent fashion. She pressed his hands, moved up closer to him and laid her head on his shoulder. They had not been long in this position when he sought to move away from her gently and began talking, not without sadness: "Can a man possibly be in a stranger situation? I am compelled to leave you and to impose the greatest violence upon myself at a moment when I ought to abandon myself to the sweetest feelings. I must not at this moment take possession of the happiness which awaits me in your arms. Ah, if only the postponement does not cheat me of my fairest hopes!"

The beautiful lady inquired anxiously for the cause of this strange utterance.

"Just as I was finishing my studies in Bologna," he replied, "and was making the utmost efforts to prepare myself for my future career, I became seriously ill with an ailment which threatened to shatter my physical and mental powers, if not to destroy my life. In my extreme distress and in the most violent pain, I made a vow to the Mother of God that if she allowed me to recover, I would spend a year in strict fasting and abstain from all enjoyment, of whatever nature it might be. For ten months now I have kept my vow most faithfully and, in view of the great benefit I received, these months have in no way appeared long, since it was not difficult for me to do without many an accustomed and familiar pleasure. But what an eternity the two months that still remain will become for me, since only after they have run their course may I partake of a bliss that transcends all understanding. Don't let the time hang heavy and don't withdraw from me the favor which you have so willingly proffered me."

The beautiful woman, who was not particularly satisfied with this explanation, took courage again when her friend continued after some reflection: "I scarcely dare to make a proposal to you and to indicate the means by which I can be released from my vow sooner. If I were to find someone who would undertake to keep the vow as strictly and unfailingly as

ich das Gelübde zu halten übernähme und die Hälfte der noch übrigen Zeit mit mir teilte, so würde ich umso geschwinder frei sein, und nichts würde sich unsern Wünschen entgegenstellen. Sollten Sie nicht, meine süße Freundin, um unser Glück zu beschleunigen, willig sein, einen Teil des Hindernisses, das uns entgegensteht, hinwegzuräumen? Nur der zuverlässigsten Person kann ich einen Anteil an meinem Gelübde übertragen; es ist streng, denn ich darf des Tages nur zweimal Brot und Wasser genießen, darf des Nachts nur wenige Stunden auf einem harten Lager zubringen und muß ungeachtet meiner vielen Geschäfte eine große Anzahl Gebete verrichten. Kann ich, wie es mir heute geschehen ist, nicht vermeiden, bei einem Gastmahl zu erscheinen, so darf ich deswegen doch nicht meine Pflicht hintansetzen, vielmehr muß ich den Reizungen aller Leckerbissen, die an mir vorübergehen, zu widerstehen suchen. Können Sie sich entschließen, einen Monat lang gleichfalls alle diese Gesetze zu befolgen, so werden Sie alsdann sich selbst in dem Besitz eines Freundes desto mehr erfreuen, als Sie ihn durch ein so lobenswürdiges Unternehmen gewissermaßen selbst erworben haben."

Die schöne Dame vernahm ungern die Hindernisse, die sich ihrer Neigung entgegensetzten; doch war ihre Liebe zu dem jungen Manne durch seine Gegenwart dergestalt vermehrt worden, daß ihr keine Prüfung zu streng schien, wenn ihr nur dadurch der Besitz eines so werten Gutes versichert werden konnte. Sie sagte ihm daher mit den gefälligsten Ausdrücken: „Mein süßer Freund! das Wunder, wodurch Sie Ihre Gesundheit wiedererlangt haben, ist mir selbst so wert und verehrungswürdig, daß ich es mir zur Freude und Pflicht mache, an dem Gelübde teilzunehmen, das Sie dagegen [34] zu erfüllen schuldig sind. Ich freue mich, Ihnen einen so sichern Beweis meiner Neigung zu geben; ich will mich auf das genaueste nach Ihrer Vorschrift richten, und ehe Sie mich lossprechen, soll mich nichts von dem Wege entfernen, auf den Sie mich einleiten."

Nachdem der junge Mann mit ihr aufs genaueste diejenigen Bedingungen abgeredet, unter welchen sie ihm die Hälfte seines Gelübdes ersparen konnte, entfernte er sich mit der Versicherung, daß er sie bald wieder besuchen und nach der

I do, and who would share with me half of the remaining period, I would be free all the sooner and nothing would stand in the way of our wishes. Would you not be willing, my sweet friend, in order to hasten our bliss, to remove a part of the hindrance which stands in our way? I can transfer a share in my vow only to the most trustworthy person. It is stringent, for I may only eat bread and water twice a day, may spend only a few hours of every night on a hard bed and must say a large number of prayers, regardless of my many professional duties. If, as happened to me today, I cannot avoid appearing at a banquet, I must not on that account neglect my duty, but must rather seek to resist the attractions of all the delicacies which pass by me. If you, too, can resolve to follow all these laws for a month, you will then rejoice all the more in possessing a friend, since you will in a sense have won him yourself through such a meritorious undertaking."

The beautiful lady heard with displeasure of the hindrances that blocked her inclination. However, her love for the young man had been so much increased by his presence, that no test seemed too hard to her if it could only assure her the possession of such a worthy prize. She therefore said to him in the most gracious terms: "My sweet friend! The miracle through which you have regained your health is so precious and venerable to me, too, that I will make it my joy and duty to share in the vow which you are bound to fulfill. I am glad to give you such certain proof of my affection. I will follow your instructions most precisely, and until you release me nothing shall take me off the road into which you are leading me."

After the young man had discussed with her in the minutest detail the conditions under which she could spare him half of his vow, he left with the assurance that he would visit her again soon, to inquire how she had succeeded in persevering

glücklichen [35] Beharrlichkeit in ihrem Vorsatze fragen würde, und so mußte sie ihn gehen lassen, als er ohne Händedruck, ohne Kuß, mit einem kaum bedeutenden Blicke von ihr schied. Ein Glück für sie war die Beschäftigung, die ihr der seltsame Vorsatz gab, denn sie hatte manches zu tun, um ihre Lebensart völlig zu verändern. Zuerst wurden die schönen Blätter und Blumen hinausgekehrt, die sie zu seinem Empfang hatte streuen lassen; dann kam an die Stelle des wohlge-polsterten Ruhebettes ein hartes Lager, auf das sie sich, zum erstenmal in ihrem Leben nur von Wasser und Brot kaum gesättigt, des Abends niederlegte. Des andern Tages war sie beschäftigt, Hemden zuzuschneiden und zu nähen, deren sie eine bestimmte Zahl für ein Armen- und Krankenhaus fertig zu machen versprochen hatte. Bei dieser neuen und un-bequemen Beschäftigung unterhielt sie ihre Einbildungskraft immer mit dem Bilde ihres süßen Freundes und mit der Hoffnung künftiger Glückseligkeit, und bei ebendiesen Vor-stellungen schien ihre schmale Kost ihr eine herzstärkende Nahrung zu gewähren.

So verging eine Woche, und schon am Ende derselben fingen die Rosen ihrer Wangen an, einigermaßen zu ver-bleichen. Kleider, die ihr sonst wohl paßten, waren zu weit und ihre sonst so raschen und muntern Glieder matt und schwach geworden, als der Freund wieder erschien und ihr durch seinen Besuch neue Stärke und Leben gab. Er ermahnte sie, in ihrem Vorsatze zu beharren, munterte sie durch sein Beispiel auf und ließ von weitem die Hoffnung eines un-gestörten Genusses durchblicken. Nur kurze Zeit hielt er sich auf und versprach, bald wiederzukommen.

Die wohltätige Arbeit ging aufs neue muntrer fort, und von der strengen Diät ließ man keineswegs nach. Aber auch, leider! hätte sie durch eine große Krankheit nicht mehr erschöpft werden können. Ihr Freund, der sie am Ende der Woche abermals besuchte, sah sie mit dem größten Mitleiden an und stärkte sie durch den Gedanken, daß die Hälfte der Prüfung schon vorüber sei.

Nun ward ihr das ungewohnte Fasten, Beten und Arbeiten mit jedem Tage lästiger, und die übertriebene Enthaltsamkeit schien den gesunden Zustand eines an Ruhe und reichliche Nahrung gewöhnten Körpers gänzlich zu zerrütten. Die

in her resolve. And so she had to let him go, when he took his leave without pressing her hand, without a kiss, with only a barely meaningful glance. It was lucky for her that the strange resolve kept her busy, for she had much to do to change her way of life completely. First the beautiful flowers and leaves which she had had scattered for his reception were swept out; then, in place of the well-padded couch a hard bed was brought in, on which she lay down at night for the first time in her life, after barely satisfying her hunger on bread and water. The following day she was busy cutting out and sewing shirts, of which she had promised to supply a definite number for a poorhouse and hospital. During this new and uncomfortable occupation she entertained her imagination with the image of her sweet friend and with the hope of future bliss; and with these very images her frugal fare seemed to afford her a nourishment that strengthened her heart.

Thus a week passed and at the end of it the roses in her cheeks already began to pale somewhat. Clothes that normally fitted her well had become too wide for her, and her usually swift and vigorous limbs had become weary and weak when her friend appeared again and through his visit gave her new strength and life. He exhorted her to persevere in her resolution, encouraged her by his example and faintly hinted at the hope of an undisturbed enjoyment in the far distance. He stayed only a short time and promised to come again soon.

The work of benevolence went on more briskly once more, and there was no let-up in her strict diet. But, alas; she could not have been more exhausted by a severe illness. Her friend, who visited her again at the end of the week, looked at her with the greatest sympathy and strengthened her with the thought that half the test was already over.

The unaccustomed fasting, praying and working now became more burdensome to her with every day and the exaggerated abstinence seemed to ruin completely the healthy condition of a body used to rest and plentiful nurture. The

Schöne konnte sich zuletzt nicht mehr auf den Füßen halten und war genötigt, ungeachtet der warmen Jahreszeit sich in doppelte und dreifache Kleider zu hüllen, um die beinah völlig verschwindende innerliche Wärme einigermaßen zusammenzuhalten. Ja sie war nicht länger imstande, aufrecht zu bleiben, und sogar gezwungen, in der letzten Zeit das Bett zu hüten.

Welche Betrachtungen mußte sie da über ihren Zustand machen! Wie oft ging diese seltsame Begebenheit vor ihrer Seele [36] vorbei, und wie schmerzlich fiel [37] es ihr, als zehn Tage vergingen, ohne daß der Freund erschienen wäre, der sie diese äußersten Aufopferungen kostete! Dagegen aber bereitete sich in diesen trüben Stunden ihre völlige Genesung vor, ja sie ward entschieden. Denn als bald darauf ihr Freund erschien und sich an ihr Bett auf eben dasselbe Taburett setzte, auf dem er ihre erste Erklärung vernommen hatte, und ihr freundlich, ja gewissermaßen zärtlich zusprach, die kurze Zeit noch standhaft auszudauern, unterbrach sie ihn mit Lächeln und sagte: „Es bedarf weiter keines Zuredens, mein werter Freund, und ich werde mein Gelübde diese wenigen Tage mit Geduld und mit der Überzeugung ausdauern, daß Sie es mir zu meinem Besten auferlegt haben. Ich bin jetzt zu schwach, als daß ich Ihnen meinen Dank ausdrücken könnte, wie ich ihn empfinde. Sie haben mich mir selbst erhalten; Sie haben mich mir selbst gegeben, und ich erkenne, daß ich mein ganzes Dasein von nun an Ihnen schuldig bin.

„Wahrlich! mein Mann war verständig und klug und kannte das Herz einer Frau; er war billig genug, sie über eine Neigung nicht zu schelten, die durch seine Schuld in ihrem Busen entstehen konnte, ja er war großmütig genug, seine Rechte der Forderung der Natur hintanzusetzen. Aber Sie, mein Herr, Sie sind vernünftig und gut; Sie haben mich fühlen lassen, daß außer der Neigung noch etwas in uns ist, das ihr das Gleichgewicht halten kann, daß wir fähig sind, jedem gewohnten Gut zu entsagen und selbst unsere heißesten Wünsche von uns zu entfernen. Sie haben mich in diese Schule durch Irrtum und Hoffnung geführt; aber beide sind nicht mehr nötig, wenn wir uns erst mit dem guten und mächtigen Ich bekannt gemacht haben, das so still und ruhig in uns wohnt und so lange, bis es die Herrschaft im Hause

beautiful lady was finally unable to stand on her feet and was compelled, in spite of the warm season, to cover herself with double and triple layers of clothing to conserve somehow the inner warmth that had almost completely vanished. Indeed she was no longer able to remain upright and in the end was even compelled to keep to her bed.

What reflections she was compelled to make concerning her condition! How often did this strange event pass before her mind, and how painful it was to her when ten days passed without her friend appearing, he who cost her these extreme sacrifices! On the other hand, during these gloomy hours her complete recovery was being prepared, indeed it was decided. For when her friend appeared soon after that and sat down beside her bed on that same stool on which he had heard her first declaration, and admonished her in friendly, indeed in tender tones, to hold out steadfastly for the short period still remaining, she interrupted him with a smile and said: "I need no further urging, my dear friend, and I will endure my vow during these few days with patience and in the conviction that you have imposed it on me for my own good. I am too weak now to be able to express my gratitude to you as I feel it. You have saved me for myself; you have given me to myself, and I recognize that from now on I owe you my whole existence.

"Truly, my husband was understanding and clever and knew a woman's heart. He was fair enough not to scold her for an inclination that might arise in her heart through his fault; indeed he was generous enough to place his rights behind the demands of nature. But you, sir, are reasonable and good. You have made me feel that there is something in us other than desire which can balance it so that we are capable of renouncing everything of value to which we are accustomed and to give up even our most cherished wishes. You have led me into this school through error and hope; but both are no longer necessary, once we have become acquainted with the good and mighty 'I' which dwells within us so silently and so calmly and makes its presence known incessantly, at least through delicate reminders, until it becomes master in the

gewinnt, wenigstens durch zarte Erinnerungen seine Gegenwart unaufhörlich merken läßt. Leben Sie wohl! Ihre Freundin
wird Sie künftig mit Vergnügen sehen; wirken Sie auf Ihre
Mitbürger wie auf mich; entwickeln Sie nicht allein die Ver-
wirrungen, die nur zu leicht über Besitztümer entstehen,
sondern zeigen Sie ihnen auch durch sanfte Anleitung und
durch Beispiel, daß in jedem Menschen die Kraft der Tugend
im Verborgenen keimt; die allgemeine Achtung wird Ihr Lohn
sein, und Sie werden mehr als der erste Staatsmann und der
größte Held den Namen Vater des Vaterlandes verdienen."

house. Farewell! Your friend will see you in future with pleasure; influence your fellow citizens as you have influenced me. Do not merely unravel the confusions that arise only too easily over property, but show them also through gentle guidance and by example that in every man the power of virtue secretly dwells. Your reward will be general esteem and you will deserve the name of Father of Our Country more than the foremost statesman and the greatest hero."

# Ernst Theodor Amadeus Hoffmann

## (1776–1822)

HOFFMANN WAS a man of many interests: he was equally gifted as a painter, writer and musician (he added the "Amadeus" to his name out of admiration for Mozart). He was born in Königsberg, East Prussia, into a family of jurists, studied law himself and embarked on a juristic career. Through the vicissitudes of the Napoleonic wars and his own irresponsible satirical bent, he lost several legal posts. For a while he made his living as musical director in theaters at Bamberg and Dresden, and through his journalistic efforts. At the same time he devoted himself to musical composition and to creative writing. In 1814, he was finally appointed Councillor of the Court of Appeals at Berlin, a post which he held for life. He went on composing, wrote pioneering musical criticism, and published the many tales on which his fame rests.

His personal life was tragic. He was grotesquely ugly and he knew it. Disappointed in love, he indulged himself excessively in drink, so that he undermined his health and died at the early age of forty-six.

Hoffmann's influence on world literature has been great, out of proportion to the intrinsic worth of his work. One need only mention the names of Musset, Gautier, Baudelaire, Poe, Dostoevsky, Hans Christian Andersen, as writers who are indebted to his art. His world is that of the grotesque, macabre and supernatural which forms one of the aspects of European romanticism. He made elaborate use of such para-

psychological phenomena as animal magnetism, *Doppelgänger*, and automata in his works.

*Don Juan* is one of Hoffmann's earliest tales and is a remarkably original and profound essay, in fictional form, on Mozart's genius. The story is typically Hoffmannesque in its introduction of telepathy and in its bitter attack on philistinism. But above all it is a glorious tribute to Hoffmann's musical idol, Mozart.

# DON JUAN

## EINE FABELHAFTE BEGEBENHEIT
### DIE SICH MIT EINEM REISENDEN ENTHUSIASTEN ZUGETRAGEN

### von E. T. A. Hoffmann

EIN DURCHDRINGENDES Läuten, der gellende Ruf: Das Theater
fängt an! weckte mich aus dem sanften Schlaf, in den ich
versunken war; Bässe brummen durcheinander—ein Paukenschlag—Trompetenstöße—ein klares A, von der Hoboe ausge-
halten—Violinen stimmen ein: ich reibe mir die Augen. Sollte
der allezeit geschäftige Satan mich im Rausche—? Nein! ich
befinde mich in dem Zimmer des Hotels, wo ich gestern abend
halb gerädert abgestiegen. Gerade über meiner Nase hängt
die stattliche Troddel der Klingelschnur; ich ziehe sie heftig
an, der Kellner erscheint.

„Aber was, um's Himmelswillen, soll die konfuse Musik da
neben mir bedeuten? gibt es denn ein Konzert hier im
Hause?"

„Ew.[1] Exzellenz—(ich hatte mittags an der Wirtstafel[2]
Champagner getrunken!)—Ew. Exzellenz wissen vielleicht
noch nicht, daß dieses Hotel mit dem Theater verbunden ist.
Diese Tapetentür führt auf einen kleinen Korridor, von dem
Sie unmittelbar in Nr. 23 treten: das ist die Fremdenloge."

„Was?—Theater?—Fremdenloge?"

„Ja, die kleine Fremdenloge zu zwei, höchstens drei Personen—nur so für vornehme Herren, ganz grün tapeziert, mit
Gitterfenstern, dicht beim Theater! Wenn's Ew. Exzellenz
gefällig ist—wir führen heute den Don Juan von dem be-

42

# DON JUAN

A FABULOUS INCIDENT
THAT HAPPENED TO A TRAVELLING ENTHUSIAST

by E. T. A. Hoffmann

A PENETRATING peal, the shrill cry: "The show is beginning!"
woke me out of the gentle sleep into which I had sunk.
Basses rumble in confusion—a bass drum beats—trumpets
blare—a clear A, sustained by the oboe—violins tune up: I
rub my eyes. Can it be that Satan, ever busy, has caught me
in a state of intoxication? No, I am in the room of the hotel
where I put up last night, half dead from exhaustion. Right
above my nose hangs the elegant tassel of the bell rope; I
give it a violent tug, the waiter appears.

"What in Heaven's name can be the meaning of the confused music near me? Is there a concert here in the house?"

"Your Excellency!" (I had drunk champagne in the inn at
noon!) "Perhaps Your Excellency doesn't know yet that this
hotel is connected with the theater. This door covered with
wallpaper leads to a small hallway, out of which you step
directly into No. 23: that is the visitors' box."

"What?—theater?—a visitors' box?"

"Yes, the small visitors' box for two or, at the most, three
people—only for gentlemen of quality, decorated all in green,
with latticed windows, close to the stage. If it please Your
Excellency—today we're performing Don Juan by the famous

43

rühmten Herrn Mozart aus Wien auf. Das Legegeld, einen Taler[3] acht Groschen, stellen wir in Rechnung."[4]

Das letzte sagte er, schon die Logentür aufdrückend, so rasch war ich bei dem Worte Don Juan durch die Tapetentür in den Korridor geschritten. Das Haus war, für den mittelmäßigen Ort, geräumig, geschmackvoll verziert und glänzend erleuchtet. Logen und Parterre waren gedrängt voll. Die ersten Akkorde der Ouvertüre überzeugten mich, daß ein ganz vortreffliches Orchester, sollten die Sänger nur im mindesten etwas leisten, mir den herrlichsten Genuß des Meisterwerks verschaffen würde.—In dem Andante ergriffen mich die Schauer des furchtbaren, unterirdischen *regno all pianto*;[5] grausenerregende Ahnungen des Entsetzlichen erfüllten mein Gemüt. Wie ein jauchzender Frevel klang mir die jubelnde Fanfare im siebenten Takte des Allegro; ich sah aus tiefer Nacht feurige Dämonen ihre glühenden Krallen ausstrecken— nach dem Leben froher Menschen, die auf des bodenlosen Abgrunds dünner Decke lustig tanzten. Der Konflikt der menschlichen Natur mit den unbekannten, gräßlichen Mächten, die ihn, sein Verderben erlauernd, umfangen, trat klar vor meines Geistes Augen. Endlich beruhigt sich der Sturm; der Vorhang fliegt auf. Frostig und unmutvoll in seinen Mantel gehüllt, schreitet Leporello in finstrer Nacht vor dem Pavillon einher: *Notte e giorno facticar.*[6]—Also italienisch?—Hier am deutschen Ort italienisch? *Ah che piacere!*[7] ich werde alle Rezitative, alles so hören, wie es der große Meister in seinem Gemüt empfing und dachte! Da stürzt Don Juan heraus; hinter ihm Donna Anna, bei dem Mantel den Frevler festhaltend. Welches Ansehen! Sie könnte höher, schlanker gewachsen, majestätischer im Gange sein: aber welch' ein Kopf!—Augen, aus denen Liebe, Zorn, Haß, Verzweiflung, wie aus einem Brennpunkt eine Strahlenpyramide blitzender Funken werfen, die, wie griechisches Feuer, unauslöschlich das Innerste durchbrennen! des dunklen Haares aufgelöste Flechten wallen in Wellenringeln den Nacken hinab. Das weiße Nachtkleid enthüllt verräterisch nie gefahrlos belauschte Reize. Von der entsetzlichen Tat umkrallt, zuckt das Herz in gewaltsamen Schlägen.—Und nun— welche Stimme! *Non sperar se non m'uccidi.*[8]—Durch den Sturm der Instrumente leuchten, wie glühende Blitze, die aus

Herr Mozart from Vienna. The entrance fee, a thaler and eight groschen, we can add to the bill."

He said the last words as he was already pushing open the loge door, so swiftly had I stepped into the hall through the papered door at the sound of the words "Don Juan." For this moderate-sized town the house was spacious, decorated in good taste and brilliantly illuminated. Boxes and orchestra were filled to overflowing. The first chords of the overture convinced me that, if the singers gave even a minimum performance, a very excellent orchestra would afford me the most glorious enjoyment of the masterpiece. During the andante I was gripped by the horrors of the terrible, infernal *regno al pianto*; horror inspiring premonitions of the terrible filled my mind. Like an exultant cry of outrage, the jubilant fanfare in the seventh bar of the allegro sounded to me; out of the deep night I saw fiery demons stretch out their glowing claws for the lives of happy people who were dancing merrily on the thin cover of the bottomless abyss. The conflict of man's nature with the unknown, gruesome powers which surround him, waiting to destroy him, stood clearly before my mind's eye. Finally the storm calms down; the curtain rises quickly. Frosty and peevish, wrapped in his cloak, Leporello paces in front of the pavilion in the dark night: "*Notte e giorno facticar.*"—In Italian then?—Italian here in this German town? *Ah che piacere!* I shall hear all the recitatives, everything just as the great master conceived and created it in his mind! Then Don Juan rushes out; behind him Donna Anna, holding the villain tightly by his cloak. What a sight! She could be taller, slimmer in build, more majestic in her walk: but what a head!—Eyes out of which love, anger, hatred, despair hurl flashing sparks, as from the focus of a pyramid of light; eyes inextinguishable, which burn through to the core like Greek fire. The loosened tressses of her dark hair flow down the nape of her neck in waved ringlets. The white nightdress treacherously reveals charms which are never espied without danger. Clawed by the horrible deed, her heart quivers with powerful beats.—And now—what a voice! "*Non sperar se non m'uccidi.*" Through the storm of the instruments the notes, cast of ethereal metal, shine like glowing flashes of lightning.—In vain Don Juan seeks to tear himself loose.—

ätherischem Metall gegossenen Töne!—Vergebens sucht sich
Don Juan loszureißen.—Will er es denn? Warum stößt er
nicht mit kräftiger Faust das Weib zurück und entflieht?
Macht ihn die böse Tat kraftlos, oder ist es der Kampf von
Haß und Liebe im Innern, der ihm Mut und Stärke raubt?—
Der alte Papa hat seine Torheit, im Finstern den kräftigen
Gegner anzufallen, mit dem Leben gebüßt; Don Juan und
Leporello treten im rezitierenden Gespräch weiter vor ins
Proszenium.[9] Don Juan wickelt sich aus dem Mantel und
steht da in rotem, gerissenem Samt mit silberner Stickerei,
prächtig gekleidet. Eine kräftige, herrliche Gestalt: das Ge-
sicht ist männlich schön; eine erhabene Nase, durchbohrende
Augen, weich geformte Lippen; das sonderbare Spiel eines
Stirnmuskels über den Augenbrauen bringt sekundenlang
etwas von Mephistopheles [10] in die Physiognomie, das, ohne
dem Gesicht die Schönheit zu rauben, einen unwillkürlichen
Schauer erregt. Es ist, als könne er die magische Kunst der
Klapperschlange üben; es ist, als könnten die Weiber, von
ihm angeblickt, nicht mehr von ihm lassen, und müßten, von
der unheimlichen Gewalt gepackt, selbst ihr Verderben voll-
enden.—Lang und dürr, in rot- und weißgestreifter [11] Weste,
kleinem roten Mantel, weißem Hut mit roter Feder, trippelt
Leporello um ihn her. Die Züge seines Gesichts mischen sich
seltsam zu dem Ausdruck von Gutherzigkeit, Schelmerei,
Lüsternheit und ironisierender Frechheit; gegen das grauliche
Kopf- und Barthaar stechen seltsam die schwarzen Augenbrauen ab. Man merkt es, der alte Bursche verdient Don
Juans helfender Diener zu sein.—Glücklich sind sie über die
Mauer geflüchtet.—Fackeln—Donna Anna und Don Ottavio
erscheinen: ein zierliches, geputztes, gelecktes Männlein, von
einundzwanzig Jahren höchstens. Als Annas Bräutigam
wohnte er, da man ihn so schnell herbeirufen konnte, wahrscheinlich im Hause; auf den ersten Lärm, den er gewiß hörte,
hätte er herbeieilen und den Vater retten können: er mußte
sich aber erst putzen, und mochte überhaupt nachts nicht
gern sich herauswagen.—*„Ma qual mai s'offre, o dei, spet-*
*tacolo funesto agli occhi miei!"* [12] Mehr als Verzweiflung
über den grausamsten Frevel liegt in den entsetzlichen,
herzzerschneidenden Tönen dieses Rezitativs und Duetts. Don
Juans gewaltsames Attentat, das ihr Verderben nur drohte, dem

Does he really want to? Why does he not beat the woman back with his powerful fist and flee? Does the evil deed make him powerless, or is it the conflict between hatred and love within him which robs him of his courage and strength?— The old papa has paid with his life for the folly of attacking his powerful opponent in the dark; Don Juan and Leporello advance further onto the proscenium in spoken conversation. Don Juan unwraps his cloak and there he stands splendidly dressed in a suit of red, slashed velvet with silver embroidery. A powerful, splendid figure: his face has a masculine beauty; a prominent nose, piercing eyes, softly formed lips; the strange play of a muscle in the forehead, above the eyebrows, brings something Mephistophelian into his physiognomy for seconds at a time; without depriving the face of its beauty, it makes one involuntarily shudder. It is as if he were able to practice the magic art of the rattlesnake; it is as if women, once he has looked at them, could no longer let him go and, gripped by his uncanny power, were forced to complete their own destruction.—Tall and lean, in his waistcoat with red and white stripes, his little red coat, white hat with a red plume, Leporello skips around him. The features of his face intermingle strangely in an expression of good nature, roguishness, sensuality and ironical insolence; his black eyebrows contrast strangely with the grayish hair on his head and in his beard. One feels it—the old fellow deserves to be Don Juan's helpful servant.—They have successfully escaped over the wall.—Torches—Donna Anna and Don Ottavio appear: a dainty, foppish, dapper little man, twenty-one years old at the most. As Anna's fiancé he probably lived in the house, since they were able to summon him so quickly; at the first alarm, which he had certainly heard, he could have hurried over and saved the father: but he had to get all dressed up first, and he did not like to venture out at night at all.—*"Ma qual mai s'offre, o dei, spettacolo funesto agli occhi miei!"* More than despair at the brutal crime lies in the terrible, heart-rending tones of this recitative and duet. It is not only Don Juan's violent attack—which only threatened her with ruin and caused the death of her father—which tears these notes from his anguished heart: only a destructive, murderous inner struggle can produce them.—

Vater aber den Tod gab, ist es nicht allein, was diese Töne
der beängsteten Brust [13] entreißt: nur ein verderblicher,
tötender Kampf im Innern kann sie hervorbringen.—

Eben schalt die lange, hagere Donna Elvira mit sichtlichen
Spuren großer, aber verblühter Schönheit den Verräter, Don
Juan: *Tu nido d'inganni*,[14] und der mitleidige Leporello
bemerkte ganz klug: *parla come un libro stampato*,[15] als ich
jemand neben oder hinter mir zu bemerken glaubte. Leicht
konnte man die Logentür hinter mir geöffnet haben und
hineingeschlüpft sein—das fuhr mir wie ein Stich durchs
Herz. Ich war so glücklich, mich allein in der Loge zu befinden, um ganz ungestört das so vollkommen dargestellte
Meisterwerk mit allen Empfindungsfasern, wie mit Poly-
penarmen, zu umklammern, und in mein Selbst hineinzu-
ziehn! ein einziges Wort, das obendrein albern sein konnte,
hätte mich auf eine schmerzhafte Weise herausgerissen aus
dem herrlichen Moment der poetisch-musikalischen Begeisterung! Ich beschloß, von meinem Nachbar gar keine
Notiz zu nehmen, sondern, ganz in die Darstellung vertieft,
jedes Wort, jeden Blick zu vermeiden. Den Kopf in die Hand
gestützt, dem Nachbar den Rücken wendend, schaute ich
hinaus.—Der Gang der Darstellung entsprach dem vortreff-
lichen Anfange. Die kleine, lüsterne, verliebte Zerlina tröstete
mit gar lieblichen Tönen und Weisen den gutmütigen Tölpel
Masetto. Don Juan sprach sein inneres, zerrissenes Wesen,
den Hohn über die Menschlein um ihn her, nur aufgestellt zu
seiner Lust, in ihr mattliches Tun und Treiben verderbend
einzugreifen, in der wilden Arie: *Fin ch'han dal vino* [16]—
ganz unverhohlen aus. Gewaltiger als bisher zuckte hier der
Stirnmuskel.—Die Masken erscheinen. Ihr Terzett [17] ist ein
Gebet, das in rein glänzenden Strahlen zum Himmel steigt.—
Nun fliegt der Mittelvorhang auf. Da geht es lustig her;
Becher erklingen, in fröhlichem Gewühl wälzen sich die
Bauern und allerlei Masken umher, die Don Juans Fest
herbeigelockt hat.—Jetzt kommen die drei zur Rache Ver-
schworenen. Alles wird feierlicher, bis der Tanz angeht.
Zerlina wird gerettet, und in dem gewaltig donnernden Finale
tritt mutig Don Juan mit gezogenem Schwert seinen Feinden
entgegen. Er schlägt dem Bräutigam den stählernen Galanteriedegen aus der Hand, und bahnt sich durch das gemeine

Tall, thin Donna Elvira, with visible traces of great but faded beauty, was just scolding the betrayer Don Juan, "*Tu nido d'inganni*," and the sympathetic Leporello remarked quite cleverly, "*parla come un libro stampato*," when I thought I noticed someone near or behind me. Someone could easily have opened the loge door behind me and slipped in—this thought went through my heart like a needle. I was so happy to be alone in the box, so that I could embrace the masterpiece that was being performed so perfectly, with every sensory fibre as with the tentacles of an octopus, and to absorb it into my inner being; a single word, which might moreover be a silly one, would have torn me painfully out of the glorious moment of poetic-musical ecstasy! I resolved to take no notice whatever of my neighbor but, wholly engrossed in the performance, to avoid every word, every look. With my head in my hand, my back turned to my neighbor, I looked out.—The sequel of the performance bore out the excellent beginning. Sensual, infatuated little Zerlina consoled the good-natured bumpkin Masetto, in very lovely tones and airs. In the wild aria, "*Fin ch'han dal vino*," Don Juan frankly expressed his inner torn soul, his scorn of the people around him, existing only for his pleasure; so that he may bring ruin into their insipid doings and dealings.—The masks appear. Their terzetto is a prayer which rises to heaven in pure and shining rays.—Now the central curtain rises quickly. There is a merry scene; cups ring, in a merry throng peasants and all sorts of masks whirl about, attracted by Don Juan's party.— Now the three conspirators appear, sworn to vengeance. Everything becomes more solemn until the dance begins. Zerlina is rescued, and in the powerfully thundering finale Don Juan bravely goes to meet his enemies with drawn sword. He knocks the steel dress sword out of the fiancé's hand and makes a way for himself into the open through the common rabble, throwing them into a confusion as the gallant Roland caused among the host of the tyrant Cymork, so that they all fall over each other in a very comical disorder.—

Gesindel, das er, wie der tapfere Roland [18] die Armee des
Tyrannen Cymork, durcheinander wirft, daß alles gar possierlich übereinander purzelt, den Weg ins Freie.—

Schon oft glaubte ich dicht hinter mir einen zarten,
warmen Hauch gefühlt, das Knistern eines seidenen Gewandes
gehört zu haben: das ließ mich wohl die Gegenwart eines
Frauenzimmers [19] ahnen, aber ganz versunken in die poetische
Welt, die mir die Oper aufschloß, achtete ich nicht darauf.
Jetzt, da der Vorhang gefallen war, schaute ich nach meiner
Nachbarin.—Nein—keine Worte drücken mein Erstaunen
aus: Donna Anna, ganz in dem Kostüme, wie ich sie eben auf
dem Theater gesehen, stand hinter mir, und richtete auf mich
den durchdringenden Blick ihres seelenvollen Auges.—Ganz
sprachlos starrte ich sie an; ihr Mund (so schien es mir)
verzog sich zu einem leisen ironischen Lächeln, in dem ich
mich spiegelte und meine alberne Figur erblickte. Ich fühlte
die Notwendigkeit, sie anzureden, und konnte doch die, durch
das Erstaunen, ja ich möchte sagen, wie durch den Schreck
gelähmte Zunge nicht bewegen. Endlich, endlich fuhren mir,
beinahe unwillkürlich, die Worte heraus: „Wie ist es möglich,
Sie hier zu sehen?" worauf sie sogleich in dem reinsten
Toskanisch [20] erwiderte, daß, verstände und spräche ich nicht
italienisch, sie das Vergnügen meiner Unterhaltung entbehren
müsse, indem sie keine andere, als nur diese Sprache rede.—
Wie Gesang lauteten die süßen Worte. Im Sprechen erhöhte
sich der Ausdruck des dunkelblauen Auges, und jeder daraus
leuchtende Blitz goß einen Glutstrom in mein Inneres, von
dem alle Pulse stärker schlugen und alle Fibern erzuckten.—
Es war Donna Anna unbezweifelt. Die Möglichkeit abzu-
wägen, wie sie auf dem Theater und in meiner Loge habe
zugleich sein können, fiel mir nicht ein. So wie der glückliche
Traum das Seltsamste verbindet, und dann ein frommer
Glaube das Übersinnliche versteht, und es den sogenannten
natürlichen Erscheinungen des Lebens zwanglos anreiht: so
geriet ich auch in der Nähe des wunderbaren Weibes in eine
Art Somnambulismus, in dem ich die geheimen Beziehungen
erkannte, die mich so innig mit ihr verbanden, daß sie selbst
bei ihrer Erscheinung auf dem Theater nicht hatte von mir
weichen können.—Wie gern setzte ich dir, mein Theodor,[21]
jedes Wort des merkwürdigen Gesprächs her, das nun

A number of times I thought I felt close behind me a gentle, warm breath and heard the rustle of a silken dress: this naturally led me to suspect the presence of a woman; but, wholly engrossed in the world of poetry which the opera opened before me, I paid no attention to it. Now, after the curtain had fallen, I looked at my neighbor.—No—no words can express my astonishment: Donna Anna, in the very costume in which I had just seen her on the stage, stood behind me, fixing the penetrating glance of her soulful eyes upon me.—I stared at her utterly speechless; her lips (so it seemed to me) were pursed in a gentle, ironical smile in which I was reflected and perceived the silly figure I cut. I felt the necessity of addressing her, and yet I could not move my tongue, which was paralyzed by astonishment, yes, I might even say by terror. Finally, finally, almost against my will, these words escaped me: "How is it possible to see you here?"; to which she promptly replied in the purest Tuscan, that if I did not understand or speak Italian she would have to forego the pleasure of conversing with me, as she spoke no other tongue but this.—These sweet words sounded like music. As she spoke, the expression in her dark blue eyes was heightened and every flash of lightning that came from them poured a stream of fire into my soul, making my pulse beat faster and all my fibres quiver.—It was Donna Anna, without a doubt. It did not occur to me to weigh the possibility how she could have been on the stage and in my loge at the same time. Just as a happy dream combines the strangest things, and as a pious faith understands the supernatural, and then fitting it without effort into the so-called natural phenomena of life, so too, in the presence of the amazing woman, I fell into a kind of somnambulism in which I recognized the mysterious bonds which united me so intimately with her, so that she had not been able to keep away from me even when she was on the stage.—How I would like, my dear Theodor, to put down for you every word of the remarkable conversation that now began between the signora and myself; but when I want to write down in German what she said, I find every word

zwischen der Signora und mir begann: allein, indem ich das, was sie sagte, deutsch hinschreiben will, finde ich jedes Wort steif und matt, jede Phrase [22] ungelenk, das auszudrücken, was sie leicht und mit Anmut toskanisch sagte.

Indem sie über den Don Juan, über ihre Rolle sprach, war es, als öffneten sich mir nun erst die Tiefen des Meisterwerks, und ich konnte hell hineinblicken und einer fremden Welt phantastische Erscheinungen deutlich erkennen. Sie sagte, ihr ganzes Leben sei Musik, und oft glaubte sie manches im Innern geheimnisvoll verschlossene, was keine Worte aussprächen, singend zu begreifen. „Ja, ich begreife es dann wohl", fuhr sie mit brennendem Auge und erhöhter Stimme fort: „aber es bleibt tot und kalt um mich, und indem man eine schwierige Roulade,[23] eine gelungene Manier beklatscht, greifen eisige Hände in mein glühendes Herz!—Aber du—du verstehst mich, denn ich weiß, daß auch d i r das wunderbare, romantische Reich aufgegangen,[24] wo die himmlischen Zauber der Töne wohnen!—"

„Wie, du herrliche, wundervolle Frau—du—du solltest mich kennen?"

„Ging nicht der zauberische Wahnsinn ewig sehnender Liebe in der Rolle der * * * in deiner neuesten Oper aus deinem Innern hervor?—Ich habe dich verstanden: dein Gemüt hat sich im Gesange mir aufgeschlossen!—Ja, (hier nannte sie meinen Vornamen) ich habe d i c h gesungen, sowie deine Melodien i c h sind."

Die Theaterglocke läutete: eine schnelle Blässe entfärbte Donna Annas ungeschminktes Gesicht; sie fuhr mit der Hand nach dem Herzen, als empfände sie einen plötzlichen Schmerz und indem sie leise sagte: Unglückliche Anna, jetzt kommen deine fürchterlichsten Momente—war sie aus der Loge verschwunden.—

Der erste Akt hatte mich entzückt, aber nach dem wunderbaren Ereignis wirkte jetzt die Musik auf eine ganz andere seltsame Weise. Es war, als ginge eine lang verheißene Erfüllung der schönsten Träume aus einer andern Welt wirklich in das Leben ein: als würden die geheimsten Ahnungen der entzückten Seele in Tönen fest gebannt und müßten sich zur wunderbarsten Erkenntnis seltsamlich gestalten.—In Donna Annas Szene fühlte ich mich von einem

stiff and pale, every phrase too clumsy to express what she said in Tuscan with lightness and grace.

As she spoke about Don Juan and about her role, it seemed as if the depth of the masterpiece opened up before me only now; I could look into it brightly and recognize clearly the fantastic phenomena of a strange world. She said that her whole life was music, and she often thought she understood in song what was mysteriously locked up in her mind, what no words could express. "Yes, I understand it well then," she continued with burning eyes and raising her voice; "but it remains dead and cold about me, and when they applaud a difficult roulade or a successful mannerism, icy hands clutch at my glowing heart!—But you—you understand me, for I know that the marvellous, romantic realm in which the heavenly magic of the tones dwells has been opened for you, too."—

"What, you glorious, wonderful woman—you—can you possibly know me?"

"Did not the magic madness of eternally yearning love, in the role of * * * in your most recent opera, come from the depths of your soul?—I understood you; your soul revealed itself to me in song.—Yes (here she called me by my first name) I sang you, just as I am your melodies."

The intermission bell rang; a swift pallor spread over Donna Anna's unpainted face. She put her hand to her heart as if she felt a sudden pain there, and with the words: "Unhappy Anna, now your most terrible moments are coming"—she had vanished from the box.—

The first act had enthralled me, but after the remarkable experience the music now affected me in an entirely different, strange way. It was as if a long-promised fulfillment of the most beautiful dreams from another world were really entering into life; as though the most secret premonitions of my enraptured soul were being captured in music and must assume strange shape in the most wonderful revelations.—In Donna Anna's scene I felt myself quiver with an intoxicated

sanften, warmen Hauch, der über mich hinwegglitt, in trunkener Wollust erbeben; unwillkürlich schlossen sich meine Augen und ein glühender Kuß schien auf meinen Lippen zu brennen: aber der Kuß war ein wie von ewig dürstender Sehnsucht lang ausgehaltener Ton.

Das Finale war in frevelnder Lustigkeit angegangen: *Già la mensa è preparata!* [25]—Don Juan saß kosend zwischen zwei Mädchen, und lüftete einen Kork nach dem andern, um den brausenden Geistern,[26] die hermetisch verschlossen, freie Herrschaft über sich zu verstatten. Es war ein kurzes Zimmer mit einem großen gotischen Fenster im Hintergrunde, durch das man in die Nacht hinaussah. Schon während Elvira den Ungetreuen an alle Schwüre erinnert, sah man es oft durch das Fenster blitzen, und hörte das dumpfe Murmeln des herannahenden Gewitters. Endlich das gewaltige Pochen. Elvira, die Mädchen entfliehen, und unter den entsetzlichen Akkorden der unterirdischen Geisterwelt, tritt der gewaltige Marmorkoloß,[27] gegen den Don Juan pygmäisch [28] dasteht, ein. Der Boden erbebt unter des Riesen donnerndem Fußtritt. —Don Juan ruft durch den Sturm, durch den Donner, durch das Geheul der Dämonen sein fürchterliches: *No!* die Stunde des Untergangs ist da. Die Statue verschwindet, dicker Qualm erfüllt das Zimmer, aus ihm entwickeln sich fürchterliche Larven. In Qualen der Hölle windet sich Don Juan, den man dann und wann unter den Dämonen erblickt. Eine Explosion, wie wenn tausend Blitze einschlügen—: Don Juan, die Dämonen, sind verschwunden, man weiß nicht wie! Leporello liegt ohnmächtig in der Ecke des Zimmers.—Wie wohltätig wirkt nun die Erscheinung der übrigen Personen, die den Juan, der von unterirdischen Mächten irdischer Rache entzogen, vergebens suchen. Es ist, als wäre man nun erst dem furchtbaren Kreise der höllischen Geister entronnen.— Donna Anna erschien ganz verändert: eine Totenblässe überzog ihr Gesicht, das Auge war erloschen, die Stimme zitternd und ungleich: aber eben dadurch in dem kleinen Duett mit dem süßen Bräutigam, der nun, nachdem ihm der Himmel des gefährlichen Rächeramts glücklich überhoben hat, gleich Hochzeit machen will, von herzzereißender Wirkung.

Der fugierte Chor hatte das Werk herrlich zu einem Ganzen gerundet, und ich eilte, in der exaltiertesten Stimmung, in

voluptuousness from a gentle, warm breath which floated over me. Involuntarily my eyes closed and a glowing kiss seemed to burn on my lips; but the kiss was a long note that seemed sustained by an eternally thirsty yearning.

The finale had began in outrageous merriment: *"Già la mensa è preparata!"*—Don Juan sat chatting between two girls, drawing one cork after the other, to permit the effervescent spirits, hitherto hermetically locked in, free reign over himself. It was a short room with a large, Gothic window in the background, through which one looked out into the night. Even while Elvira reminds the unfaithful man of all his vows, one often saw flashes of lightning through the window and heard the muffled murmur of the approaching storm. Finally the tremendous pounding. Elvira and the girls flee, and amidst the horrifying chords of the infernal spirit world, the enormous marble colossus enters; beside him Don Juan stands there like a pygmy. The ground shakes under the thundering footsteps of the giant.—Don Juan shouts through the storm, through the thunder, through the howling of the demons, his terrified *"No!"* The hour of his destruction has come. The statue vanishes, thick smoke fills the room, out of it horrible masks emerge. Don Juan writhes in the torments of hell; from time to time one catches sight of him among the demons. An explosion, as though a thousand bolts of lightning struck—: Don Juan and the demons have vanished, one does not know how! Leporello lies unconscious in the corner of the room.—How beneficial is the effect produced by the appearance of the other persons who look in vain for Don Juan who has been removed from earthly vengeance by the infernal powers. It is as if one had only now escaped from the fearful circle of the hellish spirits.—Donna Anna seemed quite changed: a deathlike pallor covered her face, her eyes were dull, her voice trembling and uneven; but for this very reason the effect is heartrending in the little duet she sings with her sweet fiancé who, now that Heaven has happily absolved him from his dangerous vow of vengeance, wants to celebrate the marriage at once.

The fugal chorus had rounded the work into a splendid whole, and I hurried to my room in the most exalted frame

der ich mich je befunden, in mein Zimmer. Der Kellner rief
mich zur Wirtstafel, und ich folgte ihm mechanisch.—Die
Gesellschaft war, der Messe wegen, glänzend, und die heutige
Darstellung des Don Juan der Gegenstand des Gesprächs.
Man pries im allgemeinen die Italiener und das Eingreifende
ihres Spiels: doch zeigten kleine Bemerkungen, die hier und
da ganz schalkhaft hingeworfen wurden, daß wohl keiner die
tiefere Bedeutung der Oper aller Opern auch nur ahnte.—
Don Ottavio hatte sehr gefallen. Donna Anna war einem zu
leidenschaftlich gewesen. Man müsse, meinte er, auf dem
Theater sich hübsch mäßigen und das zu sehr Angreifende
vermeiden. Die Erzählung des Überfalls habe ihn ordentlich
konsterniert.[29] Hier nahm er eine Prise Tabak und schaute
ganz unbeschreiblich dummklug seinen Nachbar an, welcher
behauptete: Die Italienerin sei aber übrigens eine recht
schöne Frau, nur zu wenig besorgt um Kleidung und Putz;
eben in jener Szene sei ihr eine Haarlocke aufgegangen, und
habe das Demiprofil des Gesichts beschattet! Jetzt fing ein
anderer ganz leise zu intonieren an: *Fin ch'han dal vino*—
worauf eine Dame bemerkte: am wenigsten sei sie mit dem
Don Juan zufrieden: der Italiener sei viel zu finster, viel zu
ernst gewesen, und habe überhaupt den frivolen, luftigen
Charakter nicht leicht genug genommen.—Die letzte Explosion wurde sehr gerühmt. Des Gewäsches satt eilte ich in
mein Zimmer.

## IN DER FREMDENLOGE NR. 23

Es war mir [30] so eng, so schwül in dem dumpfen Gemach!—
Um Mitternacht glaubte ich deine Stimme zu hören, mein
Theodor! Du sprachst deutlich meinen Namen aus und es
schien an der Tapetentür zu rauschen. Was hält mich ab, den
Ort meines wunderbaren Abenteuers noch einmal zu betreten?—Vielleicht sehe ich dich und sie, die mein ganzes
Wesen erfüllt!—Wie leicht ist es, den kleinen Tisch hinein-
zutragen—zwei Lichter—Schreibzeug! Der Kellner sucht
mich mit dem bestellten Punsch; er findet das Zimmer leer,
die Tapetentür offen: er folgt mir in die Loge und sieht
mich mit zweifelndem Blick an. Auf meinen Wink setzt er
das Getränk auf den Tisch und entfernt sich, mit einer Frage
auf der Zunge, noch einmal sich nach mir umschauend. Ich

of mind which I had ever experienced. The waiter called me to a meal and I followed him mechanically.—The company was brilliant because of the fair, and the topic of conversation was tonight's performance of Don Juan. There was general praise for the Italians and the incisive nature of their playing; but little remarks, rather facetiously thrown in here and there, showed that probably no one had any idea of the deeper significance of this opera of all operas.—They had all liked Don Ottavio. Donna Anna had been too passionate for one. He felt that in the theatre one had to observe a nice moderation and avoid all excess of emotion. The narration of the attack had caused him real consternation. At this point he took a pinch of snuff and looked with an indescribably stupid-sly expression at his neighbor, who asserted that the Italian woman, however, was in other respects a really beautiful woman, but too little concerned about her dress and jewelry; in that very scene one of her curls had come loose and had cast a shadow on the semiprofile of her face. Now another man began to intone very softly: *"Fin ch'han dal vino,"*—at which a lady remarked, that she was least satisfied with Don Juan; the Italian had been much too sinister, much too serious and in general had not interpreted the frivolous, airy character lightly enough.—The final explosion was highly praised. Tired of this rubbish I hurried to my room.

## IN VISITORS' BOX NO. 23

I felt so constricted, so oppressed in the musty room!— At midnight I thought I heard your voice, my Theodor! You uttered my name clearly, and there seemed to be a rustling at the tapestried door. What prevents me from entering the site of my wonderful adventure once more?—Perhaps I will see you and her who fills my whole being!—How easy it is to carry in the little table—two candles—writing materials! The waiter looks for me with the punch I had ordered; he finds the room empty, the tapestried door stands open; he follows me into the box and looks at me with a doubtful eye. At a sign from me he puts the beverage on the table and goes away with a question on his tongue, looking back at me again. Turning my back to him, I lean over the railing of the box

lehne mich, ihm den Rücken wendend, über der Loge Rand,
und sehe in das verödete Haus, dessen Architektur, von meinen
beiden Lichtern magisch beleuchtet, in wunderlichen Reflexen
fremd und feenhaft hervorspringt. Den Vorhang bewegt die
das Haus durchschneidende Zugluft.—Wie wenn er hinauf-
wallte? wenn Donna Anna, geängstet von gräßlichen Larven,
erschiene?—Donna Anna! rufe ich unwillkürlich: der Ruf
verhallt in dem öden Raum, aber die Geister der Instrumente im Orchester werden wach—ein wunderbarer Ton
zittert herauf; es ist als säusle in ihm der geliebte Name fort!—
Nicht erwehren kann ich mich des heimlichen Schauers, aber
wohltätig durchbebt er meine Nerven.—

Ich werde meiner Stimmung Herr und fühle mich aufgelegt,
dir, mein Theodor, wenigstens anzudeuten, wie ich jetzt erst
das herrliche Werk des göttlichen Meisters in seiner tiefen
Charakteristik richtig aufzufassen glaube.—Nur der Dichter
versteht den Dichter; nur ein romantisches Gemüt kann
eingehen in das Romantische; nur der poetisch exaltierte
Geist, der mitten im Tempel die Weihe empfing, das verstehen, was der Geweihte in der Begeisterung ausspricht.—
Betrachtet man das Gedicht (den Don Juan), ohne ihm eine
tiefere Bedeutung zu geben, sodaß man nur das Geschichtliche
in Anspruch nimmt: so ist es kaum zu begreifen, wie Mozart
eine solche Musik dazu denken und dichten konnte. Ein
Bonvivant, der Wein und Mädchen über die Maßen liebt,
der mutwilligerweise den steinernen Mann als Repräsentanten
des alten Vaters, den er bei Verteidigung seines eigenen
Lebens niederstach, zu seiner lustigen Tafel bittet—wahrlich,
hierin liegt nicht viel Poetisches, und ehrlich gestanden, ist
ein solcher Mensch es wohl nicht wert, daß die unterirdischen
Mächte ihn als ein ganz besonderes Kabinettstück der Hölle
auszeichnen; daß der steinerne Mann, von dem verklärten
Geiste beseelt, sich bemüht vom Pferde zu steigen, um den
Sünder vor dem letzten Stündlein [31] zur Buße zu ermahnen;
daß endlich der Teufel seine besten Gesellen ausschickt, um
den Transport in sein Reich auf die gräßlichste Weise zu
veranstalten.—Du kannst es mir glauben, Theodor! den Juan
stattete die Natur, wie ihrer Schoßkinder liebstes,[32] mit
alledem aus, was den Menschen, in näherer Verwandtschaft
mit dem Göttlichen, über den gemeinen Troß, über die

and look into the deserted auditorium, the architecture of which, magically illuminated by my two candles, stands out weird and fairy-like in the strange reflexions. The curtain is stirred by the draft which cuts through the house.—Suppose it were to go up? Suppose Donna Anna were to appear, frightened by gruesome monsters?—"Donna Anna!" I cry involuntarily; my cry dies away in the deserted house, but the spirits of the instruments in the orchestra become alive—a wonderful tone quivers up to me; it is as if the beloved name kept whispering through it.—I cannot escape a mysterious shudder that sends a pleasant tremor through my nerves.

I become master of my mood and feel inclined, my dear Theodor, at least to indicate to you that I believe I really grasp the glorious work of the divine master in its profound spirit only now.—Only a poet understands a poet; only a romantic disposition can enter into the romantic spirit; only the poetically exalted spirit, which received its consecration in the center of the temple, can understand what the initiated expresses under inspiration.—If one studies the poem (Don Juan), without giving it a deeper significance so that one considers only the story element in itself, it is scarcely understandable how Mozart could imagine and compose such music for it. A bon vivant, who loves wine and girls to excess, who arrogantly invites the stone man to his gay dinner table, as the representative of the old father whom he stabbed to death in defense of his own life—really there is not much poetry in this; and to tell the truth such a man is really not worth being singled out by the infernal powers as a special specimen of hell; that the stone man, animated by his transfigured spirit, should take the trouble to descend from his horse to urge the sinner to repentance before his last hour on earth; nor, finally, the devil should send out his best helpers to arrange for the transport into his kingdom in the most gruesome fashion.—You may believe me, Theodor, Nature equipped Juan, as the dearest of her bosom children, with everything that elevates a man, in his closer affinity with the divine, above the common throng, above the factory products which are discarded from the workshop like zeros in front of which some integer must take up its position if they are to

Fabrikarbeiten, die als Nullen, vor die, wenn sie gelten sollen, sich erst ein Zähler stellen muß, aus der Werkstätte geschleudert werden, erhebt; was ihn bestimmt zu besiegen, zu herrschen. Ein kräftiger, herrlicher Körper, eine Bildung, woraus der Funke hervorstrahlt, der, die Ahnungen des Höchsten entzündend, in die Brust fiel; ein tiefes Gemüt, ein schnell ergreifender Verstand.—Aber das ist die entsetzliche Folge des Sündenfalls,[33] daß der Feind die Macht behielt, dem Menschen aufzulauern, und ihm selbst in dem Streben nach dem Höchsten, worin er seine göttliche Natur ausspricht, böse Fallstricke zu legen. Dieser Konflikt der göttlichen und der dämonischen Kräfte erzeugt den Begriff des irdischen, sowie der erfochtene Sieg den Begriff des überirdischen Lebens.—Don Juan begeisterten die Ansprüche auf das Leben, die seine körperliche und geistige Organisation herbeiführte, und ein ewig brennendes Sehnen, von dem sein Blut siedend die Adern durchfloß, trieb ihn, daß er, gierig und ohne Rast, alle Erscheinungen der irdischen Welt aufgriff, in ihnen vergebens Befriedigung hoffend!—Es gibt hier auf Erden wohl nichts, was den Menschen in seiner innigsten Natur so hinaufsteigert, als die Liebe; sie ist es, die so geheimnisvoll und so gewaltig wirkend, die innersten Elemente des Daseins zerstört und verklärt; was Wunder also, daß Don Juan in der Liebe die Sehnsucht, die seine Brust zerreißt, zu stillen hoffte, und daß der Teufel hier ihm die Schlinge über den Hals warf? In Don Juans Gemüt kam durch des Erbfeindes List der Gedanke, daß durch die Liebe, durch den Genuß des Weibes, schon auf Erden das erfüllt werden könne, was bloß als himmlische Verheißung in unserer Brust wohnt und eben jene unendliche Sehnsucht ist, die uns mit dem Überirdischen in unmittelbaren Rapport setzt. Vom schönen Weibe zum schönern rastlos fliehend; bis zum Überdruß, bis zur zerstörenden Trunkenheit ihrer Reize mit der glühendsten Inbrunst genießend, immer in der Wahl sich betrogen glaubend, immer hoffend, das Ideal endlicher Befriedigung zu finden, mußte doch Juan zuletzt alles irdische Leben matt und flach finden, und indem er überhaupt den Menschen verachtete, lehnte er sich auf gegen die Erscheinung, die, ihm als das Höchste im Leben geltend, so bitter ihn getäuscht hatte. Jeder Genuß des Weibes war nun nicht

have any value; and this destined him to conquer and to command. A vigorous, splendid physique, a personality from which a spark radiated which, kindling premonitions of the highest powers, reached the heart; a profound sensibility, a swift, alert intellect.—But this is the horrible result of the Fall, that the Evil One retained the power of lying in wait for man and setting wicked snares for him even in his striving for the highest in which he expresses his divine nature. This conflict between divine and demonic powers creates the concept of life, just as triumphant victory creates that of life beyond.—Don Juan was inspired by those claims on life which were produced by his physical and mental organization, and an eternally burning longing, which made his blood course through his veins at boiling point, impelled him to grasp avidly and relentlessly at the manifestations of the earthly world, hoping in vain for satisfaction in them.—There is probably nothing here on earth that elevates man in his innermost nature as much as love; it is love which, working so mysteriously and so powerfully, destroys and transfigures the innermost elements of existence. What wonder then that Don Juan hoped to still in love the longing that was tearing his heart asunder and that the Devil here slipped the noose around his neck? Through trickery of the archfiend the thought came into Don Juan's mind that through love, through the enjoyment of woman there could be fulfilled even on earth what dwells in our hearts merely as a promise of heaven, and is that very infinite longing which puts us into immediate rapport with the supernatural. Restlessly fleeing from a beautiful woman to a more beautiful one; enjoying their charms with the most burning ardor, to the point of surfeit, to the point of destructive intoxication; always believing he had been deceived in his choice; always hoping to find the ideal of eventual satisfaction—Juan was finally bound to find all earthly life insipid and flat; and while he despised man in general he rebelled against the manifestation which, valued by him as the highest thing in life, had so bitterly deceived him. Every enjoyment of a woman was now no longer the satisfaction of his senses but a blasphemous mocking of nature and the Creator. A profound contempt for the common aspects of life, which he felt was beneath him; a bitter scorn

mehr Befriedigung seiner Sinnlichkeit, sondern frevelnder Hohn gegen die Natur und den Schöpfer. Tiefe Verachtung der gemeinen Ansichten des Lebens, über die er sich erhoben fühlte, und bitterer Spott über Menschen, die in der glücklichen Liebe, in der dadurch herbeigeführten bürgerlichen Vereinigung, auch nur im mindesten die Erfüllung der höheren Wünsche, die die Natur feindselig in unsere Brust legte, erwarten konnten, trieben ihn an, da vorzüglich sich aufzulehnen, und, Verderben bereitend, dem unbekannten, schicksallenkenden Wesen, das ihm wie ein schadenfrohes, mit den kläglichen Geschöpfen seiner spottenden Laune ein grausames Spiel treibendes Ungeheuer erschien, kühn entgegenzutreten, wo von einem solchen Verhältnis die Rede war.—Jede Verführung einer geliebten Braut, jedes durch einen gewaltigen, nie zu verschmerzendes Unheil bringenden Schlag gestörte Glück der Liebenden ist ein herrlicher Triumph über jene feindliche Macht, der ihn immer mehr hinaushebt aus dem beengenden Leben—über die Natur— über den Schöpfer!—Er will auch wirklich immer mehr aus [34] dem Leben, aber nur um hinabzustürzen in den Orkus.[35] Annas Verführung, mit den dabei eingetretenen Umständen, ist die höchste Spitze, zu der er sich erhebt.—

Donna Anna ist, rücksichtlich der höchsten Begünstigung der Natur, dem Don Juan entgegengestellt. Sowie Don Juan ursprünglich ein wunderbar kräftiger, herrlicher Mann war, so ist sie ein göttliches Weib, über deren reines Gemüt der Teufel nichts vermochte. Alle Kunst der Hölle konnte nur sie irdisch verderben.—Sowie der Satan dieses Verderben vollendet hat, durfte auch, nach der Fügung des Himmels, die Hölle die Vollstreckung des Rächeramts nicht länger verschieben.—Don Juan ladet den erstochenen Alten höhnend im Bilde ein zum lustigen Gastmahl, und der verklärte Geist, nun erst den gefallenen Menschen durchschauend und sich um ihn betrübend, verschmäht es nicht, in furchtbarer Gestalt ihn zur Buße zu ermahnen. Aber so verderbt, so zerrissen ist sein Gemüt, daß auch des Himmels Seligkeit keinen Strahl der Hoffnung in seine Seele wirft und ihn zum bessern Sein entzündet!—

Gewiß ist dir, mein Theodor, aufgefallen, daß ich von Annas Verführung gesprochen; und so gut ich es in dieser Stunde,

of people who were able to expect, in happy love and in the
bourgeois union which it produced, even the slightest fulfillment of the higher aspirations which nature has spitefully
implanted in our hearts;—all this impelled him to rebel especially in this area and, whenever there was talk of such a relationship, boldly to challenge (by his acts of destruction) that
unknown power which guides our destiny, and which seemed
to him to be a malicious monster playing a cruel game with
the wretched creatures of its mocking whim.—Every seduction of a beloved bride, every happiness of lovers destroyed
by a blow so powerful that it caused an irreparable catastrophe is a glorious triumph over that hostile power, lifting
him ever higher above the constraints of life—above nature—
above the Creator!—He really wants more and more to leave
life, but only to plunge into Orcus. The seduction of Anna,
with the attendant circumstances, is the highest pinnacle to
which he rises.—

With respect to the highest favors of nature, Donna Anna
is the counterpart to Don Juan. Just as Don Juan was orig-
inally a wonderfully vigorous, splendid man, so she is a divine
woman, over whose pure mind the devil had no power. All
the arts of hell could destroy her only physically.—As soon as
Satan has completed this ruin, hell dared no longer postpone
the execution of the act of vengeance which had been decreed
by Heaven.—Don Juan mockingly invites the effigy of the
stabbed old man to his gay banquet and the transfigured spirit,
only now recognizing in him the fallen man, and grieving for
him, does not disdain, in his awesome shape, to urge him to
repentance. But so corrupt, so rent is his soul that even the
bliss of Heaven casts no ray of hope into his soul nor does it
inspire him to a better existence!—

It must certainly have surprised you, my Theodor, to hear
me speak of Anna's seduction; and to the best of my ability

wo tief aus dem Gemüt hervorgehende Gedanken und Ideen
die Worte überflügeln, vermag, sage ich dir mit wenigen
Worten, wie mir in der Musik, ohne alle Rücksicht auf den
Text, das ganze Verhältnis der beiden im Kampf begriffenen
Naturen (Don Juan und Donna Anna) erscheint.—Schon
oben äußerte ich, daß Anna dem Juan gegenübergestellt ist.
Wie, wenn Donna Anna vom Himmel dazu bestimmt gewesen
wäre, den Juan in der Liebe, die ihn durch des Satans Künste
verdarb, die ihm innewohnende göttliche Natur erkennen zu
lassen, und ihn der Verzweiflung seines nichtigen Strebens zu
entreißen?—Zu spät, zur Zeit des höchsten Frevels, sah er sie,
und da konnte ihn nur die teuflische Lust erfüllen, sie zu
verderben.—Nicht gerettet wurde sie! Als er hinausfloh, war
die Tat geschehen. Das Feuer einer übermenschlichen Sinnlichkeit, Glut aus der Hölle, durchströmte ihr Innerstes, und
machte jeden Widerstand vergeblich. Nur E r , nur Don
Juan konnte den wollüstigen Wahnsinn in ihr entzünden,
mit dem sie ihn umfing, der mit der übermächtigen, zerstörenden Wut höllischer Geister im Innern sündigte. Als er
nach vollendeter Tat entfliehen wollte, da umschlang, wie
ein gräßliches, giftigen Tod sprühendes Ungeheuer, sie der
Gedanke ihres Verderbens mit folternden Qualen.—Ihres
Vaters Fall durch Don Juans Hand, die Verbindung mit dem
kalten, unmännlichen, ordinären Don Ottavio, den sie einst
zu lieben glaubte—selbst die im Innersten ihres Gemüts
in verzehrender Flamme wütende Liebe, die in dem Augenblick des höchsten Genusses aufloderte, und nun gleich der
Glut des vernichtenden Hasses brennt: Alles dieses zerreißt
ihre Brust. Sie fühlt, nur Don Juans Untergang kann der von
tödlichen Martern beängsteten Seele Ruhe verschaffen; aber
diese Ruhe ist ihr eigener irdischer Untergang.—Sie fordert
daher unablässig ihren eiskalten Bräutigam zur Rache auf,
sie verfolgt selbst den Verräter, und erst, als ihn die unterirdischen Mächte in den Orkus hinabgezogen haben, wird
sie ruhiger—nur vermag sie nicht dem hochzeitlustigen
Bräutigam nachzugeben: *lascia, o caro, un anno ancora, allo
sfogo del mio cor!* [36] Sie wird dieses Jahr nicht überstehen;
Don Ottavio wird niemals d i e umarmen, die ein frommes
Gemüt davon rettete, des Satans geweihte Braut zu bleiben.
   Wie lebhaft im Innersten meiner Seele fühlte ich alles

at this hour, when thoughts and ideas which come from the depths of my mind, outdistance my words, I will tell you in few words how the music, without any regard for the text, seems to me to reflect the whole relationship of the two natures locked in combat (Don Juan and Donna Anna).—I have already said above that Anna is the counterpart of Juan. Suppose Donna Anna had been destined by Heaven to let Juan recognize the divine nature that is innate in him, in the love which destroyed him through the wiles of Satan, and to snatch him from the despair of his worthless ambition?— Too late; at the time of his supreme crime he saw her, and then he could only be filled with the devilish desire to destroy her.—She was not saved. When he fled, the deed had been done. The fire from a superhuman sensuality, a fire from hell, streamed through her innermost being and made all resistance vain. *He* alone, only Don Juan could kindle in her the voluptuous frenzy with which she embraced him, he who sinned with the superhuman, destructive fury of hellish spirits within him. When, after doing the deed, he wanted to flee, the thought of her ruin ensnared her with tormenting pains like a horrible monster spewing poisonous death.—Her father's death at Don Juan's hand, her union with the cold, unmanly, common Don Ottavio whom she once thought she loved, even the love that was raging in her heart with a consuming flame, flaring up at the moment of supreme enjoyment and is now burning like the fire of destructive hatred—all this is tearing her heart to shreds. She feels that only Don Juan's destruction can bring peace to her soul, which is a prey to mortal torment; but this peace is her own earthly destruction.—She therefore incessantly spurs her ice-cold fiancé to vengeance, she herself pursues her betrayer, and she grows calmer only when the infernal powers have dragged him down to Orcus—only she cannot yield to her bridegroom who is eager for marriage: *"lascia, o caro, un anno ancora, allo sfogo del mio cor!"* She will not outlive this year; Don Ottavio will never embrace the woman who was saved by her pious soul from remaining Satan's consecrated bride.

How vividly I felt all this in my innermost soul in the

dieses in den die Brust zerreißenden Akkorden des ersten
Rezitativs und der Erzählung von dem nächtlichen Überfall!—Selbst die Szene der Donna Anna im zweiten Akt:
*Crudele*,[37] die, oberflächlich betrachtet, sich nur auf den Don
Ottavio bezieht, spricht in geheimen Anklängen, in den
wunderbarsten Beziehungen, jene innere, alles irdische Glück
verzehrende Stimmung der Seele aus. Was soll selbst in den
Worten der sonderbare, von dem Dichter vielleicht unbewußt
hingeworfene Zusatz: *forse un giorno il cielo ancora sentirà
pietà di me!* [38]—

Es schlägt zwei Uhr—Ein warmer elektrischer Hauch
gleitet über mich her—ich empfinde den leisen Geruch feinen
italienischen Parfüms, der gestern zuerst mich die Nachbarin
vermuten ließ; mich umfängt ein seliges Gefühl, das ich nur
in Tönen aussprechen zu können glaube. Die Luft streicht
heftiger durch das Haus—die Saiten des Flügels im Orchester
rauschen—Himmel! wie aus weiter Ferne, auf den Fittichen
schwellender Töne eines luftigen Orchesters getragen, glaube
ich Annas Stimme zu hören: *Non mi dir bell'idol mio!* [39]—
Schließe dich auf, du fernes, unbekanntes Geisterreich—du
Dschinnistan [40] voller Herrlichkeit, wo ein unaussprechlicher,
himmlischer Schmerz, wie die unsäglichste Freude, der entzückten Seele alles auf Erden Verheißene über alle Maßen
erfüllt! Laß mich eintreten in den Kreis deiner holdseligen
Erscheinungen! Mag der Traum, den du, bald zum Grausen
erregenden, bald zum freundlichen Boten an den irdischen
Menschen erkoren [41]—mag er meinen Geist, wenn der Schlaf
den Körper in bleiernen Banden festhält, den ätherischen
Gefilden zuführen!—

### GESPRÄCH DES MITTAGS AN DER WIRTSTAFEL, ALS NACHTRAG

KLUGER MANN (mit der Dose, stark auf den Deckel derselben
schnippend): Es ist doch fatal, daß wir nun so bald keine
ordentliche Oper mehr hören werden! aber das kommt von
dem häßlichen Übertreiben!

MULATTENGESICHT: Ja ja! hab's ihr oft genug gesagt! Die
Rolle der Donna Anna griff sie immer ordentlich an!—
Gestern war sie vollends gar wie besessen. Den ganzen
Zwischenakt hindurch soll sie in Ohnmacht gelegen haben,

heartrending chords of the first recitative and the narrative of the nocturnal attack!—Even Donna Anna's scene in the second act: *"Crudele,"* which, on a superficial view, refers only to Don Ottavio, expresses in hidden harmonies, in the most wonderful relationships, that inner mood of the soul that consumes all earthly happiness. What meaning is there even in the words of the strange passage added by the author perhaps unconsciously: *"forse un giorno il cielo ancora sentirà pietà di me!"*—

The clock strikes two!—A warm, electric breath glides over me—I smell the faint fragrance of fine Italian perfume which yesterday gave me the first inkling of the presence of my neighbor; I am enveloped by a feeling of bliss, which I think I can express only in tones. The air stirs more violently through the house—the strings of the grand piano in the orchestra roar—Heavens! I think I hear Anna's voice as though from a great distance, borne on the pinions of swelling tones of an ethereal orchestra: *"Non mi dir bell'idol mio!"*— Open up, you distant, unknown spirit realm—you jinnestan full of glory in which an inexpressible, celestial pain, akin to the most ineffable joy, fulfills for the enraptured soul, beyond all measure, everything that was promised it on earth! Let me enter the circle of your lovely apparitions! May the dream which you have chosen, either to arouse horror or to serve as a friendly messenger to earthly man—may it lead my spirit to the ethereal fields when sleep holds the body fast in bonds of lead!—

## Conversation at noon in the dining room, by way of an epilogue

CLEVER MAN (snuffbox in hand, tapping vigorously on the lid): It's really unfortunate that we won't get to hear a decent opera for some time to come. But that's what comes of these hideous exaggerations.

MULATTO-FACE: Yes, yes. I've told her often enough. The part of Donna Anna always affected her deeply. Yesterday she was altogether like a woman possessed. Throughout the entr'acte she's said to have been unconscious, and in the scene

und in der Szene im zweiten Akt hatte sie gar Nervenzufälle—

UNBEDEUTENDER: O sagen Sie—!

MULATTENGESICHT: Nun ja! Nervenzufälle, und war doch wahrlich nicht vom Theater zu bringen.

ICH: Um des Himmels willen—die Zufälle sind doch nicht von Bedeutung? wir hören doch Signora bald wieder?

KLUGER MANN (mit der Dose, eine Prise nehmend): Schwerlich, denn Signora ist heute morgen Punkt zwei Uhr gestorben.

in the second act she even had nervous attacks—

INSIGNIFICANT PERSON: Oh, I say—!

MULATTO-FACE: Really. Nervous attacks, and they just couldn't get her out of the theater.

I: For Heaven's sake—I hope the attacks weren't serious? We will hear the signora again soon, won't we?

CLEVER MAN (with his snuffbox, taking a pinch): Hardly, for the signora died this morning at two o'clock sharp.

# Adalbert Stifter

(1805–1868)

STIFTER WAS born of peasant and artisan stock in a village
in the Bohemian Forest. He lost his father at an early age
and was brought up by his mother to whom he owed much.
His studies at the University of Vienna ranged over the fields
of law, mathematics, the physical sciences, but he was drawn
especially to painting and literature. Disappointed in love, he
married a woman to whom he was emotionally indifferent,
but with whom he developed an exemplary life.

Stifter's first writings began to appear and to attract attention while he was a young tutor in an aristocratic family.
From then on he published steadily. The excesses of the
Revolution of 1848 "broke his heart," for he loved order and
steady, natural development. His interest in education was
recognized by the Government, which appointed him a school
inspector in Upper Austria, a post he held till 1865. But he
was stricken with cancer and took his own life in a fit of deep
depression.

Stifter's work consists of two massive novels, *Der Nach-
sommer* (Indian Summer) and *Witiko*, and of various collections of novellas and sketches, among them the collection
*Bunte Steine* (Colored Stones) which includes *Bergkristall*.

Stifter's development as an artist was from romanticism
(his early work stands under the influence of Jean Paul,
Hoffmann and James Fenimore Cooper) to the serene, ob-
jective clarity of Goethe, whose piety towards life (*Lebens-
frömmigkeit*) he shares. He was also touched by the new

interest in the small things of everyday life that characterizes realism in literature. In his famous preface to *Bunte Steine* he anticipates Walt Whitman's remark that "a leaf of grass is no less than the journey-work of the stars." So Stifter sees the everyday work of nature as much more wonderful and awesome than the dramatic and catastrophic spectacles she sometimes stages. He therefore emphasizes in his writings the quiet, gentle, simple, conserving forces in life. His limpid, crystalline style corresponds perfectly to the intellectual and emotional tone of his world.

All these qualities are apparent in *Bergkristall*. One can hardly speak of a plot; the children are lost on a mountain and are found again. Yet one feels an extraordinary tension in reading about their adventure. There is no flashy psychology; both adults and children have the same naïve, simple sets of reactions; and yet it is a world of rich and varied characters that Stifter quietly presents to us. There is no artiness in the construction of the narrative; the telling is straightforward. Yet anyone with a feeling for fine literature must recognize that the tale is a superb piece of fiction.

*Bergkristall* was first published in 1845 under the title *Der heilige Abend* (Christmas Eve). It was later rewritten and incorporated in the collection *Bunte Steine* under its present title because the glass-like clarity of rock crystal is a fitting symbol of the spirit that pervades the tale.

# BERGKRISTALL

von Adalbert Stifter

UNSERE KIRCHE feiert verschiedene Feste, welche zum Herzen dringen. Man kann sich kaum etwas Lieblicheres denken als Pfingsten und kaum etwas Ernsteres und Heiligeres als Ostern. Das Traurige und Schwermütige der Karwoche und darauf das Feierliche des Sonntags begleiten uns durch das Leben. Eines der schönsten Feste feiert die Kirche fast mitten im Winter, wo beinahe die längsten Nächte und kürzesten Tage sind, wo die Sonne am schiefsten gegen unsere Gefilde steht und Schnee alle Fluren deckt, das Fest der Weihnacht. Wie in vielen Ländern der Tag vor dem Geburtsfeste des Herrn der Christabend heißt, so heißt er bei uns der Heilige Abend, der darauffolgende Tag der Heilige Tag und die dazwischenliegende Nacht die Weihnacht. Die katholische Kirche begeht den Christtag als den Tag der Geburt des Heilandes mit ihrer allergrößten kirchlichen Feier, in den meisten Gegenden wird schon die Mitternachtstunde als die Geburtsstunde des Herrn mit prangender Nachtfeier geheiligt, zu der die Glocken durch die stille, finstere, winterliche Mitternachtluft laden, zu der die Bewohner mit Lichtern oder auf wohlbekannten Pfaden aus schneeigen Bergen an bereiften Wäldern vorbei und durch knarrende Obstgärten zu der Kirche eilen, aus der die feierlichen Töne kommen und die aus der Mitte des in beeiste Bäume gehüllten Dorfes mit den langen beleuchteten Fenstern emporragt.

Mit dem Kirchenfeste ist auch ein häusliches verbunden.

# ROCK CRYSTAL

## by Adalbert Stifter

OUR CHURCH celebrates various holidays which affect the heart deeply. One can scarcely imagine anything more charming than Whitsuntide or anything more earnest and sacred than Easter. The sad and melancholy character of Holy Week, followed by the solemnity of Easter Sunday, accompanies us through life. One of the most beautiful holidays is celebrated by the Church almost in the middle of winter, when the nights are virtually longest and days shortest, when the sun shines most obliquely on our fields and snow covers them all—the feast of Christmas. In many countries the day preceding the birthday celebration of our Lord is called Christmas Eve; we call it Holy Eve; the day following, Holy Day; and the night that falls between them, the Night of Consecration. The Catholic Church celebrates Christmas day, the day on which our Saviour was born, with the very greatest ecclesiastical solemnity. In most regions the hour of our Lord's birth is sanctified from midnight on with a splendid nocturnal celebration, to which the church bells invite us through the silent, dark, wintry midnight air. The residents hasten to church with lanterns, or on dark, familiar paths from the snow-covered mountains, past frost-covered forests and through creaking orchards, to the church from which the solemn tones come and which, with its high, lighted windows, stands out in the midst of the village shrouded by ice-covered trees.

The church holiday is tied up with a domestic one. In

Es hat sich fast in allen christlichen Ländern verbreitet, daß
man den Kindern die Ankunft des Christkindleins—auch
eines Kindes, des wunderbarsten, das je auf der Welt war—
als ein heiteres, glänzendes, feierliches Ding zeigt, das durch
das ganze Leben fortwirkt und manchmal noch spät im Alter
bei trüben, schwermütigen oder rührenden Erinnerungen
gleichsam als Rückblick in die einstige Zeit mit den bunten
schimmernden Fittichen durch den öden, traurigen und
ausgeleerten Nachthimmel fliegt. Man pflegt den Kindern die
Geschenke zu geben, die das heilige Christkindlein gebracht
hat, um ihnen Freude zu machen. Das tut man gewöhnlich
am Heiligen Abende, wenn die tiefe Dämmerung eingetreten
ist. Man zündet Lichter und meistens sehr viele an, die oft
mit den kleinen Kerzlein auf den schönen grünen Ästen eines
Tannen- oder Fichtenbäumchens schweben, das mitten in der
Stube steht. Die Kinder dürfen nicht eher kommen, als bis
das Zeichen gegeben wird, daß der Heilige Christ zugegen
gewesen ist und die Geschenke, die er mitgebracht, hinter-
lassen hat. Dann geht die Tür auf, die Kleinen dürfen hinein,
und bei dem herrlichen schimmernden Lichterglanze sehen
sie Dinge auf dem Baume hängen oder auf dem Tische
herumgebreitet, die alle Vorstellungen ihrer Einbildungskraft
weit übertreffen, die sie sich nicht anzurühren getrauen und
die sie endlich, wenn sie sie bekommen haben, den ganzen
Abend in ihren Ärmchen herumtragen und mit sich in das
Bett nehmen. Wenn sie dann zuweilen in ihre Träume hinein
die Glockentöne der Mitternacht hören, durch welche die
Großen in die Kirche zur Andacht gerufen werden, dann mag
es ihnen sein,[1] als [2] zögen jetzt die Englein durch den Himmel
oder als kehre der Heilige Christ nach Hause, welcher nunmehr bei allen Kindern gewesen ist und jedem von ihnen ein
herrliches Geschenk hinterbracht hat.

Wenn dann der folgende Tag, der Christtag, kommt, so ist
er ihnen so feierlich, wenn sie früh morgens mit ihren
schönsten Kleidern angetan in der warmen Stube stehen,
wenn der Vater und die Mutter sich zum Kirchgange
schmücken, wenn zu Mittage ein feierliches Mahl ist, ein
besseres als in jedem Tage des ganzen Jahres, und wenn nachmittags oder gegen den Abend hin Freunde und Bekannte
kommen, auf den Stühlen und Bänken herumsitzen, mitein-

almost all Christian countries the custom has spread of showing children the arrival of the Christ child—He too was a child, the most wonderful that ever was on earth—as a happy, splendid, solemn thing, which continues to affect us throughout our whole lives; and sometimes, even in our old age, in the midst of troubled, melancholy or touching memories, it flies on bright, glittering wings through the desolate, sad and empty night sky like a backward glance into a time now past. It is customary to give children the gifts that the holy Christ child has brought, to give them happiness. This is usually done on Christmas Eve, when deep twilight has settled. Lights are lit—usually a great many—which often sway beside the little candles on the beautiful green branches of a fir or spruce tree that stands in the middle of the living room. The children are not permitted to come until the sign is given that the Holy Christ has been there and has left behind the gifts which He has brought. Then the door is opened, the little ones are permitted to enter, and in the splendid, glittering glow of the lights they see things hanging on the tree or spread out on the table which far surpass all the conceptions of their imagination, which they do not dare to touch, and which they finally, when they have been presented to them, carry about in their little arms all evening and take to bed with them. Sometimes they hear in their dreams the tones of the midnight bells which call the grown-ups to worship in church; then they imagine that the little angels are now moving through heaven or the Holy Christ is returning home after visiting all children and leaving each of them a splendid gift.

When the following day comes, Christmas day, it is a most solemn occasion for them. In the early morning they stand in the warm living room, dressed in their best clothes; while father and mother are dressing for church. At noon they eat a formal meal, a better one than on any other day in the year. In the afternoon or towards evening friends and acquaintances come, sit about on chairs and benches and can talk to each other or comfortably look through the windows

ander reden und behaglich durch die Fenster in die Winter-
gegend hinausschauen können, wo entweder die langsamen
Flocken niederfallen oder ein trübender Nebel um die Berge
steht oder die blutrote kalte Sonne hinabsinkt. An verschiedenen Stellen der Stube, entweder auf einem Stühlchen oder
auf der Bank oder auf dem Fensterbrettchen, liegen die
zaubrischen, nun aber schon bekannteren und vertrauteren
Geschenke von gestern abend herum.

Hierauf vergeht der lange Winter, es kommt der Frühling
und der unendlich dauernde Sommer—und wenn die Mutter
wieder vom Heiligen Christe erzählt, daß nun bald sein Festtag sein wird und daß er auch diesmal herabkommen werde,
ist es den Kindern, als sei seit seinem letzten Erscheinen eine
ewige Zeit vergangen und als liege die damalige Freude in
einer weiten nebelgrauen Ferne.

Weil dieses Fest so lange nachhält, weil sein Abglanz so
hoch in das Alter hinaufreicht, so stehen wir so gerne dabei,
wenn die Kinder dasselbe begehen und sich darüber freuen.—

In den hohen Gebirgen unsers Vaterlandes steht ein Dörfchen mit einem kleinen, aber sehr spitzigen Kirchturme, der
mit seiner roten Farbe, mit welcher die Schindeln bemalt sind,
aus dem Grün vieler Obstbäume hervorragt und wegen derselben roten Farbe in dem duftigen und blauen Dämmern
der Berge weithin ersichtlich ist. Das Dörfchen liegt gerade
mitten in einem ziemlich weiten Tale, das fast wie ein länglicher Kreis [3] gestaltet ist. Es enthält außer der Kirche eine
Schule, ein Gemeindehaus und noch mehrere stattliche
Häuser, die einen Platz gestalten, auf welchem vier Linden
stehen, die ein steinernes Kreuz in ihrer Mitte haben. Diese
Häuser sind nicht bloße Landwirtschaftshäuser, sondern sie
bergen auch noch diejenigen Handwerke in ihrem Schoße,[4]
die dem menschlichen Geschlechte unentbehrlich sind und
die bestimmt sind, den Gebirgsbewohnern ihren einzigen
Bedarf an Kunsterzeugnissen zu decken. Im Tale und an den
Bergen herum sind noch sehr viele zerstreute Hütten, wie
das in Gebirgsgegenden sehr oft der Fall ist, welche alle nicht
nur zur Kirche und Schule gehören, sondern auch jenen
Handwerken, von denen gesprochen wurde, durch Abnahme
der Erzeugnisse ihren Zoll entrichten. Es gehören sogar noch
weitere Hütten zu dem Dörfchen, die man von dem Tale aus [5]

at the wintry countryside without, where either slow snow-flakes are falling, or a darkening mist clings to the mountains, or the blood-red, cold sun is setting. Last night's magic presents, by now better known and more familiar, lie about in various parts of the living room, on a chair or on the bench or on the window sill.

Then the long winter passes, spring comes and the endless summer. When mother tells them again of the Holy Christ, that His holiday is coming soon and that He will come down this time too, the children feel that an eternity has passed since His last appearance and that the joy of that time lies in the far, foggy gray distance.

Because this holiday has such a lasting effect, because its reflected light reaches so far into our old age, we like to be present when children celebrate it and rejoice in it.

In the high mountains of our country there is a little village with a small but very pointed church steeple, which stands out from the green of many fruit trees because of the red color of its shingles; and because of this same red color it can be seen for a great distance in the delicate blue haze of the mountains. The little village is situated right in the center of a fairly wide valley, which has almost the shape of an ellipse. Besides the church it has a school, a community hall and a few other stately houses which form a square on which there are four linden trees with a stone cross in their center. These houses are no mere farmhouses; they also harbor those handicrafts which are indispensable to the human species and which serve to provide the mountain dwellers' sole needs in manufactured products. In the valley and round about the mountains there are scattered many more huts, as is very often the case in mountain regions; and the inhabitants of these not only belong to the church and the school, but they also pay their tribute to the crafts mentioned above by buying the products. Even more distant huts belong to the village; these cannot even be seen from the valley; they lie even deeper in the mountains. Their inhabitants rarely leave them to join their fellow parishioners, and in winter they often have to

gar nicht sehen kann, die noch tiefer in den Gebirgen stecken, deren Bewohner selten zu ihren Gemeindemitbrüdern herauskommen und die im Winter oft ihre Toten aufbewahren müssen, um sie nach dem Wegschmelzen des Schnees zum Begräbnisse bringen zu können. Der größte Herr, den die Dörfler im Laufe des Jahres zu sehen bekommen, ist der Pfarrer. Sie verehren ihn sehr, und es geschieht gewöhnlich, daß derselbe durch längeren Aufenthalt im Dörfchen ein der Einsamkeit gewöhnter Mann wird, daß er nicht ungerne bleibt und einfach fortlebt. Wenigstens hat man seit Menschengedenken nicht erlebt, daß der Pfarrer des Dörfchens ein auswärtssüchtiger oder seines Standes unwürdiger Mann gewesen wäre.

Es gehen keine Straßen durch das Tal, sie haben ihre zweigleisigen Wege, auf denen sie ihre Felderzeugnisse mit einspännigen Wäglein nach Hause bringen, es kommen daher wenig Menschen in das Tal, unter diesen manchmal ein einsamer Fußreisender, der ein Liebhaber der Natur ist, eine Weile in der bemalten Oberstube des Wirtes wohnt und die Berge betrachtet, oder gar ein Maler, der den kleinen spitzen Kirchturm und die schönen Gipfel der Felsen in seine Mappe zeichnet. Daher bilden die Bewohner eine eigene Welt, sie kennen einander alle mit Namen und mit den einzelnen Geschichten von Großvater und Urgroßvater her, trauern alle, wenn einer stirbt, wissen, wie er heißt, wenn einer geboren wird, haben eine Sprache, die von der der Ebene draußen abweicht, haben ihre Streitigkeiten, die sie schlichten, stehen einander bei und laufen zusammen, wenn sich etwas Außerordentliches begibt.

Sie sind sehr stetig, und es bleibt immer beim alten.[6] Wenn ein Stein aus einer Mauer fällt, wird derselbe wieder hineingesetzt, die neuen Häuser werden wie die alten gebaut, die schadhaften Dächer werden mit gleichen Schindeln ausgebessert, und wenn in einem Hause scheckige Kühe sind, so werden immer solche Kälber aufgezogen, und die Farbe bleibt bei dem Hause.

Gegen Mittag [7] sieht man von dem Dorfe einen Schneeberg, der mit seinen glänzenden Hörnern fast oberhalb der Hausdächer zu sein scheint, aber in der Tat doch nicht so nahe ist. Er sieht das ganze Jahr, Sommer und Winter, mit

keep their dead until they can bring them down for burial after the snow has melted. The greatest man whom the villagers get to see in the course of the year is the priest. They venerate him deeply, and it usually happens that he becomes accustomed to the isolation as a result of his lengthy stay in the village; and so he remains there not unwillingly and just lives on. At least as far as human memory can reach, it has never happened that the priest of the little village was anxious to leave it or was unworthy of his calling.

No highways pass through the valley; they have their double-track roads on which they bring their field products home on one-horse carts. Accordingly, few people come into the valley; among these few an occasional solitary pedestrian who is a lover of nature lives for a while in the painted upstairs room of the inn and contemplates the mountains, or even a painter, who sketches the small, pointed church steeple and the beautiful peaks of the rocks in his portfolio. And so the inhabitants form a world of their own; they all know each other by name and by the individual stories handed down from grandfather and great-grandfather. They all mourn when one of them dies, know what name is given to the newborn, have a language that deviates from that of the plains beyond, have their quarrels, which they settle, help each other, and flock together when something unusual happens.

They are very conservative and things always remain the same. When a stone falls out of a wall it is put in again, the new houses are built like the old, the damaged roofs are repaired with the same type of shingle, and if there are spotted cows on a farm, the same type of calf is always reared and the color stays with the farm.

Towards the south of the village one sees a snowy mountain whose gleaming horns seem to be almost directly above the house tops, but are in fact not so near. All year, summer and winter, it looks down into the valley with its projecting rocks

seinen vorstehenden Felsen und mit seinen weißen Flächen in das Tal herab. Als das Auffallendste, was sie in ihrer Umgebung haben, ist der Berg der Gegenstand der Betrachtung der Bewohner, und er ist der Mittelpunkt vieler Geschichten geworden. Es lebt kein Mann und Greis in dem Dorfe, der nicht von den Zacken und Spitzen des Berges, von seinen Eisspalten und Höhlen, von seinen Wässern und Geröllströmen etwas zu erzählen wüßte, was er entweder selbst erfahren oder von andern erzählen gehört hat. Dieser Berg ist auch der Stolz des Dorfes, als hätten sie ihn selber gemacht, und es ist nicht so ganz entschieden, wenn man auch die Biederkeit und Wahrheitsliebe der Talbewohner hoch anschlägt, ob sie nicht zuweilen zur Ehre und zum Ruhme des Berges lügen. Der Berg gibt den Bewohnern außer dem, daß er ihre Merkwürdigkeit ist, auch wirklichen Nutzen; denn wenn eine Gesellschaft von Gebirgsreisenden hereinkommt, um von dem Tale aus den Berg zu besteigen, so dienen die Bewohner des Dorfes als Führer, und einmal Führer gewesen zu sein, dieses und jenes erlebt zu haben, diese und jene Stelle zu kennen, ist eine Auszeichnung, die jeder gerne von sich darlegt. Sie reden oft davon, wenn sie in der Wirtsstube beieinander sitzen, und erzählen ihre Wagnisse und ihre wunderbaren Erfahrungen und versäumen aber auch nie zu sagen, was dieser oder jener Reisende gesprochen habe und was sie von ihm als Lohn für ihre Bemühungen empfangen hätten. Dann sendet der Berg von seinen Schneeflächen die Wasser ab, welche einen See in seinen Hochwäldern speisen und den Bach erzeugen, der lustig durch das Tal strömt, die Brettersäge, die Mahlmühle und andere kleine Werke treibt, das Dorf reinigt und das Vieh tränkt. Von den Wäldern des Berges kommt das Holz, und sie halten die Lawinen auf. Durch die innern [8] Gänge und Lockerheiten der Höhen sinken die Wasser durch, die dann in Adern durch das Tal gehen und in Brünnlein und Quellen hervorkommen, daraus [9] die Menschen trinken und ihr herrliches, oft belobtes Wasser dem Fremden reichen. Allein an letzteren Nutzen denken sie nicht und meinen, das sei immer go gewesen.

Wenn man auf die Jahresgeschichte des Berges sieht, so sind im Winter die zwei Zacken seines Gipfels, die sie Hörner heißen,[10] schneeweiß und stehen, wenn sie an hellen Tagen

and its white surfaces. As the most striking sight they have in the region, the mountain is the object of contemplation for the inhabitants and has become the focus of many stories. There is not a man or oldster in the village who could not tell some story about the crags and peaks of the mountain, of its crevasses and caves, its waters and rock slides—something he has either experienced himself or heard others tell. This mountain is also the pride of the village, as if they had made it themselves; and it is by no means certain, even if one puts a high value on the honesty and veracity of the valley dwellers, that they do not occasionally lie for the honor and fame of the mountain. Apart from being their main object of interest, the mountain is also actually useful; for when a party of mountain tourists arrives to climb the mountain from the valley, the inhabitants of the village serve as guides; and to have once served as a guide, to have had this or that experience, to know this or that spot, is a distinction which everyone is glad to claim for himself. They often talk about it when they sit together in the taproom; they narrate their acts of daring and their remarkable experiences; but they also never fail to tell what this or that tourist had said, and how much they got from him as a reward for their efforts. Moreover the mountain sends down from its snow fields the waters which feed a lake in its forests and make the brook which, streaming merrily through the valley, drives the sawmill, the gristmill and other small works, cleans the village and waters the cattle. The mountain forests provide them with timber and break the force of the avalanches. Through the underground channels and loose soil on the heights the waters filter, then go through the valley in veins and emerge in little fountains and springs from which people drink and offer strangers their marvelous, much lauded water. Yet they do not think of its usefulness, but believe it has always been so.

When one considers the seasonal history of the mountain, the two crags of its peak which they call horns are snow white in winter and, when they are visible on bright days,

sichtbar sind, blendend in der finstern Bläue der Luft; alle Bergfelder, die um diese Gipfel herumlagern, sind dann weiß; alle Abhänge sind so; selbst die steilrechten Wände, die die Bewohner Mauern heißen, sind mit einem angeflogenen weißen Reife bedeckt und mit zartem Eise wie mit einem Firnisse belegt, so daß die ganze Masse wie ein Zauberpalast aus dem bereiften Grau der Wälderlast emporragt, welche schwer um ihre Füße herum ausgebreitet ist. Im Sommer, wo Sonne und warmer Wind den Schnee von den Steilseiten wegnimmt, ragen die Hörner nach dem Ausdrucke der Bewohner schwarz in den Himmel und haben nur schöne weiße Äderchen und Sprenkeln auf ihrem Rücken, in der Tat aber sind sie zart fernblau, und was sie Äderchen und Sprenkeln heißen, das ist nicht weiß, sondern hat das schöne Milchblau des fernen Schnees gegen das dunklere der Felsen. Die Bergfelder um die Hörner aber verlieren, wenn es recht heiß ist, an ihren höheren Teilen wohl den Firn nicht, der gerade dann recht weiß auf das Grün der Talbäume herabsieht, aber es weicht von ihren unteren Teilen der Winterschnee, der nur einen Flaum machte, und es wird das unbestimmte Schillern von Bläulich und Grünlich sichtbar, das das Geschiebe[11] von Eis ist, das dann bloßliegt und auf die Bewohner unten hinabgrüßt.

Am Rande dieses Schillerns, wo es von ferne wie ein Saum von Edelsteinsplittern aussieht, ist es in der Nähe ein Gemenge wilder, riesenhafter Blöcke, Platten und Trümmer, die sich drängen und verwirrt ineinandergeschoben sind. Wenn ein Sommer gar heiß und lang ist, werden die Eisfelder weit hinauf entblößt, und dann schaut eine viel größere Fläche von Grün und Blau in das Tal, manche Kuppen und Räume werden entkleidet, die man sonst nur weiß erblickt hatte, der schmutzige Saum des Eises wird sichtbar, wo es Felsen, Erde und Schlamm schiebt, und viel reichlichere Wasser als sonst fließen in das Tal. Dies geht fort, bis es nach und nach wieder Herbst wird, das Wasser sich verringert, zu einer Zeit einmal ein grauer Landregen die ganze Ebene des Tales bedeckt, worauf, wenn sich die Nebel von den Höhen wieder lösen, der Berg seine weiche Hülle abermals umgetan hat und alle Felsen, Kegel und Zacken in weißem Kleide dastehen.

So spinnt es sich ein Jahr um das andere mit geringen Ab-

they stand out in the dark blue of the air with dazzling brilliance. All the mountain fields which lie about these peaks are then white; all the slopes are so; even the perpendicular walls, which the people call stone walls, are covered with a coating of white hoarfrost and overlaid with delicate ice as with a varnish, so that the whole mass towers like an enchanted palace above the frosty gray of the mass of forest which is spread out thickly about its feet. In the summer, when the sun and the warm wind remove the snow from the steep mountain sides, the horns, as the inhabitants say, jut out black into the sky and have only beautiful, little white veins and speckles on their backs. But actually they are a delicate, distant blue and what they call little veins and speckles are not white but possess the beautiful milk blue of the distant snow in contrast to the darker blue of the rocks. Even when it is really hot, the mountain fields around the horns do not lose their old snow in the higher regions; they look down just then in all their whiteness on the green trees in the valley. But from the lower regions the recent winter snow, which merely formed a down, recedes and a vague iridescence of blue and green becomes visible; this is the sérac, which is exposed and sends its greetings to the inhabitants below.

At the edge of this iridescence, where from a distance it looks like a border of jewel fragments, it is, from close up, a mixture of wild, gigantic blocks, slabs and debris, crowded together and piled in confusion over each other. When a summer is very hot and long, the ice fields are bared for a great distance up, and then a much greater expanse of green and blue looks down into the valley; many knolls and spaces, which would normally be seen as white, are stripped bare; the dirty border of the ice becomes visible, there where it shoves rocks, earth and mud; and water flows into the valley much more plentifully than is usual. This continues until it gradually becomes autumn again; the water supply decreases; at some time a gray, steady rain covers the whole plain and then, when the mists lift from the heights again, the mountain has put on its soft wrap once more, and all the rocks, cones and crags stand there in a white cloak.

This goes on year after year with slight variations and will

wechslungen ab und wird sich fortspinnen, solange die Natur
so bleibt und auf den Bergen Schnee und in den Tälern
Menschen sind. Die Bewohner des Tales heißen die geringen
Veränderungen große, bemerken sie wohl und berechnen an
ihnen den Fortschritt des Jahres. Sie bezeichnen an den
Entblößungen die Hitze und die Ausnahmen der Sommer.

Was nun noch die Besteigung des Berges betrifft,[12] so geschieht dieselbe von dem Tale aus. Man geht nach der Mittagsrichtung zu auf einem guten, schönen Wege, der über
einen sogenannten Hals in ein anderes Tal führt. Hals heißen
sie einen mäßig hohen Bergrücken, der zwei größere und
bedeutendere Gebirge miteinander verbindet und über den
man zwischen den Gebirgen von einem Tale in ein anderes
gelangen kann. Auf dem Halse, der den Schneeberg mit
einem gegenüberliegenden großen Gebirgszuge verbindet,
ist lauter [13] Tannenwald. Etwa auf der größten Erhöhung
desselben, wo nach und nach sich der Weg in das jenseitige
Tal hinabzusenken beginnt, steht eine sogenannte Unglücksäule. Es ist einmal ein Bäcker, welcher Brot in seinem Korbe
über den Hals trug, an jener Stelle tot gefunden worden. Man
hat den toten Bäcker mit dem Korbe und mit den umringen-
den Tannenbäumen auf ein Bild gemalt, darunter eine Erklärung und eine Bitte um ein Gebet geschrieben, das Bild auf
eine rot angestrichene hölzerne Säule getan und die Säule an
der Stelle des Unglückes aufgerichtet. Bei dieser Säule biegt
man von dem Wege ab und geht auf der Länge des Halses
fort, statt über seine Breite in das jenseitige Tal hinüberzu-
wandern. Die Tannen bilden dort einen Durchlaß, als ob eine
Straße zwischen ihnen hin ginge. Es führt auch [14] manchmal
ein Weg in dieser Richtung hin, der dazu dient, das Holz
von den höheren Gegenden zu der Unglücksäule herabzu-
bringen, der aber dann wieder mit Gras verwächst.

Wenn man auf diesem Wege fortgeht, der sachte bergan
führt, so gelangt man endlich auf eine freie,[15] von Bäumen
entblößte Stelle. Dieselbe ist dürrer Heideboden, hat nicht
einmal [16] einen Strauch, sondern ist mit schwachem Heide-
kraute, mit trockenen Moosen und Dürrbodenpflanzen be-
wachsen. Die Stelle wird immer steiler, und man geht lange
hinan; man geht aber immer in einer Rinne, gleichsam wie in
einem ausgerundeten Graben, hinan, was den Nutzen hat, daß

go on as long as Nature remains what she is and there is snow on the mountains and people in the valleys. The inhabitants of the valley call the slight variations great ones, note them well and calculate the progress of the year by them. They measure the heat and the exceptional summers by the exposure of the mountain.

Now as far as the ascent of the mountain is concerned, it its undertaken from the valley. One walks in a southerly direction on a good, beautiful road that leads into another valley by way of a so-called "neck." By "neck" they mean a moderately high mountain range which connects two bigger and more important mountain ranges and over which one can get from one valley to another between the ranges. The neck that connects the snow mountain with a large mountain range that lies opposite is covered with pine forest. At about the highest point of the neck, where the road gradually begins to descend into the valley on the other side, there stands a so-called "accident pillar." One time a baker, who was carrying bread over the "neck" in his basket, was found dead at that spot. A picture of the dead baker with his basket and the surrounding pine trees was made; an explanation and a request for a prayer were written under it; the picture was attached to a wooden post painted red; and the post was erected at the spot of the accident. At this pillar one turns off from the road and continues along the length of the neck, instead of going across the breadth of the ridge into the valley beyond. The pines form an opening there, as if a highway led between them. At times a road does actually lead in this direction, serving to transport the timber from the higher regions to the accident column; but then it is overgrown with grass.

When one continues on this road, which leads gently uphill, one finally reaches an open spot bare of trees. This area is dry heath soil, with not even a shrub on it, but it is overgrown with scant heather, dry mosses and heath plants. The area becomes steeper and steeper, and one climbs for a long time. But one always keeps climbing in a trench, a sort of rounded ditch, which has the advantage that one cannot easily get lost in that great, treeless, undifferentiated area. After a

man auf der großen, baumlosen und überall gleichen Stelle
nicht leicht irren kann. Nach einer Zeit erscheinen Felsen, die
wie Kirchen gerade aus dem Grasboden aufsteigen und
zwischen deren Mauern man längere Zeit hinangehen kann.
Dann erscheinen wieder kahle, fast pflanzenlose Rücken, die
bereits in die Lufträume der höheren Gegenden ragen und
gerade zu dem Eise führen. Zu beiden Seiten dieses Weges
sind steile Wände, und durch diesen Damm hängt der
Schneeberg mit dem Halse zusammen. Um das Eis zu überwinden, geht man eine geraume Zeit an der Grenze desselben,
wo es von den Felsen umstanden ist, dahin, bis man zu dem
ältesten Firn gelangt, der die Eisspalten überbaut und in den
meisten Zeiten des Jahres den Wanderer trägt. An der
höchsten Stelle des Firns erheben sich die zwei Hörner aus
dem Schnee, wovon eines das höhere, mithin die Spitze des
Berges ist. Diese Kuppen sind schwer zu erklimmen; da sie
mit einem oft breiteren, oft engeren Schneegraben—dem
Firnschrunde—umgeben sind, der übersprungen werden muß,
und da ihre steilrechten Wände nur kleine Absätze haben, in
welche der Fuß eingesetzt werden muß, so begnügen sich die
meisten Besteiger des Berges damit, bis zu dem Firnschrunde
gelangt zu sein und dort die Rundsicht, soweit sie nicht durch
das Horn verdeckt ist, zu genießen. Die [17] den Gipfel besteigen
wollen, müssen dies mit Hilfe von Steigeisen, Stricken und
Klammern tun.

Außer diesem Berge stehen an derselben Mittagseite noch
andere, aber keiner ist so hoch, wenn sie sich auch früh im
Herbste mit Schnee bedecken und ihn bis tief in den Frühling hinein behalten. Der Sommer aber nimmt denselben
immer weg, und die Felsen glänzen freundlich im Sonnenscheine, und die tiefer gelegenen Wälder zeigen ihr sanftes
Grün von breiten blauen Schatten durchschnitten, die so
schön sind, daß man sich in seinem Leben nicht satt daran
sehen kann.

An den andern Seiten des Tales, nämlich von Mitternacht,
Morgen und Abend [18] her, sind die Berge langgestreckt und
niederer, manche Felder und Wiesen steigen ziemlich hoch
hinauf, und oberhalb ihrer sieht man verschiedene Wald-
blößen, Alpenhütten und dergleichen, bis sie an ihrem Rande
mit feingezacktem Walde am Himmel hingehen, welche

while rocks appear which rise straight out of the grassy floor like churches, and between these walls one can climb for quite a time. Then bald ridges, almost bare of plants, appear again; these already jut out into the atmosphere of the higher regions and lead directly to the ice. On both sides of this road there are steep walls and this defile connects the snow mountain with the neck. To scale the ice one walks for a considerable time along its border, where it is surrounded by rocks, until one reaches the older, perpetual snow which bridges the crevasses and supports the traveler most of the year. At the highest level of the perpetual snow the two horns rise out of the snow; one of these is the higher, and is therefore the peak of the mountain. These peaks are very difficult to climb; since they are surrounded by a snow ditch, now broader, now narrower—the glacial cleft—over which one must jump; and since its perpendicular walls have only small ledges into which the foot can be inserted, most of the mountain climbers are content to have reached the glacial cleft and to enjoy from there the panorama, in so far as it is not cut off by the horn. Those who want to climb the summit must do so with the help of crampons, ropes and clamps.

There are other mountains besides this one on the same southern side, but none is so high, though they are covered with snow early in autumn and keep the snow until late into the spring. But the summer always takes it away, and the rocks gleam friendly in the sunshine, and the forests lying lower down show a gentle green intersected by broad blue shadows which are so beautiful that one could not tire of looking at them all one's life.

On the other sides of the valley, that is to the north, east and west, the mountains stretch away at a lower level. Some fields and meadows climb to a fairly high level, and above them one sees various clearings, Alpine huts and such like, until they merge with the sky at their border as a serrated forest. This serration indicates their lesser elevation, while

Auszackung eben ihre geringe Höhe anzeigt, während die mittäglichen Berge, obwohl sie noch großartigere Wälder hegen, doch mit einem ganz glatten Rande an dem glänzenden Himmel hinstreichen.

Wenn man so ziemlich mitten in dem Tale steht, so hat man die Empfindung, als ginge nirgends ein Weg in dieses Becken herein und keiner daraus hinaus; allein diejenigen, welche öfter im Gebirge gewesen sind, kennen diese Täuschung gar wohl: in der Tat führen nicht nur verschiedene Wege und darunter sogar manche durch die Verschiebungen der Berge fast auf ebenem Boden in die nördlichen Flächen hinaus, sondern gegen Mittag, wo das Tal durch steilrechte Mauern fast geschlossen scheint, geht sogar ein Weg über den obenbenannten Hals.

Das Dörflein heißt Gschaid, und der Schneeberg, der auf seine Häuser herabschaut, heißt Gars.

Jenseits des Halses liegt ein viel schöneres und blühenderes Tal, als das von Gschaid ist, und es führt von der Unglücksäule der gebahnte Weg hinab. Es hat an seinem Eingange einen stattlichen Marktflecken, Millsdorf, der sehr groß ist, verschiedene Werke hat und in manchen Häusern städtische Gewerbe und Nahrung treibt. Die Bewohner sind viel wohlhabender als die in Gschaid, und obwohl nur drei Wegstunden [19] zwischen den beiden Tälern liegen, was für die an große Entfernungen gewöhnten und Mühseligkeiten liebenden Gebirgsbewohner eine unbedeutende Kleinigkeit ist, so sind doch Sitten und Gewohnheiten in den beiden Tälern so verschieden, selbst der äußere Anblick derselben ist so ungleich, als ob eine große Anzahl Meilen zwischen ihnen läge. Das ist in Gebirgen sehr oft der Fall und hängt nicht nur von der verschiedenen Lage der Täler gegen die Sonne ab, die sie oft mehr oder weniger begünstigt, sondern auch von dem Geiste der Bewohner, der durch gewisse Beschäftigungen nach dieser oder jener Richtung gezogen wird. Darin stimmen aber alle überein, daß sie an Herkömmlichkeiten und Väterweise hängen, großen Verkehr [20] leicht entbehren, ihr Tal außerordentlich lieben und ohne demselben kaum leben können.

Es vergehen oft Monate, oft fast ein Jahr, ehe ein Bewohner von Gschaid in das jenseitige Tal hinüber kommt und den großen Marktflecken Millsdorf besucht. Die Millsdorfer hal-

the southern mountains, although they support even more magnificent forests, stretch along the gleaming sky with a quite smooth border.

When one stands in about the middle of the valley, one has the feeling that no road leads into this basin and none out of it; but those who have often been in the mountains are quite familiar with this illusion; in fact, not only do various roads lead into the northern plains, and among them some which lie almost on level ground because of the dislocation of the mountains, but towards the south, where the valley seems almost blocked by perpendicular walls, there is even a road over the above-mentioned neck.

The little village is called Gschaid, and the snow mountain that looks down on its houses is called Gars.

On the other side of the neck there is a much more beautiful and more fertile valley than that of Gschaid, and the beaten road from the accident pillar leads down to it. At its entrance there is a stately market town, Millsdorf, which is very large, has various factories, and some houses in which the trades and professions of the city are carried on. Its inhabitants are much more prosperous than those of Gschaid; and although only three hours' walking distance lies between the two valleys, which is an insignificant trifle for mountain dwellers, who are used to great distances and love hardships, the customs and habits in the two valleys are so different, and they are so unlike even in external appearance that one would think a great number of miles lay between them. This is very often the case in the mountains; it depends not only on the different position of the valleys with relation to the sun, which often favors them more or less, but also on the mentality of the inhabitants who are drawn in this or that direction by certain occupations. But they are all alike in this, that they cling to tradition and to the ways of their forefathers, easily dispense with outside communication, love their valley inordinately and can scarcely live without it.

Months often pass, often almost a year, before an inhabitant of Gschaid crosses over into the valley beyond and visits the large market town of Millsdorf. The people of

ten es ebenso, obwohl sie ihrerseits doch Verkehr mit dem
Lande draußen pflegen und daher nicht so abgeschieden sind
wie die Gschaider. Es geht sogar ein Weg, der eine Straße
heißen könnte, längs ihres Tales, und mancher Reisende und
mancher Wanderer geht hindurch, ohne nur im geringsten
zu ahnen, daß mitternachtwärts seines Weges jenseits des
hohen herabblickenden Schneebergs noch ein Tal sei, in dem
viele Häuser zerstreut sind und in dem das Dörflein mit dem
spitzigen Kirchturme steht.

Unter den Gewerben des Dorfes, welche bestimmt sind,
den Bedarf des Tales zu decken, ist auch das eines Schusters,
das nirgends entbehrt werden kann, wo die Menschen nicht
in ihrem Urzustande sind. Die Gschaider aber sind so weit
über diesem Stande, daß sie recht gute und tüchtige Gebirgsfußbekleidung brauchen. Der Schuster ist mit einer kleinen
Ausnahme der einzige im Tale. Sein Haus steht auf dem
Platze in Gschaid, wo überhaupt die besseren stehen, und
schaut mit seinen grauen Mauern, weißen Fenstersimsen und
grün angestrichenen Fensterläden auf die vier Linden hinaus.
Es hat im Erdgeschosse die Arbeitsstube, die Gesellenstube,
eine größere und kleinere Wohnstube, ein Verkaufstübchen,
nebst Küche und Speisekammer und allen zugehörigen Ge-
lassen; im ersten [21] Stockwerke oder eigentlich im Raume des
Giebels hat es die Oberstube oder eigentliche Prunkstube.
Zwei Prachtbetten, schöne geglättete Kästen mit Kleidern
stehen da, dann ein Gläserkästchen mit Geschirren, ein Tisch
mit eingelegter Arbeit, gepolsterte Sessel, ein Mauerkästchen
mit den Ersparnissen, dann hängen an den Wänden Heiligen-
bilder, zwei schöne Sackuhren, gewonnene Preise im Schießen,
und endlich sind auch Scheibengewehre und Jagdbüchsen
nebst ihrem Zugehöre in einem eigenen, mit Glastafeln ver-
sehenen Kasten aufgehängt. An das Schusterhaus ist ein
kleineres Häuschen, nur durch den Einfahrtsschwibbogen
getrennt, angebaut, welches genau dieselbe Bauart hat und
zum Schusterhause wie ein Teil zum Ganzen gehört. Es hat
nur eine Stube mit den dazu gehörigen Wohnteilen. Es hat
die Bestimmung, dem Hausbesitzer, sobald er das Anwesen
seinem Sohne oder Nachfolger übergeben hat, als sogenanntes
Ausnahmstübchen zu dienen, in welchem er mit seinem
Weibe so lange haust, bis beide gestorben sind, die Stube

Millsdorf behave in the same way, although they for their part do associate with the country outside and are therefore not so isolated as the people of Gschaid. There is even a road that might be called a highway, stretching along their valley; and many a tourist and many a wanderer traverses it without in the least suspecting that to the north of his road, beyond the tall snow mountain that looks down on him, there is another valley, in which many houses are scattered and in which the little village with the pointed steeple is situated.

Among the trades of the village which are meant to supply the needs of the valley there is also that of a shoemaker—a trade that no place can dispense with where people do not live in the primitive state. The people of Gschaid, however, are so far above this state that they need really good and sturdy mountain footwear. The shoemaker is, with a small exception, the only one in the valley. His house stands on the square in Gschaid where, in general, the better houses stand and looks out at the four linden trees with its gray walls, white window sills and green painted shutters. On its ground floor it has a work room, the journeyman's room, a larger and a smaller living room, a little sales room, besides the kitchen and pantry and all the little rooms that go with these. On the second floor, which is really under the gables, is the upper room or best room. Two handsome beds, beautiful polished wardrobes with clothes in them stand in it, also a glass cabinet filled with china, an inlaid table, upholstered easy chairs, a little wall safe containing his savings. On the walls hang pictures of saints, two beautiful pocket watches, trophies won in shooting. And finally, target and hunting rifles, together with their accessories, are hung in a special cabinet with glass panels. A smaller house is built on to the shoemaker's house, separated from it only by the arch over the driveway; it is built in the same style of architecture exactly, and belongs to the cobbler's house as a part to the whole. It has only one room plus the requisite living accommodation. Its purpose is to serve as a so-called "old folks' room" for the owner of the house after he has turned over his property to his son or successor. He will live in it with his wife until both have died, when the room will again stand empty awaiting a new occupant.

wieder leer steht und auf einen neuen Bewohner wartet.

Das Schusterhaus hat nach rückwärts [22] Stall und Scheune; denn jeder Talbewohner ist, selbst wenn er ein Gewerbe treibt, auch Landbebauer und zieht hieraus seine gute und nachhaltige Nahrung. Hinter diesen Gebäuden ist endlich der Garten, der fast bei keinem besseren Hause in Gschaid fehlt und von dem sie ihre Gemüse, ihr Obst und für festliche Gelegenheiten ihre Blumen ziehen. Wie oft im Gebirge, so ist auch in Gschaid die Bienenzucht in diesen Gärten sehr verbreitet.

Die kleine Ausnahme, deren oben Erwähnung geschah, und die Nebenbuhlerschaft der Alleinherrlichkeit des Schusters ist ein anderer Schuster, der alte Tobias, der aber eigentlich kein Nebenbuhler ist, weil er nur mehr [23] flickt, hierin viel zu tun hat und es sich nicht im entferntesten beikommen läßt,[24] mit dem vornehmen Platzschuster in einen Wettstreit einzugehen, insbesondere, da der Platzschuster ihn häufig mit Lederflecken, Sohlenabschnitten und dergleichen Dingen unentgeltlich versieht. Der alte Tobias sitzt im Sommer am Ende des Dörfchens unter Holunderbüschen und arbeitet. Er ist umringt von Schuhen und Bundschuhen, die aber sämtlich alt, grau, kotig und zerrissen sind. Stiefel mit langen Röhren sind nicht da, weil sie im Dorfe und in der Gegend nicht getragen werden; nur zwei Personen haben solche, der Pfarrer und der Schullehrer, welche aber beides, flicken und neue Ware machen, nur bei dem Platzschuster lassen. Im Winter sitzt der alte Tobias in seinem Stübchen hinter den Holunderstauden und hat warm geheizt, weil das Holz in Gschaid nicht teuer ist.

Der Platzschuster ist, ehe er das Haus angetreten hat, ein Gemsewildschütze gewesen und hat überhaupt in seiner Jugend, wie die Gschaider sagen, nicht gut getan. Er war in der Schule immer einer der besten Schüler gewesen, hatte dann von seinem Vater das Handwerk gelernt, ist auf Wanderung [25] gegangen und ist endlich wieder zurückgekehrt. Statt, wie es sich für einen Gewerbsmann ziemt und wie sein Vater es zeitlebens getan, einen schwarzen Hut zu tragen, tat er einen grünen auf, steckte noch alle bestehenden Federn darauf und stolzierte mit ihm und mit dem kürzesten Lodenrocke,[26] den es im Tale gab, herum, während sein Vater

The shoemaker's house has a stable and barn at the rear; for every valley dweller, even when he has a trade, is a farmer too, and derives a good and lasting sustenance from the soil. Behind these buildings there is, finally, the garden, which almost none of the better houses in Gschaid lacks, and from which they obtain their vegetables, fruit and flowers for festive occasions. As often in the mountains, so, too, in Gschaid bee-keeping is general in these gardens.

The small exception mentioned above, a rival of the unlimited monopoly of the shoemaker, is another shoemaker, old Tobias. He is, however, not a real competitor, because he now only mends, is kept busy at it and hasn't the remotest intention of entering into competition with the elegant shoemaker on the square, especially as the latter frequently supplies him gratis with scraps of leather, remnants of soles and such things. In the summer, old Tobias sits at the end of the little village working under the elder bushes. He is surrounded by shoes and peasant boots, all of them old, gray, muddy and torn. Boots with high tops are not there, because they are not worn in the village or in the region. Only two people have them, the priest and schoolteacher, but they have only the shoemaker on the square do both their mending and new work. In the winter old Tobias sits in his little room behind the elder bushes and is warm because wood is not expensive in Gschaid.

Before taking over the house, the shoemaker on the square was a chamois poacher; he was in general, as the people of Gschaid say, a good-for-nothing in his youth. He had always been one of the best pupils in school, had then learned the trade from his father, had gone on the road as a journeyman and finally come home again. Instead of wearing a black hat as befits a tradesman and as his father had done all his life, he put on a green one, put every possible kind of feather on it and strutted about in this hat and in the shortest Loden jacket in the valley, whereas his father always wore a jacket of dark, if possible black, color, and which also had to be very

immer einen Rock von dunkler, womöglich schwarzer Farbe
hatte, der auch, weil er einem Gewerbsmanne angehörte,
immer sehr weit herabgeschnitten sein mußte. Der junge
Schuster war auf allen Tanzplätzen und Kegelbahnen zu
sehen. Wenn ihm jemand eine gute Lehre gab, so pfiff er ein
Liedlein. Er ging mit seinem Scheibengewehre zu allen
Schießen der Nachbarschaft und brachte manchmal einen
Preis nach Hause, was er für einen großen Sieg hielt. Der
Preis bestand meistens aus Münzen, die künstlich [27] gefaßt
waren und zu deren Gewinnung der Schuster mehr gleiche
Münzen ausgeben mußte, als der Preis enthielt, besonders da
er wenig haushälterisch mit dem Gelde war. Er ging auf alle
Jagden, die in der Gegend abgehalten wurden, und hatte sich
den Namen eines guten Schützen erworben. Er ging aber
auch manchmal allein mit seiner Doppelbüchse und mit
Steigeisen fort, und einmal sagte man, daß er eine schwere
Wunde im Kopfe erhalten habe.

In Millsdorf war ein Färber, welcher gleich am Anfange des
Marktfleckens, wenn man auf dem Wege von Gschaid hinüber kam, ein sehr ansehnliches Gewerbe hatte, mit vielen
Leuten und sogar, was im Tale etwas Unerhörtes war, mit
Maschinen arbeitete. Außerdem besaß er noch eine ausge-
breitete Feldwirtschaft. Zu der Tochter dieses reichen Färbers
ging der Schuster über das Gebirge, um sie zu gewinnen. Sie
war wegen ihrer Schönheit weit und breit [28] berühmt, aber
auch wegen ihrer Eingezogenheit, Sittsamkeit und Häuslich-
keit belobt. Dennoch, hieß es,[29] soll der Schuster ihre Aufmerksamkeit erregt haben. Der Färber ließ ihn nicht in sein
Haus kommen; und hatte die schöne Tochter schon früher
keine öffentlichen Plätze und Lustbarkeiten besucht und war
selten außer dem Hause ihrer Eltern zu sehen gewesen: so
ging sie jetzt schon gar nirgends mehr hin als in die Kirche
oder in ihren Garten oder in den Räumen des Hauses herum.

Einige Zeit nach dem Tode seiner Eltern, durch welchen
ihm das Haus derselben zugefallen war, das er nun allein
bewohnte, änderte sich der Schuster gänzlich. So wie er früher
getollt hatte, so saß er jetzt in seiner Stube und hämmerte
Tag und Nacht an seinen Sohlen. Er setzte prahlend einen
Preis darauf, wenn es jemand gäbe, der bessere Schuhe und
Fußbekleidungen machen könne. Er nahm keine andern

long because it was worn by a tradesman. The young shoemaker was to be seen on every dance floor and bowling alley. When anyone tried to give him good advice, he whistled a little song. He went to every shooting match in the neighborhood with his target rifle and sometimes brought home a prize, which he considered a great triumph. The prize consisted mostly of coins in an artistic setting, but to win them the shoemaker had to spend more coins of the same kind than the prize amounted to, especially as he was not economical with money. He went to every hunt that was held in the region and had gained the name of a good marksman. But sometimes he went away alone with his double-barreled shotgun and climbing irons, and once, it was said, he had received a serious wound in his head.

In Millsdorf there was a dyer who had a considerable business right at the entrance to the market town, where one came over on the road from Gschaid. He employed many people and even used machinery, which was something unheard of in the valley. Besides, he owned an extensive farm. To win the daughter of this rich dyer the shoemaker crossed the range. She was noted for her beauty far and wide but she was also praised for her modesty, virtue and domesticity. Nevertheless, it was said, the shoemaker had attracted her attention. The dyer would not admit him to his house; if the beautiful daughter had, even before this, never gone to public places of amusement and had rarely been seen outside the house of her parents, she now went absolutely nowhere except to church, or she walked about in her garden or in the rooms of her home.

Some time after the death of his parents, through which he had acquired their house in which he now lived alone, the shoemaker changed completely. As he had formerly led a wild life, so he now sat in his room, hammering away at his soles day and night. He boastingly offered a prize to anyone who could make better shoes and bootwear than he. He employed none but the best workmen and drilled away at them

Arbeiter als die besten und trillte sie noch sehr herum, wenn sie in seiner Werkstätte arbeiteten, daß sie ihm folgten und die Sache so einrichteten, wie er befahl. Wirklich brachte er es jetzt auch dahin, daß nicht nur das ganze Dorf Gschaid, das zum größten Teile die Schusterarbeit aus benachbarten Tälern bezogen hatte, bei ihm arbeiten ließ,[30] daß das ganze Tal bei ihm arbeiten ließ und daß endlich sogar einzelne von Millsdorf und anderen Tälern herein kamen und sich ihre Fußbekleidungen von dem Schuster in Gschaid machen ließen. Sogar in die Ebene hinaus verbreitete sich sein Ruhm, daß manche, die in die Gebirge gehen wollten, sich die Schuhe dazu von ihm machen ließen.

Er richtete das Haus sehr schön zusammen, und in dem Warengewölbe glänzten auf den Brettern die Schuhe, Bundstiefel und Stiefel; und wenn am Sonntage die ganze Bevölkerung des Tales hereinkam und man bei den vier Linden des Platzes stand, ging man gerne zu dem Schusterhause hin und sah durch die Gläser in die Warenstube, wo die Käufer und Besteller waren.

Nach seiner Vorliebe zu den Bergen machte er auch jetzt die Gebirgsbundschuhe am besten. Er pflegte in der Wirtsstube zu sagen: es gäbe keinen, der ihm einen fremden Gebirgsbundschuh zeigen könne, der sich mit einem seinigen vergleichen lasse. „Sie wissen es nicht," pflegte er beizufügen, „sie haben es in ihrem Leben nicht erfahren, wie ein solcher Schuh sein muß, daß der gestirnte Himmel der Nägel recht auf der Sohle sitze und das gebührende Eisen enthalte, daß der Schuh außen hart sei, damit kein Geröllstein, wie scharf er auch sei, empfunden werde und daß er sich von innen doch weich und zärtlich wie ein Handschuh an die Füße lege."

Der Schuster hatte sich ein sehr großes Buch machen lassen, in welches er alle verfertigte Ware eintrug, die Namen derer beifügte, die den Stoff geliefert und die Ware gekauft hatten, und eine kurze Bemerkung über die Güte des Erzeugnisses beischrieb. Die gleichartigen Fußbekleidungen hatten ihre fortlaufenden Zahlen, und das Buch lag in der großen Lade seines Gewölbes. Wenn die schöne Färberstochter von Millsdorf auch nicht aus der Eltern Hause kam, wenn sie auch weder Freunde noch Verwandte besuchte, so

when they worked in his shop, until they obeyed him and did things exactly as he ordered them to do. And really he now brought matters to the point where not only the whole village of Gschaid, which for the most part had had its shoe work done in neighboring valleys, now patronized him, but that the whole valley had him do their work and finally even some people from Millsdorf and other valleys came over and had the shoemaker of Gschaid make their footwear. His fame spread even to the plain, so that some who wanted to go into the mountains had him make their shoes.

He fixed up the house handsomely, and in his salesroom the shoes, laced boots and high boots shone on the shelves. On Sundays, when the whole population of the valley came in and stood around at the four linden trees on the square, they liked to go over to the shoemaker's house and look through the windows into the salesroom in which shoes were being bought and orders taken.

In accordance with his love for the mountains, his best work was now his laced mountain shoes. He used to say in the taproom: no one could show him a laced mountain shoe made elsewhere that could compare with his. "They don't know," he would add, "they haven't had the practical experience in all their lives how such a shoe should be made: so that the starry heaven of nails should sit properly on the sole and that there should be the necessary iron, that the shoe should be hard on the outside, so that no loose stone, however sharp it might be, would be felt, and that it would yet settle on the foot softly and tenderly like a glove on the inside."

The shoemaker had had a very large book made into which he entered all the goods he had finished, adding the names of those who had supplied the material and bought the goods and a brief remark about the quality of the product. Footwear of the same type had serial numbers, and the book lay in the large drawer of the shop.

Even though the fair daughter of the dyer of Millsdorf did not leave her parents' house, even though she visited neither friends nor relatives, the shoemaker of Gschaid could yet

konnte es der Schuster von Gschaid doch so machen, daß sie
ihn von ferne sah, wenn sie in die Kirche ging, wenn sie in
dem Garten war und wenn sie aus den Fenstern ihres Zimmers auf die Matten blickte. Wegen dieses unausgesetzten
Sehens hatte es die Färberin durch langes, inständiges und
ausdauerndes Flehen für ihre Tochter dahin gebracht, daß
der halsstarrige Färber nachgab und daß der Schuster, weil er
denn nun doch besser geworden, die schöne, reiche Mills-
dorferin als Eheweib nach Gschaid führte.

Aber der Färber war desungeachtet auch ein Mann, der
seinen Kopf hatte.[31] Ein rechter Mensch, sagte er, müsse sein
Gewerbe treiben, daß es blühe und vorwärts komme, er müsse
daher sein Weib, seine Kinder, sich und sein Gesinde ernähren,
Hof und Haus im Stande des Glanzes halten und sich noch ein
Erkleckliches erübrigen, welches letztere doch allein imstande
sei, ihm Ansehen und Ehre in der Welt zu geben; darum er-
halte seine Tochter nichts als eine vortreffliche Ausstattung,
das andere ist Sache des Ehemanns, daß er es mache und für
alle Zukunft es besorge. Die Färberei in Millsdorf und die
Landwirtschaft auf dem Färberhause sei für sich ein ansehnliches und ehrenwertes Gewerbe, das seiner Ehre willen [32] bestehen und wozu alles, was da sei, als Grundstock dienen
müsse, daher er nichts weggebe. Wenn einmal er und sein
Eheweib, die Färberin, tot seien, dann gehöre Färberei und
Landwirtschaft in Millsdorf ihrer einzigen Tochter, nämlich
der Schusterin in Gschaid, und Schuster und Schusterin
könnten dann damit tun, was sie wollten; aber alles dieses
nur, wenn die Erben es wert wären, das Erbe zu empfangen;
wären sie es nicht wert, so ging das Erbe auf die Kinder
derselben, und wenn keine vorhanden wären, mit der Ausnahme des lediglichen Pflichtteiles auf andere Verwandte über.

Der Schuster verlangte auch nichts, er zeigte im Stolze,
daß es ihm nur um die schöne Färberstochter in Millsdorf
zu tun gewesen [33] und daß er sie schon ernähren und erhalten
könne, wie sie zu Hause ernährt und erhalten worden ist. Er
kleidete sie als sein Eheweib nicht nur schöner als alle
Gschaiderinnen und alle Bewohnerinnen des Tales, sondern
auch schöner, als sie sich je zu Hause getragen hatte, und
Speise, Trank und übrige Behandlung mußte besser und
rücksichtsvoller sein, als sie das gleiche im väterlichen Hause

bring it about that she saw him from a distance when she went to church, when she was in the garden, and when she looked out on the meadows from the windows of her room. Because of this constant looking, the dyer's wife had succeeded, through long, insistent and persevering supplication on behalf of her daughter, in making the stiffnecked dyer yield, so that the shoemaker, because he had improved after all, led the beautiful rich girl from Millsdorf home to Gschaid as his wife.

Nevertheless the dyer was a headstrong man too. A real man, he said, must carry on his trade in such a way that it will flourish and progress; he must therefore support his wife, his children, himself and his servants, maintain his house and farm in a prosperous state. He must besides lay aside a considerable sum, which alone will procure for him respect and honor in the world. For this reason his daughter would get nothing but an excellent trousseau; the rest was the concern of her husband, to look after her now and to provide for her future. The dyeworks in Millsdorf and the farm adjoining the house were in themselves a respectable and honorable business; they would have to continue for the sake of his honor and serve as the basis for everything else that was there; so he would give away nothing. Once he and his wife were dead, the dyeworks and the farm in Millsdorf would belong to their only daughter, that is the wife of the shoemaker of Gschaid, and they could both do what they pleased with it. But all this only if the heirs were worthy of receiving the inheritance; if they were not, the inheritance would go to their children, and if there were none, to other relatives, except for what was legally theirs.

The shoemaker, too, asked for nothing; he demonstrated in his pride that his interest had been confined to the fair daughter of the dyer of Millsdorf and that he could certainly support and maintain her as she had been supported and maintained at home. He dressed her, as his wife, not only more handsomely than all the women of Gschaid and all the inhabitants of the valley, but even more handsomely than she had ever dressed at home; and food, drink and all other services had to be better and choicer than she had enjoyed

genossen hatte. Und um dem Schwiegervater zu trotzen, kaufte er mit erübrigten Summen nach und nach immer mehr Grundstücke so ein, daß er einen tüchtigen Besitz beisammen hatte.

Weil die Bewohner von Gschaid so selten aus ihrem Tale kommen und nicht einmal oft nach Millsdorf hinüber gehen, von dem sie durch Bergrücken und durch Sitten geschieden sind, weil ferner ihnen gar kein Fall vorkommt, daß ein Mann sein Tal verläßt und sich in dem benachbarten ansiedelt (Ansiedlungen in großen Entfernungen kommen öfter vor), weil endlich auch kein Weib oder Mädchen gerne von einem Tale in ein anderes auswandert, außer in dem ziemlich seltenen Falle, wenn sie der Liebe folgt und als Eheweib und zu dem Ehemann in ein anderes Tal kommt: so geschah es, daß die schöne Färberstochter von Millsdorf, da sie Schusterin in Gschaid geworden war, doch immer von allen Gschaidern als Fremde angesehen wurde, und wenn man ihr auch nichts Übles antat, ja wenn man sie ihres schönen Wesens und ihrer Sitten wegen sogar liebte, doch immer etwas vorhanden war, das wie Scheu oder, wenn man will, wie Rücksicht aussah und nicht zu dem Innigen und Gleichartigen kommen ließ,[34] wie Gschaiderinnen gegen Gschaiderinnen, Gschaider gegen Gschaider hatten. Es war so, ließ sich nicht abstellen und wurde durch die bessere Tracht und durch das erleichterte häusliche Leben der Schusterin noch vermehrt.

Sie hatte ihrem Manne nach dem ersten Jahre einen Sohn und in einigen Jahren darauf ein Töchterlein geboren. Sie glaubte aber, daß er die Kinder nicht so liebe, wie sie sich vorstellte, daß es sein solle, und wie sie sich bewußt war, daß sie dieselben liebe; denn sein Angesicht war meistens ernsthaft und mit seinen Arbeiten beschäftigt. Er spielte und tändelte selten mit den Kindern und sprach stets ruhig mit ihnen, gleichsam so, wie man mit Erwachsenen spricht. Was Nahrung und Kleidung und andere äußere Dinge anbelangte, hielt er die Kinder untadelig.

In der ersten Zeit der Ehe kam die Färberin öfter nach Gschaid, und die jungen Eheleute besuchten auch Millsdorf zuweilen bei Kirchweihen oder anderen festlichen Gelegenheiten. Als aber die Kinder auf der Welt waren, war die Sache anders geworden. Wenn schon Mütter ihre Kinder lieben und

in her father's house. And to spite his father-in-law, he bought more and more land with sums of money that he had saved, so that he amassed a considerable estate.

Because the inhabitants of Gschaid so rarely leave their valley and do not even frequently go to Millsdorf, from which they are separated by mountains and customs; and because it never happens to them that a man leaves his valley and settles in the neighboring one (settlements in distant places occur more often); and finally because no wife or girl likes to emigrate from one valley to another, except in the fairly rare case when she follows the call of love and joins her husband as his wedded wife in another valley—it happened that the fair daughter of the dyer of Millsdorf was still regarded as a stranger by all the people of Gschaid even after she had become the wife of the shoemaker of Gschaid. And even though they did her no harm, indeed though they even loved her because of her beauty and good manners, there was always something present that looked like shyness or, if you will, deference and did not permit that intimacy and equality that the men and women of Gschaid had for each other to develop. It was so, could not be stopped and was even increased by the better clothes the shoemaker's wife wore and the easier life she led at home.

After the first year she had borne her husband a son and a few years later a little daughter. But she felt that he did not love the children as she imagined he should and as she was conscious of loving them herself; for his countenance was mostly serious and he was busy with his work. He rarely played and dallied with the children, and always spoke quietly to them, just as one speaks to grown-ups. But as far as food and clothing and other externals were concerned, he kept the children above reproach.

In the first period of the marriage the dyer's wife came to Gschaid fairly often, and the young couple visited Millsdorf at times, at church fairs or on other festive occasions. But when the children came, matters were different. Though mothers may love their children and yearn for them, this is

sich nach ihnen sehnen, so ist dieses von Großmüttern öfter noch in höherem Grade der Fall: sie verlangen zuweilen mit wahrlich krankhafter Sehnsucht nach ihren Enkeln. Die Färberin kam sehr oft nach Gschaid herüber, um die Kinder zu sehen, ihnen Geschenke zu bringen, eine Weile dazubleiben und dann mit guten Ermahnungen zu scheiden. Da aber das Alter und die Gesundheitsumstände der Färberin die öfteren Fahrten nicht mehr so möglich machten, und der Färber aus dieser Ursache Einsprache tat, wurde auf etwas anderes gesonnen, die Sache wurde umgekehrt, und die Kinder kamen jetzt zur Großmutter. Die Mutter brachte sie selber öfter in einem Wagen, öfter aber wurden sie, da sie noch im zarten Alter waren, eingemummt einer Magd mitgegeben, die sie in einem Fuhrwerke über den Hals brachte. Als sie aber größer waren, gingen sie zu Fuße entweder mit der Mutter oder mit einer Magd nach Millsdorf, ja da der Knabe geschickt, stark und klug geworden war, ließ man ihn allein den bekannten Weg über den Hals gehen, und wenn es sehr schön war, und er bat, erlaubte man auch, daß ihn die kleine Schwester begleite. Dies ist bei den Gschaidern gebräuchlich, weil sie an starkes Fußgehen gewöhnt sind und die Eltern überhaupt, namentlich aber ein Mann wie der Schuster, es gerne sehen und eine Freude daran haben, wenn ihre Kinder tüchtig werden.

So geschah es, daß die zwei Kinder den Weg über den Hals öfter zurücklegten als die übrigen Dörfler zusammengenommen, und da schon ihre Mutter in Gschaid gewissermaßen wie eine Fremde behandelt wurde, so wurden durch diesen Umstand auch die Kinder fremd, sie waren kaum Gschaider und gehörten halb nach Millsdorf hinüber.

Der Knabe Konrad hatte schon das ernste Wesen seines Vaters, und das Mädchen Susanna, nach ihrer Mutter so genannt, oder, wie man es zur Abkürzung nannte, Sanna, hatte viel Glauben zu seinen Kenntnissen, seiner Einsicht und seiner Macht und gab sich unbedingt unter seine Leitung, gerade so wie die Mutter sich unbedingt unter die Leitung des Vaters gab, dem sie alle Einsicht und Geschicklichkeit zutraute.

An schönen Tagen konnte man morgens die Kinder durch das Tal gegen Mittag wandern sehen, über die Wiese gehen

often the case to an even higher degree with grandmothers; they sometimes yearn for their grandchildren with a truly morbid craving. The dyer's wife came over to Gschaid very often to see the children, to bring them gifts, to remain there a while and then to depart with some good advice to them. But since the age and the health of the dyer's wife made the fairly frequent visits impossible, and because the dyer raised objections on this account, another plan was devised; the matter was reversed and the children now came to the grandmother. Their mother herself often brought them in a carriage; more frequently, however, they were bundled up, because they were still of a tender age, and handed over to a maid, who brought them over the neck in a carriage. But when they were bigger, they went to Millsdorf on foot either with their mother or with a maid. Indeed, since the boy had become alert, strong and clever, he was allowed to take the familiar road over the neck alone; and when the weather was very beautiful and he requested it, he was allowed to take his little sister with him. This is customary with the people of Gschaid because they are accustomed to a good deal of walking, and parents in general, especially a man like the shoemaker, are glad and happy to see their children growing capable.

So it happened that the two children took the road over the neck more often than all the rest of the villagers taken together. Since their mother had always been treated more or less as a stranger in Gschaid, the children too became strangers because of this circumstance; they were scarcely Gschaid children and half belonged to Millsdorf.

The boy Conrad already had the serious character of his father, and the girl Susanna, named after her mother, or Sanna, as she was called for short, had much faith in his knowledge, judgment and power, and yielded absolutely to his leadership, just as her mother yielded absolutely to the leadership of the father, to whom she attributed unerring judgment and ability.

On fine days one could see the children hiking in the morning southwards through the valley, walking over the

und dort anlangen, wo der Wald des Halses gegen sie
herschaut. Sie näherten sich dem Walde, gingen auf seinem
Wege allgemach über die Erhöhung hinan, und kamen, ehe
der Mittag eingetreten war, auf den offenen Wiesen auf der
anderen Seite gegen Millsdorf hinunter. Konrad zeigte Sanna
die Wiesen, die dem Großvater gehörten, dann gingen sie
durch seine Felder, auf denen er ihr die Getreidearten erklärte, dann sahen sie auf Stangen unter dem Vorsprunge des
Daches die langen Tücher zum Trocknen herabhängen, die
sich im Winde schlängelten oder närrische Gesichter machten, dann hörten sie seine Walkmühle und seinen Lohstampf,
die er an seinem Bache für Tuchmacher und Gerber angelegt
hatte, dann bogen sie noch um eine Ecke der Felder und
gingen in kurzem [35] durch die Hintertür in den Garten der
Färberei, wo sie von der Großmutter empfangen wurden.
Diese ahnte immer, wenn die Kinder kamen, sah zu den
Fenstern aus und erkannte sie von weitem, wenn Sannas
rotes Tuch recht in der Sonne leuchtete.

Sie führte die Kinder dann durch die Waschstube und
Presse in das Zimmer, ließ sie niedersetzen, ließ nicht zu, daß
sie Halstücher oder Jäckchen lüfteten, damit sie sich nicht
verkühlten,[36] und behielt sie beim Essen da. Nach dem Essen
durften sie sich lüften, spielen, durften in den Räumen des
großväterlichen Hauses herumgehen oder sonst tun, was sie
wollten, wenn es nur nicht unschicklich oder verboten war.
Der Färber, welcher immer bei dem Essen war, fragte sie um
ihre Schulgegenstände aus und schärfte ihnen besonders ein,
was sie lernen sollten. Nachmittags wurden sie von der
Großmutter schon, ehe die Zeit kam, zum Aufbruche getrieben, daß sie ja nicht zu spät kämen. Obgleich der Färber
keine Mitgift gegeben hatte und vor seinem Tode von seinem
Vermögen nichts wegzugeben gelobt hatte, glaubte sich die
Färberin an diese Dinge doch nicht so strenge gebunden,
und sie gab den Kindern nicht allein während ihrer Anwesen-
heit allerlei, worunter nicht selten ein Münzstück und zuweilen gar von ansehnlichem Werte war, sondern sie band
ihnen auch immer zwei Bündelchen zusammen, in denen
sich Dinge befanden, von denen sie glaubte, daß sie notwendig wären oder daß sie den Kindern Freude machen
könnten. Und wenn oft die nämlichen Dinge im Schuster-

meadow and reaching the place where the forest of the neck looks down toward it. They would approach the forest, walk gradually up the slope on the road, and before noon were coming down the open meadows on the other side toward Millsdorf. Conrad showed Sanna the meadows that belonged to their grandfather; then they went through his fields, in which he explained to her the various kinds of grain; then they saw the long cloths hanging on poles under the projecting roof to dry, coiling snakelike in the wind or making comical faces; then they heard his fulling mill and his bark crusher which he had built beside his brook for cloth makers and tanners; then they turned another corner of the fields and in a short while entered the garden of the dyeworks by a back door, where they were received by their grandmother. She always had a premonition when the children were coming, looked out of the windows and recognized them from a distance when Sanna's red kerchief shone brightly in the sun.

She would then lead the children through the laundry and ironing room into the living room, made them sit down, would not let them loosen their kerchiefs or little jackets, so that they might not catch cold, and kept them there for dinner. After dinner they were allowed to undo their things, play, walk around in the rooms of grandfather's house or do whatever they wished, as long as it was not improper or forbidden. The dyer, who was always present at dinner, questioned them about their studies at school, and especially impressed on them what they ought to learn. In the afternoon their grandmother would urge them, even before it was time, to start out so that they would not arrive too late. Although the dyer had given no dowry and had vowed to give away no part of his fortune before his death, his wife did not consider herself strictly bound to these vows, and she not only gave the children all sorts of things while they were present, often including coins of considerable value, but she always tied up two bundles for them in which there were things she thought they needed, or which would give the children pleasure. And even if the same things were often in the shoemaker's house in Gschaid, and of excellent quality, the grandmother gave them nevertheless, for the joy of giving, and the children

hause in Gschaid in aller Trefflichkeit vorhanden waren, so gab sie die Großmutter in der Freude des Gebens doch, und die Kinder trugen sie als etwas Besonderes nach Hause. So geschah es nun, daß die Kinder am Heiligen Abende schon unwissend die Geschenke in Schachteln gut versiegelt und verwahrt nach Hause trugen, die ihnen in der Nacht einbeschert werden sollten.

Weil die Großmutter die Kinder immer schon vor der Zeit zum Fortgehen drängte, damit sie nicht zu spät nach Hause kämen, so erzielte sie hiedurch, daß die Kinder gerade auf dem Wege bald an dieser, bald an jener Stelle sich aufhielten. Sie saßen gerne an dem Haselnußgehege, das auf dem Halse ist, und schlugen mit Steinen Nüsse auf oder spielten, wenn keine Nüsse waren, mit Blättern oder mit Hölzlein oder mit den weichen, braunen Zäpfchen, die im ersten Frühjahre von den Zweigen der Nadelbäume herabfielen. Manchmal erzählte Konrad dem Schwesterchen Geschichten, oder wenn sie zu der roten Unglücksäule kamen, führte er sie ein Stück auf dem Seitenwege links gegen die Höhen hinan und sagte ihr, daß man da auf den Schneeberg gelange, daß dort Felsen und Steine seien, daß die Gemsen herumspringen und große Vögel fliegen. Er führte sie oft über den Wald hinaus, sie betrachteten dann den dürren Rasen und die kleinen Sträucher der Heidekräuter; aber er führte sie wieder zurück und brachte sie immer vor der Abenddämmerung nach Hause, was ihm stets Lob eintrug.

Einmal war am Heiligen Abende, da die erste Morgendämmerung in dem Tale von Gschaid in Helle übergegangen war, ein dünner, trockener Schleier über den ganzen Himmel gebreitet, so daß man die ohnedem schiefe und ferne Sonne im Südosten nur als einen undeutlichen roten Fleck sah, überdies war an diesem Tage eine milde, beinahe laulichte Luft unbeweglich im ganzen Tale und auch an dem Himmel, wie die unveränderte und ruhige Gestalt der Wolken zeigte. Da sagte die Schustersfrau zu ihren Kindern: „Weil ein so angenehmer Tag ist, weil es so lange nicht geregnet hat und die Wege fest sind, und weil es auch der Vater gestern unter der Bedingung erlaubt hat, wenn der heutige Tag dazu geeignet ist, so dürft ihr zur Großmutter nach Millsdorf gehen; aber ihr müßt den Vater noch vorher fragen."

took them home as something special. And so it happened that on Christmas Eve the children would, without knowing it, carry home well-sealed and packed boxes containing the gifts that were to be presented to them that night.

Because their grandmother always urged the children to start for home sooner than was necessary, so that they might not arrive too late, all she achieved by this maneuver was that the children stopped on the way now at one spot, now at another. They liked to sit by the hazel-nut bushes on the neck, and they cracked the nuts open with stones or, if there were no nuts, they played with leaves or little bits of wood or with the soft brown little cones which fell from the branches of the pine trees in the early spring. Sometimes Conrad told his little sister stories, or when they came to the red accident pillar, he took her up a piece on the side road to the left towards the heights, and told her that you got to the snow mountain that way, that there were rocks and stones there, that the chamois leaped about and the big birds flew there. He often took her beyond the forest; they would then gaze at the dry grass and the little shrubs of heather; but he led her back and always brought her home again before dark, which always earned him praise.

Once, on the day before Christmas, when the first dawn in the valley of Gschaid had changed into full day, a thin, dry veil was spread over the whole sky, so that the sun in the southeast, which in any case was low and distant, could only be seen as an indistinct red spot. On this day, moreover, the air in the whole valley and in the sky too was mild, almost tepid and motionless, as was proved by the unchanged and calm shape of the clouds. So the shoemaker's wife said to her children: "Since it is such a pleasant day, because it hasn't rained for such a long time, and the roads are firm, and because father gave permission for it on condition that today would be suitable for it, you may go to grandmother's at Millsdorf; but you must first ask father again."

Die Kinder, welche noch in ihren Nachtkleidchen dastanden, liefen in die Nebenstube, in welcher der Vater mit einem Kunden sprach, und baten um die Wiederholung der gestrigen Erlaubnis, weil ein so schöner Tag sei. Sei wurde ihnen erteilt, und sie liefen wieder zur Mutter zurück.

Die Schustersfrau zog nun ihre Kinder vorsorglich an, oder eigentlich, sie zog das Mädchen mit dichten, gut verwahrenden Kleidern an; denn der Knabe begann sich selber anzukleiden und stand viel früher fertig da, als die Mutter mit dem Mädchen hatte ins reine kommen können.[37] Als sie dieses Geschäft vollendet hatte, sagte sie: „Konrad, gib wohl acht: weil ich dir das Mädchen mitgehen lasse, so müsset ihr beizeiten fort gehen, ihr müsset an keinem Platze stehen bleiben, und wenn ihr bei der Großmutter gegessen habt, so müsset ihr gleich wieder umkehren und nach Hause trachten; denn die Tage sind jetzt sehr kurz, und die Sonne geht gar bald unter.“

„Ich weiß es schon, Mutter“, sagte Konrad.

„Und siehe gut auf Sanna, daß sie nicht fällt oder sich erhitzt.“

„Ja, Mutter.“

„So, Gott behüte euch, und geht noch zum Vater und sagt, daß ihr jetzt fortgehet.“

Der Knabe nahm eine von seinem Vater kunstvoll aus Kalbfellen genähte Tasche an einem Riemen um die Schulter, und die Kinder gingen in die Nebenstube, um dem Vater Lebewohl zu sagen. Aus dieser kamen sie bald heraus und hüpften, von der Mutter mit einem Kreuze [38] besegnet, fröhlich auf die Gasse.

Sie gingen schleunig längs des Dorfplatzes hinab und dann durch die Häusergasse und endlich zwischen den Planken der Obstgärten in das Freie [39] hinaus. Die Sonne stand schon über dem mit milchigen Wolkenstreifen durchwobenen Wald der morgendlichen Anhöhen, und ihr trübes, rötliches Bild schritt durch die laublosen Zweige der Holzäpfelbäume mit den Kindern fort.

In dem ganzen Tale war kein Schnee, die größeren Berge, von denen er schon viele Wochen herabgeglänzt hatte, waren damit bedeckt, die kleineren standen in dem Mantel ihrer Tannenwälder und im Fahlrot ihrer entblößten Zweige un-

The children, who were still standing there in their night clothes, ran into the adjoining room in which the father was talking to a customer, and asked for a repetition of yesterday's permission, because it was such a beautiful day. It was given them and they ran back again to their mother.

The shoemaker's wife now dressed her children carefully, or rather she dressed the girl in heavy, protective clothing; for the boy began to dress himself and stood all dressed much sooner than the mother could finish with the girl. When she had completed this task she said: "Pay attention, Conrad; because I'm letting the girl go along with you, you must set out in good time, you must not stop anywhere, and when you've had dinner at grandmother's, you must turn around at once and get home; for the days are very short now, and the sun sets soon."

"I know that, mother," said Conrad.

"And look after Sanna carefully, so that she doesn't fall or get overheated."

"Yes, mother."

"There, God protect you, and go to father first and tell him that you're leaving now."

The boy took a bag which his father had sewn together skillfully out of calfskins and slung it over his shoulder by a strap; and the children went into the adjoining room to say good-by to their father. They soon emerged from it and skipped happily out into the street, blessed by their mother with a sign of the cross.

They quickly went down along the village square and then through the street of houses and finally between the board fences of the orchards out into the open. The sun already stood above the forest on the eastern heights, interlaced with milky strips of cloud, and its dull, reddish image accompanied the children through the leafless branches of the crab apple trees.

There was no snow in the whole valley; the larger mountains which had been glistening with it for many weeks now, were covered by it; the smaller ones stood free from snow, and calm, wrapped in the cloak of their pine forests and in

beschneit und ruhig da. Der Boden war noch nicht gefroren, und er wäre vermöge der vorhergegangenen langen regenlosen Zeit ganz trocken gewesen, wenn ihn nicht die Jahreszeit mit einer zarten Feuchtigkeit überzogen hätte, die ihn aber nicht schlüpfrig, sondern eher fest und widerprallend machte, daß sie leicht und gering darauf fortgingen. Das wenige Gras, welches noch auf den Wiesen und vorzüglich an den Wassergräben derselben war, stand in herbstlichem Ansehen. Es lag kein Reif und bei näherem Anblicke nicht einmal ein Tau, was nach der Meinung der Landleute baldigen Regen bedeutet.

Gegen die Grenzen der Wiesen zu war ein Gebirgsbach, über welchen ein hoher Steg führte. Die Kinder gingen auf den Steg und schauten hinab. Im Bache war schier kein Wasser, ein dünner Faden von sehr stark blauer Farbe ging durch die trockenen Kiesel des Gerölles, die wegen Regenlosigkeit ganz weiß geworden waren, und sowohl die Wenigkeit als auch die Farbe des Wassers zeigten an, daß in den größeren Höhen schon Kälte herrschen müsse, die den Boden verschließe, daß er mit seiner Erde das Wasser nicht trübe, und die das Eis erhärte, daß es in seinem Innern nur wenige klare Tropfen abgeben könne.

Von dem Stege liefen die Kinder durch die Gründe fort und näherten sich immer mehr den Waldungen.

Sie trafen endlich die Grenze des Holzes und gingen in demselben weiter.

Als sie in die höheren Wälder des Halses hinaufgekommen waren, zeigten sich die langen Furchen des Fahrweges nicht mehr weich, wie es unten im Tale der Fall gewesen war, sondern sie waren fest, und zwar nicht aus Trockenheit, sondern, wie die Kinder sich bald überzeugten, weil sie gefroren waren. An manchen Stellen waren sie so überfroren, daß sie die Körper der Kinder trugen. Nach der Natur der Kinder gingen sie nun nicht mehr auf dem glatten Pfade neben dem Fahrwege, sondern in den Gleisen, und versuchten, ob dieser oder jener Furchenaufwurf sie schon trage. Als sie nach Verlauf einer Stunde auf der Höhe des Halses angekommen waren, war der Boden bereits so hart, daß er klang und Schollen wie Steine hatte.

An der roten Unglücksäule des Bäckers bemerkte Sanna zuerst, daß sie heute gar nicht dastehe. Sie gingen zu dem

the pale red of their bare branches. The ground was not frozen yet and it would have been quite dry because of the long time that had passed without rain, if the season had not covered it with a delicate moisture which, however, did not make it slippery but rather firm and resilient, so that they walked lightly and easily on it. The little grass that was still on the meadows and especially in the water ditches, had an autumnal look about it. There was no hoarfrost and, on closer inspection, not even a dew, which the country folk interpret as signifying imminent rain.

Toward the edges of the meadows there was a mountain brook which was crossed by a high footbridge. The children walked over the footbridge and looked down. There was almost no water in the brook; a thin thread of very strong blue color went through the dry pebbles of the gravel which had turned quite white because of the lack of rain. Both the scantiness and color of the water indicated that at the greater heights there prevailed already a cold which sealed up the soil, so that the earth did not make the water muddy and froze the ice so that it could only give off a few clear drops at its core.

From the footbridge the children ran on across the lower ground and came closer and closer to the forests.

They finally met the edge of the forest and continued on in it.

When they had come up into the higher forests of the neck, the long ruts of the road were no longer soft as had been the case down below in the valley, but they were firm, and that not because of dryness but, as the children soon convinced themselves, because they were frozen. At some spots they were so frozen over that they could support the bodies of the children. As was natural for children, they no longer walked on the smooth path beside the roadway but in the tracks, trying out whether this or that clump of earth would bear their weight. When, after the passing of an hour, they had come to the top of the neck, the soil was already so hard that it resounded and had clods as hard as stone.

Sanna was the first to notice, at the red accident pillar erected to the baker, that it wasn't there at all today. They

Platze hinzu und sahen, daß der runde, rot angestrichene
Balken, der das Bild trug, in dem dürren Grase liege, das wie
dünnes Stroh an der Stelle stand und den Anblick der liegenden Säule verdeckte. Sie sahen zwar nicht ein, warum die
Säule liege, und ob sie umgeworfen worden oder ob sie von
selber umgefallen sei, das sahen sie, daß sie an der Stelle, wo
sie in die Erde ragte, sehr morsch war und daß sie daher sehr
leicht habe umfallen können; aber da sie einmal lag, so machte
es ihnen Freude, daß sie das Bild und die Schrift so nahe
betrachten konnten, wie es sonst nie der Fall gewesen war.
Als sie alles—den Korb mit den Semmeln, die bleichen Hände
des Bäckers, seine geschlossenen Augen, seinen grauen Rock
und die umstehenden Tannen—betrachtet hatten, als sie die
Schrift gelesen und laut gesagt hatten, gingen sie wieder
weiter.

Abermals nach einer Stunde wichen die dunklen Wälder zu
beiden Seiten zurück, dünnstehende Bäume, teils einzelne
Eichen, teils Birken und Gebüschgruppen empfingen sie,
geleiteten sie weiter, und nach kurzem liefen sie auf den
Wiesen in das Millsdorfer Tal hinab.

Obwohl dieses Tal bedeutend tiefer liegt als das von
Gschaid und auch um so viel wärmer war, daß man die Ernte
immer um vierzehn Tage früher beginnen konnte als in
Gschaid, so war doch auch hier der Boden gefroren, und als
die Kinder bis zu den Loh- und Walkwerken des Großvaters
gekommen waren, lagen auf dem Wege, auf dem die Räder
oft Tropfen herausspritzten, schöne Eistäfelchen. Den Kindern ist das gewöhnlich ein sehr großes Vergnügen.

Die Großmutter hatte sie kommen gesehen, war ihnen
entgegen gegangen, nahm Sanna bei den erfrorenen Händchen
und führte sie in die Stube.

Sie nahm ihnen die wärmeren Kleider ab, sie ließ in dem
Ofen nachlegen und fragte sie, wie es ihnen im Herübergehen
gegangen sei.

Als sie hierauf die Antwort erhalten hatte, sagte sie: „Das
ist schon recht, das ist gut, es freut mich gar sehr, daß ihr
wieder gekommen seid; aber heute müßt ihr bald fort, der
Tag ist kurz, und es wird auch kälter, am Morgen war es in
Millsdorf nicht gefroren."

„In Gschaid auch nicht", sagte der Knabe.

went over to the place and saw that the round, red post which supported the picture was lying in the dried grass which was like thin straw and hid the pillar lying there from view. But they could not understand why the pillar was lying there, whether it had been knocked over or had fallen down by itself; this they saw, that it was very rotten at the spot where it projected from the ground and could therefore have fallen over easily. But because it was now lying on the ground they were glad to be able to study the picture and the writing from so close a distance as never before. When they had examined everything—the basket with rolls, the baker's pale hands, his closed eyes, his gray coat and the pines surrounding him—and when they had read the writing and spoken it out loud, they went on again.

After another hour the dark forests on both sides receded, thin stands of trees, partly individual oaks, partly birches and groups of bushes received them, led them on, and after a short while they ran down the meadows into the Millsdorf valley.

Although this valley lies appreciably deeper than that of Gschaid, and was accordingly so much warmer that one could always begin harvesting about two weeks sooner than in Gschaid, the ground was frozen here, too. When the children had reached their grandfather's tannery and fulling mill, there were beautiful little sheets of ice lying on the road, on which the wheels often splashed drops of water. This is often a great source of pleasure for children.

Their grandmother had seen them coming, had gone to meet them, took Sanna by her frozen little hands and led her into the living room.

She took off their warmer clothes, had fresh fuel added to the fire and asked them how things had gone on their way over.

When she had received the answer, she said: "That's quite right, that's good, I'm very glad that you've come again; but today you must go back soon, the day is short and it's getting colder, too, this morning there was no frost in Millsdorf."

"Nor in Gschaid," said the boy.

„Siehst du, darum müßt ihr euch sputen, daß euch gegen Abend nicht zu kalt wird", antwortete die Großmutter.

Hierauf fragte sie, was die Mutter mache,[40] was der Vater mache und ob nichts Besonderes in Gschaid geschehen sei.

Nach diesen Fragen bekümmerte sie sich um das Essen, sorgte, daß es früher bereitet wurde als gewöhnlich, und richtete selber den Kindern kleine Leckerbissen zusammen, von denen sie wußte, daß sie eine Freude damit erregen würde. Dann wurde der Färber gerufen, die Kinder bekamen an dem Tische aufgedeckt wie große Personen und aßen nun mit Großvater und Großmutter, und die letzte legte ihnen hiebei besonders Gutes vor. Nach dem Essen streichelte sie Sannas unterdessen sehr rot gewordene Wangen.

Hierauf ging sie geschäftig hin und her und steckte das Kalbfellränzchen des Knaben voll und steckte ihm noch allerlei in die Taschen. Auch in die Täschchen von Sanna tat sie allerlei Dinge. Sie gab jedem ein Stück Brot, es auf dem Wege zu verzehren, und in dem Ränzchen, sagte sie, seien noch zwei Weißbrote, wenn etwa der Hunger zu groß würde.

„Für die Mutter habe ich einen guten gebrannten Kaffee mitgegeben", sagte sie, „und in dem Fläschchen, das zugestopft und gut verbunden ist, befindet sich auch ein schwarzer Kaffeeaufguß, ein besserer, als die Mutter bei euch gewöhnlich macht, sie soll ihn nur kosten, wie er ist, er ist eine wahre Arznei, so kräftig, daß nur ein Schlückchen den Magen so wärmt, daß es den Körper in den kältesten Wintertagen nicht frieren kann. Die anderen Sachen, die in der Schachtel und in den Papieren im Ränzchen sind, bringt unversehrt nach Hause."

Da sie noch ein Weilchen mit den Kindern geredet hatte, sagte sie, daß sie gehen sollten.

„Habe acht, Sanna", sagte sie, „daß du nicht frierst erhitze dich nicht; und daß ihr nicht über die Wiesen hinauf und unter den Bäumen lauft. Etwa kommt gegen Abend ein Wind,[41] da müßt ihr langsamer gehen. Grüßet Vater und Mutter, und sagt, sie sollen recht glückliche Feiertage haben."

Die Großmutter küßte beide Kinder auf die Wangen und schob sie durch die Tür hinaus. Nichtsdestoweniger ging sie aber auch selber mit, geleitete sie durch den Garten, ließ sie

"You see? That's why you must hurry, so you don't feel too cold toward evening," the grandmother answered.

Then she asked them how their mother was, how their father was and if anything special had happened in Gschaid.

After these questions she concerned herself with the meal, saw to it that it was prepared sooner than usual, and herself prepared little delicacies for the children which she knew would make them happy. Then the dyer was called, the children were served at the table like grown-ups, and now ate with their grandfather and grandmother, and the latter served them particularly good things. After dinner she patted Sanna's cheeks which had meanwhile become very red.

After this she walked about busily and filled the boy's calfskin satchel and put all sorts of other things into his pockets. She also put all sorts of things in Sanna's little pockets. She gave each of them a piece of bread to eat on the way, and told them that there were two more pieces of white bread in the satchel in case their hunger became too great.

"For mother I've sent along some good roasted coffee," she said, "and in the little bottle which is corked and tied there is some black liquid coffee, better than your mother usually makes at home; let her taste it just as it is, it's a real tonic, so strong that just one litle sip warms the stomach, so that the body can't be chilled even on the coldest winter days. The other things there in the box and in the papers in the satchel you must bring home intact."

After talking to the children for a while longer she told them they should go.

"Be careful, Sanna," she said, "that you don't get chilled and don't get overheated; and that you don't go up over the meadows and under the trees. If a wind rises towards evening, you must walk slower. Give our love to father and mother and tell them to have a really happy holiday."

The grandmother kissed both children on the cheeks and pushed them out through the door. However, she accompanied them herself, led them through the garden, let them out by

durch das Hinterpförtchen hinaus, schloß wieder und ging in
das Haus zurück.

Die Kinder gingen an den Eistäfelchen neben den Werken
des Großvaters vorbei, sie gingen durch die Millsdorfer Felder
und wendeten sich gegen die Wiesen hinan.

Als sie auf den Anhöhen gingen, wo, wie gesagt wurde,
zerstreute Bäume und Gebüschgruppen standen, fielen äußerst
langsam einzelne Schneeflocken.

„Siehst du, Sanna", sagte der Knabe, „ich habe es gleich
gedacht, daß wir Schnee bekommen; weißt du, da wir von
Hause weggingen, sahen wir noch die Sonne, die so blutrot war
wie eine Lampe bei dem Heiligen Grabe,[42] und jetzt ist nichts
mehr von ihr zu erblicken, und nur der graue Nebel ist über
den Baumwipfeln oben. Das bedeutet allemal Schnee."

Die Kinder gingen freudiger fort, und Sanna war recht
froh, wenn sie mit dem dunkeln Ärmel ihres Röckchens eine
der fallenden Flocken auffangen konnte und wenn dieselbe
recht lange nicht auf dem Ärmel zerfloß. Als sie endlich an
dem äußersten Rand der Millsdorfer Höhen angekommen
waren, wo es gegen die dunkeln Tannen des Halses hineingeht,
war die dichte Waldwand schon recht lieblich gesprenkelt
von den immer reichlicher herabfallenden Flocken. Sie gingen
nunmehr in den dicken Wald hinein, der den größten Teil
ihrer noch bevorstehenden Wanderung einnahm.

Es geht von dem Waldrande noch immer aufwärts, und
zwar bis man zur roten Unglücksäule kommt, von wo sich,
wie schon oben angedeutet wurde, der Weg gegen das Tal
von Gschaid hinabwendet. Die Erhebung des Waldes von
der Millsdorfer Seite aus ist sogar so steil, daß der Weg
nicht gerade hinangeht, sondern daß er in sehr langen
Abweichungen von Abend nach Morgen und von Morgen
nach Abend hinanklimmt. An der ganzen Länge des Weges
hinauf zur Säule und hinab bis zu den Wiesen von Gschaid
sind hohe, dichte, ungelichtete Waldbestände, und sie werden
erst ein wenig dünner, wenn man in die Ebene gelangt ist
und gegen die Wiesen des Tales von Gschaid hinauskommt.
Der Hals ist auch, wenn er gleich nur eine kleine Verbindung
zwischen zwei großen Gebirgshäuptern abgibt, doch selbst
so groß, daß er, in die Ebene gelegt, einen bedeutenden
Gebirgsrücken abgeben würde.

the little back gate, closed it again and went into the house.

The children walked past their grandfather's factory on the little sheets of ice, walked through the Millsdorf fields and turned toward the meadows.

When they were walking on the slopes where, as we have said, scattered trees and groups of bushes stood, individual snowflakes were falling very slowly.

"See, Sanna," said the boy, "I knew right away that we'd get snow. You know when we left the house we could still see the sun which was blood-red like a lamp at the Holy Sepulcher, and now it can't be seen at all, and there's only the gray mist over the treetops above. That always means snow."

The children walked on more joyfully and Sanna was really happy when she could catch one of the falling flakes on the dark sleeve of her little coat and it didn't melt on her sleeve for a long time. When they finally reached the outermost edge of the Millsdorf heights, where you enter the dark pines of the neck, the dense wall of forest was already beautifully speckled with the snowflakes which were falling more and more plentifully. They now entered the dense forest, which made up the greatest part of the walk that was still before them.

The way from the edge of the forest is still steadily upwards, indeed until one comes to the accident pillar, from which point, as has already been indicated above, the road turns down toward the valley of Gschaid. The ascent of the forest from the Millsdorf side is actually so steep that the road does not go straight up but climbs up in long turns from west to east and from east to west. Throughout the length of the road up to the pillar and down to the meadows of Gschaid there are high, dense, uncleared stands of forest, and they become a little thinner only when one has reached the plain and comes out to the meadows of the valley of Gschaid. Even though it forms only a small connection between two large summits, the neck itself is so large that, placed in the plain, it would form a considerable mountain ridge.

Das erste, was die Kinder sahen, als sie die Waldung betraten, war, daß der gefrorne Boden sich grau zeigte, als ob er mit Mehl besät wäre, daß die Fahne manches dünnen Halmes des am Wege hin und zwischen den Bäumen stehenden dürren Grases mit Flocken beschwert war, und daß auf den verschiedenen grünen Zweigen der Tannen und Fichten, die sich wie Hände öffneten, schon weiße Fläumchen saßen.

„Schneit es denn jetzt bei dem Vater zu Hause auch?" fragte Sanna.

„Freilich", antwortete der Knabe, „es wird auch kälter, und du wirst sehen, daß morgen der ganze Teich gefroren ist."

„Ja, Konrad", sagte das Mädchen.

Es verdoppelte beinahe seine kleinen Schritte, um mit denen des dahinschreitenden Knaben gleichbleiben zu können.

Sie gingen nun rüstig in den Windungen fort, jetzt von Abend nach Morgen, jetzt von Morgen nach Abend. Der von der Großmutter vorausgesagte Wind stellte sich nicht ein, im Gegenteile war es so stille, daß sich nicht ein Ästchen oder Zweig rührte, ja sogar es schien im Walde wärmer, wie es in lockeren Körpern, dergleichen ein Wald auch ist, immer im Winter zu sein pflegt, und die Schneeflocken fielen stets reichlicher, so daß der ganze Boden schon weiß war, daß der Wald sich grau zu bestäuben anfing und daß auf dem Hute und den Kleidern des Knaben sowie auf denen des Mädchens der Schnee lag.

Die Freude der Kinder war sehr groß. Sie traten auf den weichen Flaum, suchten mit dem Fuße absichtlich solche Stellen, wo er dichter zu liegen schien, um dorthin zu treten und sich den Anschein zu geben, als wateten sie bereits. Sie schüttelten den Schnee nicht von den Kleidern ab.

Es war große Ruhe eingetreten. Von den Vögeln, deren doch manche auch zuweilen im Winter in dem Walde hin und her fliegen und von denen die Kinder im Herübergehen sogar mehrere zwitschern gehört hatten, war nichts zu vernehmen, und sie sahen auch keine auf irgendeinem Zweige sitzen oder fliegen, und der ganze Wald war gleichsam ausgestorben.

Weil nur die bloßen Fußstapfen der Kinder hinter ihnen blieben und weil vor ihnen der Schnee rein und unverletzt war, so war daraus zu erkennen, daß sie die einzigen waren,

The first thing that the children saw when they entered the woods was that the frozen ground looked gray, as if someone had sown flour on it, that the heads of some of the thin blades of dried grass which stood along the road and between the trees were heavy with snowflakes, and that little bits of white fluff were already sitting on the different green branches of the firs and spruces which opened up like hands.

"Is it snowing at home now too, at father's?" asked Sanna.

"Of course," the boy replied, "it's getting colder too, and you'll see that tomorrow the whole pond will be frozen."

"Yes, Conrad," said the girl.

She almost doubled her short steps, to keep up with those of the boy, who was striding along.

They now walked briskly on the winding road, from west to east and from east to west. The wind which their grandmother had predicted did not appear; on the contrary, it was so still that not a twig or branch stirred; in fact it actually seemed to be warmer in the woods, as it always is in winter in rarer areas like forests. The snowflakes fell more and more plentifully, so that the whole ground was already white, the forest began to be covered with a gray dust, and the snow lay on the boy's hat and clothes as well as on those of the girl.

The joy of the children was very great. They stepped on the soft down, deliberately felt with their feet for places where it seemed to be lying thicker, walked on those spots and pretended that they were already wading through it.

They did not shake the snow from their clothes.

A great peace had settled down. The birds, some of which fly about the forest even in the winter, and several of which the children had actually heard twittering on their way over, could no longer be heard at all; they saw none sitting on any of the branches or flying, and the whole forest was as though dead.

Because only the footprints made by the children were behind them and because the snow in front of them was pure and unbroken, it was clear that they were the only

die heute über den Hals gingen.

Sie gingen in ihrer Richtung fort, sie näherten sich öfter den Bäumen, öfter entfernten sie sich, und wo dichtes Unterholz war, konnten sie den Schnee auf den Zweigen liegen sehen.

Ihre Freude wuchs noch immer; denn die Flocken fielen stets dichter, und nach kurzer Zeit brauchten sie nicht mehr den Schnee aufzusuchen, um in ihm zu waten, denn er lag schon so dicht, daß sie ihn überall weich unter den Sohlen empfanden und daß er sich bereits um ihre Schuhe zu legen begann; und wenn es so ruhig und heimlich war, so war es, als ob sie das Knistern des in die Nadeln herabfallenden Schnees vernehmen könnten.

„Werden wir heute auch die Unglücksäule sehen?" fragte das Mädchen, „sie ist ja umgefallen, und da wird es darauf schneien, und da wird die rote Farbe weiß sein."

„Darum können wir sie doch sehen", antwortete der Knabe, „wenn auch der Schnee auf sie fällt, und wenn sie auch weiß ist, so müssen wir sie liegen sehen, weil sie eine dicke Säule ist und weil sie das schwarze eiserne Kreuz auf der Spitze hat, das doch immer herausragen wird."

„Ja, Konrad."

Indessen, da sie noch weiter gegangen waren, war der Schneefall so dicht geworden, daß sie nur mehr die allernächsten Bäume sehen konnten.

Von der Härte des Weges oder gar von den Furchenaufwerfungen war nichts zu empfinden, der Weg war vom Schnee überall gleich weich und war überhaupt nur daran zu erkennen, daß er als ein gleichmäßiger weißer Streifen in dem Walde fortlief. Auf allen Zweigen lag schon die schöne weiße Hülle.

Die Kinder gingen jetzt mitten auf dem Wege, sie furchten den Schnee mit ihren Füßlein und gingen langsamer, weil das Gehen beschwerlicher ward. Der Knabe zog seine Jacke empor an dem Halse zusammen, damit ihm nicht der Schnee in den Nacken falle, und er setzte den Hut tiefer in das Haupt, daß er geschützter sei. Er zog auch seinem Schwesterlein das Tuch, das ihm die Mutter um die Schulter gegeben hatte, besser zusammen und zog es ihm mehr vorwärts in die Stirne, daß es ein Dach bilde.

people who were walking over the neck today.

They continued in the same direction; they often approached trees, often went away from them, and where there was dense undergrowth, they could see the snow lying on the branches.

Their joy kept increasing, for the flakes were falling more and more densely, and after a short time they no longer had to look for snow to wade in; for it already lay so thick that they felt it soft under their soles everywhere, and it even began to settle about their shoes. It was so peaceful and still that it seemed as if they could hear the crackling of the snow that was falling into the pine needles.

"Will we see the accident pillar today?" asked the girl. "It fell over, you know, so the snow will fall on it and so the red color will be white."

"We can see it just the same," replied the boy, "even though the snow falls on it, and even though it's white, we must see it lying there because it's a thick post and because it has the black iron cross at the top, which will always stick out."

"Yes, Conrad."

Meanwhile, when they had gone still further, the snow fall had become so dense that they could now see only the nearest trees.

They could feel nothing of the hardness of the road or of the earth thrown out of the ruts; everywhere the road was equally soft from the snow; it could only be distinguished by the fact that it ran on in the forest as an even, white strip. The beautiful white covering was already lying on all the branches.

The children now walked in the middle of the road; they plowed through the snow with their little feet, and walked more slowly because the going was getting hard. The boy pulled his jacket up about his throat, so that the snow would not fall into the back of his neck and he pulled his hat down over his head so that he would have more protection. He also pulled the kerchief, which his mother had given his little sister, tighter about her shoulders; and pulled it further forward over her forehead so that it formed a roof.

Der von der Großmutter vorausgesagte Wind war noch immer nicht gekommen, aber dafür wurde der Schneefall nach und nach so dicht, daß auch nicht mehr die nächsten Bäume zu erkennen waren, sondern daß sie wie neblige Säcke in der Luft standen.

Die Kinder gingen fort. Sie duckten die Köpfe dichter in ihre Kleider und gingen fort.

Sanna nahm den Riemen, an welchem Konrad die Kalbfelltasche um die Schulter hängen hatte, mit den Händchen, hielt sich daran, und so gingen sie ihres Weges.

Die Unglücksäule hatten sie noch immer nicht erreicht. Der Knabe konnte die Zeit nicht ermessen, weil keine Sonne am Himmel stand und weil es immer gleichmäßig grau war.

„Werden wir bald zu der Unglücksäule kommen?" fragte Sanna.

„Ich weiß es nicht", antwortete der Knabe, „ich kann heute die Bäume nicht sehen und den Weg nicht erkennen, weil er so weiß ist. Die Unglücksäule werden wir wohl gar nicht sehen, weil so viel Schnee liegen wird, daß sie verhüllt sein wird und daß kaum ein Gräschen oder ein Arm des schwarzen Kreuzes hervorragen wird. Aber es macht nichts.[48] Wir gehen immer auf dem Wege fort, der Weg geht zwischen den Bäumen, und wenn er zu dem Platze der Unglücksäule kommt, dann wird er abwärts gehen, wir gehen auf ihm fort, und wenn er aus den Bäumen hinausgeht, dann sind wir schon auf den Wiesen von Gschaid, dann kommt der Steg, und dann haben wir nicht mehr weit nach Hause."

„Ja, Konrad", sagte das Mädchen.

Sie gingen auf ihrem aufwärtsführenden Wege fort. Die hinter ihnen liegenden Fußstapfen waren jetzt nicht mehr lange sichtbar; denn die ungemeine Fülle des herabfallenden Schnees deckte sie bald zu, daß sie verschwanden. Der Schnee knisterte in seinem Falle nun auch nicht mehr in den Nadeln, sondern legte sich eilig und heimlich auf die weiße, schon daliegende Decke nieder. Die Kinder nahmen die Kleider noch fester, um das immerwährende allseitige Hineinrieseln abzuhalten.

Sie gingen sehr schleunig, und der Weg führte noch stets aufwärts.

Nach langer Zeit war noch immer die Höhe nicht erreicht,

The wind which their grandmother had predicted had still not come; but on the other hand the snowfall gradually became so dense that even the nearest trees could no longer be discerned but stood like misty sacks in the air.

The children went on. They thrust their heads deeper into their clothes and went on.

Sanna took the strap by which Conrad's calfskin bag hung about his shoulders in her little hands, clung to it, and so they continued their way.

They had still not reached the accident pillar. The boy could not judge the time because there was no sun in the sky and it remained uniformly gray.

"Will we soon come to the accident pillar?" asked Sanna.

"I don't know," the boy replied, "I can't see the trees today and I can't make out the road because it's so white. I don't suppose we'll see the accident pillar at all because there'll be so much snow that it will be covered up, and scarcely a blade of grass or an arm of the black cross will stick out. But it doesn't matter. We'll continue on the road; the road leads between the trees and when it comes to the place of the accident pillar it will go downwards; we'll continue on it and when it comes out of the trees we'll already be on the meadows of Gschaid; then comes the footbridge and then it won't be far till home."

"Yes, Conrad," said the girl.

They continued on the ascending road. The footprints they left behind them were now no longer visible; for the uncommon density of the falling snow soon covered them up so that they vanished. The snow no longer crackled as it fell into the needles, but lay down hurriedly and stealthily on the white blanket that was already there. The children pulled their clothes even more tightly around them to keep out the constant trickle of snow from all sides.

They walked very rapidly and the road still kept leading upwards.

After a long time they had still not reached the height on

auf welcher die Unglücksäule stehen sollte und von wo der Weg gegen die Gschaider Seite sich hinunterwenden mußte.

Endlich kamen die Kinder in eine Gegend, in welcher keine Bäume standen.

„Ich sehe keine Bäume mehr“, sagte Sanna.

„Vielleicht ist nur der Weg so breit, daß wir sie wegen des Schneiens nicht sehen können“, antwortete der Knabe.

„Ja, Konrad“, sagte das Mädchen.

Nach einer Weile blieb der Knabe stehen und sagte: „Ich sehe selber keine Bäume mehr, wir müssen aus dem Walde gekommen sein, auch geht der Weg immer bergan. Wir wollen ein wenig stehen bleiben und herumsehen, vielleicht erblicken wir etwas.“

Aber sie erblickten nichts. Sie sahen durch einen trüben Raum in den Himmel. Wie bei dem Hagel über die weißen oder grünlich gedunsenen Wolken die finsteren fransenartigen Streifen herabstarren, so war es hier, und das stumme Schütten dauerte fort. Auf der Erde sahen sie nur einen runden Fleck Weiß und dann nichts mehr.

„Weißt du, Sanna“, sagte der Knabe, „wir sind auf dem dürren Grase, auf welches ich dich oft im Sommer heraufgeführt habe, wo wir saßen und wo wir den Rasen betrachteten, der nacheinander hinaufgeht, und wo die schönen Kräuterbüschel wachsen. Wir werden da jetzt gleich rechts hinabgehen!“

„Ja, Konrad.“

„Der Tag ist kurz, wie die Großmutter gesagt hat und wie du auch wissen wirst, wir müssen uns daher sputen.“

„Ja, Konrad“, sagte das Mädchen.

„Warte ein wenig, ich will dich besser einrichten“, erwiderte der Knabe.

Er nahm seinen Hut ab, setzte ihn Sanna auf das Haupt und befestigte ihn mit den beiden Bändchen unter ihrem Kinne. Das Tüchlein, welches sie umhatte, schützte sie zu wenig, während auf seinem Haupt eine solche Menge dichter Locken war, daß noch lange Schnee darauf fallen konnte, ehe Nässe und Kälte durchzudringen vermochten. Dann zog er sein Pelzjäckchen aus und zog dasselbe über die Ärmelein der Schwester. Um seine eigenen Schultern und Arme, die jetzt das bloße Hemd zeigten, band er das kleinere Tüchlein,

which the accident pillar was supposed to stand and from which the road had to turn downhill to the Gschaid side.

Finally the children came into a region in which there were no trees.

"I don't see any more trees," said Sanna.

"Perhaps the road has become so wide that we can't see them because of the snow," replied the boy.

"Yes, Conrad," said the girl.

After a while the boy stopped and said: "I don't see any trees myself now; we must have got out of the forest and the road keeps going uphill. We'll stop for a moment and look about, perhaps we'll see something."

But they saw nothing. They looked through dull space into the sky. Just as in a hailstorm the dark, fringelike strips stare down from the white or greenish bloated clouds, so it was here; and the silent pouring continued. On the ground they saw only a round spot of white and then nothing more.

"Do you know, Sanna," said the boy, "we're on the dried grass where I often brought you in summer, where we used to sit and where we looked at the grass which gradually slopes upward and where the beautiful clusters of herbs grow. We'll start going downhill to the right in a moment."

"Yes, Conrad."

"The day is short, as grandmother said and as you must know yourself, so we'll have to hurry."

"Yes, Conrad," said the girl.

"Wait a moment, I'll fix you up better," the boy replied.

He took off his hat, put it on Sanna's head and fastened it with the two little ribbons under her chin. The small kerchief she had on gave her too little protection, while he had such a thick mane of curls on his head that much more snow could fall on it before wetness and cold could penetrate through it. Then he took off his little fur jacket and drew it over his sister's little sleeves. On his own shoulders and arms which now showed his bare shirt he tied the smaller kerchief that Sanna had worn over her chest, and the larger one she

das Sanna über die Brust, und das größere, das sie über die
Schultern gehabt hatte. Das sei für ihn genug, dachte er,
wenn er nur stark auftrete, werde ihn nicht frieren.

Er nahm das Mädchen bei der Hand, und so gingen sie
jetzt fort.

Das Mädchen schaute mit den willigen Äuglein in das
ringsum herrschende Grau und folgte ihm gerne, nur daß
es mit den kleinen eilenden Füßlein nicht so nachkommen
konnte, wie er vorwärts strebte gleich einem, der es zur
Entscheidung bringen wollte.

Sie gingen nun mit der Unablässigkeit und Kraft, die
Kinder und Tiere haben, weil sie nicht wissen, wieviel ihnen
beschieden ist und wann ihr Vorrat erschöpft ist.

Aber wie sie gingen, so konnten sie nicht merken, ob sie
über den Berg hinabkämen oder nicht. Sie hatten gleich
rechts nach abwärts gebogen, allein sie kamen wieder in
Richtungen, die bergan führten, bergab und wieder bergan.
Oft begegneten ihnen Steilheiten, denen sie ausweichen
mußten, und ein Graben, in dem sie fortgingen, führte sie
in einer Krümmung herum. Sie erklommen Höhen, die sich
unter ihren Füßen steiler gestalteten, als sie dachten, und
was sie für abwärts hielten, war wieder eben, oder es war eine
Höhlung, oder es ging immer gedehnt fort.

„Wo sind wir denn, Konrad?" fragte das Mädchen.

„Ich weiß es nicht", antwortete er.

„Wenn ich nur mit diesen meinen Augen etwas zu
erblicken imstande wäre", fuhr er fort, „daß ich mich danach
richten könnte."

Aber es war rings um sie nichts als das blendende Weiß,
überall das Weiß, das aber selber nur einen immer kleineren
Kreis um sie zog und dann in einen lichten, streifenweise
niederfallenden Nebel überging, der jedes Weitere verzehrte
und verhüllte und zuletzt nichts anderes war als der unersättlich niederfallende Schnee.

„Warte, Sanna", sagte der Knabe, „wir wollen ein wenig
stehen bleiben und horchen, ob wir nicht etwas hören können,
was sich im Tale meldet, sei es nun ein Hund oder eine
Glocke oder die Mühle, oder sei es ein Ruf, der sich hören
läßt, hören müssen wir etwas, und dann werden wir wissen,
wohin wir zu gehen haben."

had had around her shoulders. This would be enough for him, he thought; if he only walked briskly he would not be cold.

He took the girl by the hand and so they now went on.

With her willing eyes the girl looked into the prevailing gray all around and gladly followed him; but her small hurrying feet could not keep pace with his, as he strove forward like someone who was bent on doing something decisive.

They now walked with the steadiness and energy which children and animals possess because they do not know what is in store for them and when their supply will run out.

But as they went on they could not make out whether they were coming down across the mountain or not. They had at once turned downhill to the right, but they again came to regions that led uphill, downhill and then again uphill. Often they met steep inclines which they were compelled to avoid; and a ditch in which they were walking led them around in a curve. They climbed heights which became steeper under their feet than they had expected, and what they took to be downhill was level ground, or it was a hollow, or it continued to stretch out.

"But where are we, Conrad?" asked the girl.

"I don't know," he replied.

"If only I could catch sight of something with these eyes of mine," he continued, "so that I could guide myself by it."

But all about them there was nothing but the dazzling white; everywhere the white which, however, drew an ever narrowing circle about them and then changed into a bright mist that fell down in streaks, consuming and enveloping everything, and was in the end nothing but the insatiable falling snow.

"Wait, Sanna," said the boy, "we'll stop for a while and listen; maybe we can hear something from the valley, whether it's a dog or a bell or the mill or a call that can be heard; we must hear something and then we'll know where we have to go."

Sie blieben nun stehen, aber sie hörten nichts. Sie blieben noch ein wenig länger stehen, aber es meldete sich nichts, es war nicht ein einziger Laut, auch nicht der leiseste, außer ihrem Atem zu vernehmen, ja in der Stille, die herrschte, war es, als sollten sie den Schnee hören, der auf ihre Wimpern fiel. Die Voraussage der Großmutter hatte sich noch immer nicht erfüllt, der Wind war nicht gekommen, ja, was in diesen Gegenden selten ist, nicht das leiseste Lüftchen rührte sich an dem ganzen Himmel.

Nachdem sie lange gewartet hatten, gingen sie wieder fort. „Es tut auch nichts,⁴⁴ Sanna", sagte der Knabe, „sei nur nicht verzagt, folge mir, ich werde dich doch noch hinüberführen.—Wenn nur das Schneien aufhörte!"

Sie war nicht verzagt, sondern hob die Füßchen, so gut es gehen wollte, und folgte ihm. Er führte sie in dem weißen, lichten, regsamen undurchsichtigen Raume fort.

Nach einer Weile sahen sie Felsen. Sie hoben sich dunkel und undeutlich aus dem weißen und undurchsichtigen Lichte empor. Da die Kinder sich näherten, stießen sie fast daran. Sie stiegen wie eine Mauer hinauf und waren ganz gerade, so daß kaum ein Schnee an ihrer Seite haften konnte.

„Sanna, Sanna", sagte er, „da sind die Felsen, gehen wir nur weiter, gehen wir weiter."

Sie gingen weiter, sie mußten zwischen die Felsen hinein und unter ihnen fort. Die Felsen ließen sie nicht rechts und nicht links ausweichen und führten sie in einem engen Wege dahin. Nach einer Zeit verloren sie dieselben wieder und konnten sie nicht mehr erblicken. So wie sie unversehens unter sie gekommen waren, kamen sie wieder unversehens von ihnen. Es war wieder nichts um sie als das Weiß, und ringsum war kein unterbrechendes Dunkel zu schauen. Es schien eine große Lichtfülle zu sein, und doch konnte man nicht drei Schritte vor sich sehen; alles war, wenn man so sagen darf, in eine einzige weiße Finsternis gehüllt, und weil kein Schatten war, so war kein Urteil über die Größe der Dinge, und die Kinder konnten nicht wissen, ob sie aufwärts oder abwärts gehen würden, bis eine Steilheit ihren Fuß faßte und ihn aufwärts zu gehen zwang.

„Mir tun die Augen weh", sagte Sanna.

„Schaue nicht auf den Schnee", antwortete der Knabe,

They now stopped but they heard nothing. They stopped a while longer but they heard no report; there wasn't a single sound, not even the faintest, to be heard except their own breathing; in fact, in the silence that prevailed it seemed they could hear the snow that fell on their eyelashes. Their grandmother's prophecy had still not come true: the wind had not come; in fact, what is rare in these regions, not the faintest breeze was stirring in the whole sky.

After waiting a long time they went on.

"It doesn't really matter, Sanna," said the boy, "don't lose heart, follow me, I'll get you over yet. If only it would stop snowing!"

She was not despondent but lifted her little feet as best she could and followed him. He led her on in the white, bright, stirring, opaque space.

After a while they saw rocks. They stood out dark and indistinct from the white and opaque light. When the children approached, they almost ran into them. They rose up like a wall and were quite perpendicular, so that snow could scarcely cling to their sides.

"Sanna, Sanna," he said, "there are the rocks, let's go on, let's go on."

They went on; they had to move in between the rocks and along under them. The rocks did not permit them to turn right or left and led them on a narrow road. After a time they lost them again and could not see them any more. Just as they had come among them unexpectedly, so they came out of them unexpectedly. Again there was nothing around them except the whiteness and all round them no interrupting darkness could be seen. It seemed to be a great expanse of light and yet one could not see three paces ahead; everything was enveloped, if one may say so, in a single white darkness; and because there was no shadow, there could be no judgment about the size of things, and the children could not know whether they would be going up or down until a steepness caught the foot and compelled it to go upwards.

"My eyes hurt," said Sanna.

"Don't look at the snow," the boy replied, "but into the

„sondern in die Wolken. Mir tun sie schon lange weh; aber es tut nichts, ich muß doch auf den Schnee schauen, weil ich auf den Weg zu achten habe. Fürchte dich nur nicht, ich führe dich doch hinunter ins Gschaid."

„Ja, Konrad."

Sie gingen wieder fort; aber wie sie auch gehen mochten, wie sie sich auch wenden mochten, es wollte kein Anfang zum Hinabwärtsgehen kommen. An beiden Seiten waren steile Dachlehnen nach aufwärts, mitten gingen sie fort, aber auch immer aufwärts. Wenn sie den Dachlehnen entrannen und sie nach abwärts beugten, wurde es gleich so steil, daß sie wieder umkehren mußten, die Füßlein stießen oft auf Unebenheiten, und sie mußten häufig Büheln ausweichen.

Sie merkten auch, daß ihr Fuß, wo er tiefer durch den jungen Schnee einsank, nicht erdigen Boden unter sich empfand, sondern etwas anderes, das wie älterer gefrorner Schnee war; aber sie gingen immer fort, und sie liefen mit Hast und Ausdauer. Wenn sie stehen blieben, war alles still, unermeßlich still; wenn sie gingen, hörten sie das Rascheln ihrer Füße, sonst nichts; denn die Hüllen des Himmels sanken ohne Laut hernieder und so reich, daß man den Schnee hätte wachsen sehen können. Sie selber waren so bedeckt, daß sie sich von dem allgemeinen Weiß nicht hervorhoben und sich, wenn sie um ein paar Schritte getrennt worden wären, nicht mehr gesehen hätten.

Eine Wohltat war es, daß der Schnee so trocken war wie Sand, so daß er von ihren Füßen und den Bundschühlein und Strümpfen daran leicht abglitt und abrieselte, ohne Ballen und Nässe zu machen.

Endlich gelangten sie wieder zu Gegenständen.

Es waren riesenhaft große, sehr durcheinander liegende Trümmer, die mit Schnee bedeckt waren, der überall in die Klüfte hineinrieselte, und an die sie sich ebenfalls fast anstießen, ehe sie sie sahen. Sie gingen ganz hinzu, die Dinge anzublicken.

Es war Eis—lauter Eis.

Es lagen Platten da, die mit Schnee bedeckt waren, an deren Seitenwänden aber das glatte grünliche Eis sichtbar war, es lagen Hügel da, die wie zusammengeschobener Schaum aussahen, an deren Seiten es aber matt nach einwärts flim-

clouds. Mine have been hurting a long time, but it doesn't matter. I have to look down on the snow because I have to look out for the road. Just don't be afraid, I'll certainly bring you down to Gschaid."

"Yes, Conrad."

They went on again; but no matter how they went, how they might turn, the beginning of the descent would not come. On both sides there were steep cliffs slanting upwards; they walked between them, but it was always upwards. When they escaped the cliffs and turned downhill, it became so steep at once that they had to turn round again; they often stubbed their little feet on rough spots and they often had to avoid hills.

They noticed, too, that wherever their feet sank deeper through the fresh snow, they encountered not earthy soil but something else that was like older, frozen snow; but they kept on going and they walked with speed and persistence. When they stopped, everything was silent, boundlessly silent; when they walked, they heard the rustling of their feet, nothing else; for the veils of heaven sank down without a sound and so plentifully that one might have been able to see the snow grow. They themselves were so thickly covered that they did not stand out from the general whiteness and, if they had been separated by a few paces, would no longer have seen each other.

It was a blessing that the snow was as dry as sand so that it slid off and trickled easily from their little laced shoes and stockings without caking and soaking them.

Finally they reached objects again.

They were gigantic fragments of debris lying helter-skelter, covered with snow which trickled into the clefts everywhere; again they almost ran into them before seeing them. They walked right up to look at them.

It was ice—nothing but ice.

Slabs lay there, covered with snow, but on whose side walls the smooth greenish ice was visible; hills lay there which looked like compressed foam, but whose sides had a faint inward glimmer and gloss, as if beams and poles of jewels had

merte und glänzte, als wären Balken und Stanken von Edel-
steinen durcheinander geworfen worden, es lagen ferner ge-
rundete Kugeln da, die ganz mit Schnee umhüllt waren, es
standen Platten und andere Körper auch schief oder gerade
aufwärts, so hoch wie der Kirchturm in Gschaid oder wie
Häuser. In einigen waren Höhlen eingefressen, durch die man
mit einem Arme durchfahren konnte, mit einem Kopfe, mit
einem Körper, mit einem ganz großen Wagen voll Heu. Alle
diese Stücke waren zusammen- oder emporgedrängt und
starrten, so daß sie oft Dächer bildeten oder Überhänge, über
deren Ränder sich der Schnee herüberlegte und herabgriff
wie lange weiße Tatzen. Selbst ein großer, schreckhaft
schwarzer Stein, wie ein Haus, lag unter dem Eise und war
emporgestellt, daß er auf der Spitze stand, daß kein Schnee
an seinen Seiten liegen bleiben konnte. Und nicht dieser Stein
allein—noch mehrere und größere staken [45] in dem Eise, die
man erst später sah und die wie eine Trümmermauer an ihm
hingingen.

„Da muß recht viel Wasser gewesen sein, weil so viel Eis
ist", sagte Sanna.

„Nein, das ist von keinem Wasser", antwortete der Bruder,
„das ist das Eis des Berges, das immer oben ist, weil es so
eingerichtet ist."

„Ja, Konrad", sagte Sanna.

„Wir sind jetzt bis zu dem Eise gekommen", sagte der
Knabe, „wir sind auf dem Berge, Sanna, weißt du, den man
von unserm Garten aus im Sonnenscheine so weiß sieht.
Merke gut auf, was ich dir sagen werde. Erinnerst du dich
noch, wie wir oft nachmittags in dem Garten saßen, wie es
recht schön war, wie die Bienen um uns summten, die Linden
dufteten und die Sonne von dem Himmel schien?"

„Ja, Konrad, ich erinnere mich."

„Da sahen wir auch den Berg. Wir sahen, wie er so blau
war, so blau wie das sanfte Firmament, wir sahen den Schnee,
der oben ist, wenn auch bei uns Sommer war, eine Hitze
herrschte und die Getreide reif wurden."

„Ja, Konrad."

„Und unten, wo der Schnee aufhört, da sieht man allerlei
Farben, wenn man genau schaut, grün, blau, weißlich—das
ist das Eis, das unten nur so klein ausschaut, weil man sehr

been thrown together; there were, moreover, round balls which were entirely enveloped in snow; there were slabs and other bodies there, standing slanting or upright, as high as the church tower or as houses in Gschaid. Into some of these caves had been eaten, through which one could push an arm, a head, a body or a big wagon loaded with hay. All these chunks were piled together or pushed up and frozen so as to form roofs or eaves, over whose edges the snow spread and reached down like long, white paws. There was even a large, terrifyingly black stone, big as a house, lying under the ice, upright on its point so that no snow could cling to its sides. And not only this stone, several more and larger ones, which one did not notice until later, forming a kind of wall of debris around it.

"There must have been a great deal of water here, because there's so much ice," said Sanna.

"No, that isn't from water," her brother replied, "that's the ice of the mountain; it's always up there because that's the way it's been arranged."

"Yes, Conrad," said Sanna.

"We have now got to the ice," said the boy, "we're on the mountain, Sanna, you know, the one we see from our garden looking so white in the sunshine. Now mark well what I'm going to tell you. Do you still remember how we often used to sit in the garden in the afternoon, how really beautiful it was, how the bees buzzed around us, the linden trees smelled sweet and the sun shone in the sky?"

"Yes, Conrad, I remember."

"We saw the mountain then, too. We saw how blue it was, as blue as the gentle firmament; we saw the snow that is at the top even when it was summer with us, it was very hot and the wheat was ripening."

"Yes, Conrad."

"And down below, where the snow stops, you see all kinds of colors if you look closely—green, blue, whitish—that's the ice which looks so small down below because we're so far

weit entfernt ist, und das, wie der Vater sagte, nicht weggeht
bis an das Ende der Welt. Und da habe ich oft gesehen,
daß unterhalb des Eises die blaue Farbe noch fortgeht, das
werden Steine sein, dachte ich, oder es wird Erde und Weidegrund sein, und dann fangen die Wälder an, die gehen herab
und immer weiter herab, man sieht auch allerlei Felsen in
ihnen, dann folgen die Wiesen, die schon grün sind, und dann
die grünen Laubwälder, und dann kommen unsere Wiesen
und Felder, die in dem Tale von Gschaid sind. Siehst du
nun, Sanna, weil wir jetzt bei dem Eise sind, so werden wir
über die blaue Farbe hinabgehen, dann durch die Wälder,
in denen die Felsen sind, dann über die Wiesen und dann
durch die grünen Laubwälder, und dann werden wir in dem
Tale von Gschaid sein und recht leicht unser Dorf finden."

„Ja, Konrad", sagte das Mädchen.

Die Kinder gingen nun in das Eis hinein, wo es zugänglich
war.

Sie waren winzig kleine, wandelnde Punkte in diesen unge-
heuren Stücken.

Wie sie so unter die Überhänge hineinsahen, gleichsam als
gäbe ihnen ein Trieb ein, ein Obdach zu suchen, gelangten
sie in einen Graben, der gerade aus dem Eise hervorging. Er
sah aus wie das Bett eines Stromes, der aber jetzt ausge-
trocknet und überall mit frischem Schnee bedeckt war. Wo
er aus dem Eise hervorkam, ging er gerade unter einem Kellergewölbe heraus, das recht schön aus Eis über ihn gespannt
war. Die Kinder gingen in dem Graben fort und gingen in
das Gewölbe hinein und immer tiefer hinein. Es war ganz
trocken, und unter ihren Füßen hatten sie glattes Eis. In der
ganzen Höhlung aber war es blau, so blau, wie gar nichts in
der Welt ist, viel tiefer und viel schöner blau als das Firmament, gleichsam wie himmelblau gefärbtes Glas, durch
welches lichter Schein hineinsinkt. Es waren dickere und
dünnere Bogen, es hingen Zacken, Spitzen und Troddeln
herab, der Gang wäre noch tiefer zurückgegangen, sie wußten
nicht, wie tief, aber sie gingen nicht mehr weiter. Es wäre
auch sehr gut in der Höhle gewesen, es war warm, es fiel kein
Schnee, aber es war so schreckhaft blau, die Kinder fürchteten
sich und gingen wieder hinaus. Sie gingen eine Weile in dem
Graben fort und kletterten dann über seinen Rand hinaus.

away, and which, as father said, doesn't go away till the world ends. And then I've often seen that the blue color continues even below the ice; they must be stones, I thought, or earth and pasture land; and then the woods begin; they go down and farther and farther down. You also see all sorts of rocks in them, then come the meadows, which are already green, and then the green leaf woods and then come our meadows and fields which are in the valley of Gschaid. Do you see now, Sanna, since we're at the ice now, we'll go down over the blue color, then through the forests where the rocks are, then over the meadows, then through the green leaf woods, and then we'll be in the valley of Gschaid and find our village casily."

"Yes, Conrad," said the girl.
The children now went into the ice where it was accessible.

They were tiny mobile points in these enormous chunks.

As they were looking in under the eaves, as if prompted by an instinct to seek shelter, they reached a ditch, a wide, deeply-furrowed ditch, which came right out of the ice. It looked like the bed of a stream, which was now dried out and entirely covered with fresh snow. At the point where it came out of the ice, it extended right under a vault-like cellar, which was quite beautifully stretched over it. The children walked on in the ditch and went into the vault and deeper and deeper into it. It was quite dry and they had smooth ice under their feet. But in the whole cavity it was blue, as blue as nothing else in the world, a much deeper and more beautiful blue than the firmament, something like sky-blue colored glass, through which a bright light sinks. There were thicker and thinner arches, jagged ends, points and tassels hung down. The corridor would have led back still further, they did not know how deep, but they did not go any further. It would have been very good in the cave, too; it was warm, no snow fell; but it was so terrifyingly blue, the children were afraid and went out again. They went on for a while in the ditch and then climbed out over its edge.

Sie gingen an dem Eise hin, sofern es möglich war, durch das Getrümmer und zwischen den Platten durchzudringen.

„Wir werden jetzt da noch hinübergehen und dann von dem Eise abwärts laufen", sagte Konrad.

„Ja", sagte Sanna und klammerte sich an ihn an.

Sie schlugen von dem Eise eine Richtung durch den Schnee abwärts ein, die sie in das Tal führen sollte. Aber sie kamen nicht weit hinab. Ein neuer Strom von Eis, gleichsam ein riesenhaft aufgetürmter und aufgewölbter Wall, lag quer durch den weichen Schnee und griff gleichsam mit Armen rechts und links um sie herum. Unter der weißen Decke, die ihn verhüllte, glimmerte es seitwärts grünlich und bläulich und dunkel und schwarz und selbst gelblich und rötlich heraus. Sie konnten es nun auf weitere [46] Strecken sehen, weil das ungeheure und unermüdliche Schneien sich gemildert hatte und nur mehr wie an gewöhnlichen Schneetagen vom Himmel fiel. Mit dem Starkmute der Unwissenheit kletterten sie in das Eis hinein, um den vorgeschobenen Strom desselben zu überschreiten und dann jenseits weiter hinabzukommen. Sie schoben sich in die Zwischenräume hinein, sie setzten den Fuß auf jedes Körperstück, das mit einer weißen Schneehaube versehen war, war es Fels oder Eis, sie nahmen die Hände zu Hilfe, krochen, wo sie nicht gehen konnten, und arbeiteten sich mit ihren leichten Körpern hinauf, bis sie die Seite des Walles überwunden hatten und oben waren.

Jenseits wollten sie wieder hinabklettern.

Aber es gab kein Jenseits.

So weit die Augen der Kinder reichen konnten, war lauter Eis. Es standen Spitzen und Unebenheiten und Schollen empor wie lauter furchtbares überschneites Eis. Statt ein Wall zu sein, über den man hinübergehen könnte und der dann wieder von Schnee abgelöst würde, wie sie sich unten dachten, stiegen aus der Wölbung neue Wände von Eis empor, geborsten und geklüftet, mit unzähligen blauen geschlängelten Linien versehen, und hinter ihnen waren wieder solche Wände und hinter diesen wieder solche, bis der Schneefall das Weitere mit seinem Grau verdeckte.

„Sanna, da können wir nicht gehen", sagte der Knabe.

„Nein", antwortete die Schwester.

„Da werden wir wieder umkehren und anderswo hinabzu-

They walked along the ice as far as it was possible to penetrate through the debris and between the slabs.

"We'll go over to that spot now, and then go downward from the ice," said Conrad.

"Yes," said Sanna, clinging to him.

They took a direction away from the ice through the snow, one that was to lead them into the valley. But they did not get far down. A new river of ice, a sort of gigantic, towering and vaulted rampart, lay straight across the soft snow and, as it were, sent out arms to the right and left of them. Under the white cover which enveloped it, greenish and bluish and dark and black and even yellowish and reddish sparks shot out sidewards. They could now see it for distant stretches, because the vast and tireless snowing had abated and now fell from the sky as on ordinary snowy days. With the courage of ignorance they climbed into the ice, in order to cross over the protruding river and to get further down on the other side. They pushed their way into the interstices, they set their feet on every object that was provided with a white hood of snow, whether it was rock or ice; they used their hands, crawled where they could not walk and worked their way up with their bodies until they had overcome the side of the rampart and were at the top.

They intended to climb down again on the other side.

But there was no other side.

As far as the eyes of the children could reach there was nothing but ice. Points and jagged pieces and clumps jutted out like sheer terrible snow-covered ice. Instead of being a rampart which one could cross and which was then again replaced by snow, as they imagined below, new walls of ice rose up from the vaulting, burst and fissured, supplied with countless blue, serpentine lines and behind them there were more such walls and behind these more still, until the snowfall concealed the rest with its gray.

"Sanna, we can't go there," said the boy.

"No," his sister replied.

"So we'll turn around again and try to go down somewhere

kommen suchen.“

„Ja, Konrad.“

Die Kinder versuchten nun, von dem Eiswalle wieder da
hinabzukommen, wo sie hinaufgeklettert waren, aber sie
kamen nicht hinab. Es war lauter Eis, als hätten sie die
Richtung, in der sie gekommen waren, verfehlt. Sie wandten
sich hierhin und dorthin und konnten aus dem Eise nicht
herauskommen, als wären sie von ihm umschlungen. Sie
kletterten abwärts und kamen wieder in Eis. Endlich, da der
Knabe die Richtung immer verfolgte, in der sie nach seiner
Meinung gekommen waren, gelangten sie in zerstreutere
Trümmer, aber sie waren auch größer und furchtbarer, wie sie
gerne am Rande des Eises zu sein pflegen, und die Kinder
gelangten kriechend und kletternd hinaus. An dem Eisessaume
waren ungeheure Steine, sie waren gehäuft, wie sie die Kinder
ihr Leben lang nicht gesehen hatten. Viele waren in Weiß
gehüllt, viele zeigten die unteren schiefen Wände sehr glatt
und fein geschliffen, als wären sie darauf geschoben worden,
viele waren wie Hütten und Dächer gegeneinander gestellt,
viele lagen aufeinander wie ungeschlachte Knollen. Nicht weit
von dem Standorte der Kinder standen mehrere mit den
Köpfen gegeneinander gelehnt, und über sie lagen breite,
gelagerte Blöcke wie ein Dach. Es war ein Häuschen, das
gebildet war, das gegen vorne offen, rückwärts und an den
Seiten aber geschützt war. Im Innern war es trocken, da der
steilrechte Schneefall keine einzige Flocke hineingetragen
hatte. Die Kinder waren recht froh, daß sie nicht mehr in dem
Eise waren und auf ihrer Erde standen.

Aber es war auch endlich finster geworden.

„Sanna“, sagte der Knabe, „wir können nicht mehr hinabgehen, weil es Nacht geworden ist und weil wir fallen oder
gar in eine Grube geraten könnten. Wir werden da unter die
Steine hineingehen, wo es trocken und so warm ist, und da
werden wir warten. Die Sonne geht bald wieder auf, dann
laufen wir hinunter. Weine nicht, ich bitte dich recht schön,
weine nicht, ich gebe dir alle Dinge zu essen, welche uns die
Großmutter mitgegeben hat.“

Sie weinte auch nicht, sondern, nachdem sie beide unter das
steinerne Überdach hineingegangen waren, wo sie nicht nur be-
quem sitzen, sondern auch stehen und herumgehen konnten,

else."

"Yes, Conrad."

The children now tried to get down from the rampart of ice at the same place where they had climbed up, but they did not get down. There was nothing but ice, as if they had missed the direction they had taken. They turned this way and that and could not get out of the ice, as if they were surrounded by it. They climbed downwards and again came into more ice. Finally, since the boy kept following the direction which he thought they had taken, they reached a mass of scattered debris, which was, however, bigger and more terrible, as is normal at the edge of ice, and the children got out of it by crawling and climbing. At the rim of the ice there were enormous stones, piled up in a way the children had never seen in all their lives. Many were wrapped in white; many showed the lower, slanting walls very smoothly and finely polished, as if they had been shoved on that side; many were placed against each other like huts and roofs, many lay on each other like crude clumps. Not far from the spot where the children were standing several such stones stood with their heads leaning toward each other, and above them lay wide, flat blocks like a roof. A little house had been formed, open in front but protected at the sides and back. Inside it was dry, since the vertical snowfall had carried in not a single snow-flake. The children were very glad that they were no longer on the ice but standing on their earth.

But it had finally become dark.

"Sanna," said the boy, "we can't go down any more because night has come, and we might fall or even land in a pit. We'll go in there under the stones where it's so dry and so warm and we'll wait there. The sun will rise again soon, then we'll go down. Don't cry, please, don't cry, I'll give you all the things to eat which grandmother gave us to take with us."

And she did not cry, but when they had both gone in under the overhanging stone roof, where they could not only sit comfortably but could also stand up and walk about, she sat

setzte sie sich recht dicht an ihn und war mäuschenstille.

„Die Mutter", sagte Konrad, „wird nicht böse sein, wir werden ihr von dem vielen Schnee erzählen, der uns aufgehalten hat, und sie wird nichts sagen; der Vater auch nicht. Wenn uns kalt wird—weißt du—, dann mußt du mit den Händen an deinen Leib schlagen, wie die Holzhauer getan haben, und dann wird dir wärmer werden."

„Ja, Konrad", sagte das Mädchen.

Sanna war nicht ganz so untröstlich, daß sie heute nicht mehr über den Berg hinabgingen und nach Hause liefen, wie er etwa glauben mochte; denn die unermeßliche Anstrengung, von der die Kinder nicht einmal gewußt hatten, wie groß sie gewesen sei, ließ ihnen das Sitzen süß, unsäglich süß erscheinen, und sie gaben sich hin.

Jetzt machte sich auch der Hunger geltend.[47] Beide nahmen fast zu gleicher Zeit ihre Brote aus den Taschen und aßen sie. Sie aßen auch die Dinge—kleine Stückchen Kuchen, Mandeln und Nüsse und andere Kleinigkeiten—, die die Großmutter ihnen in die Tasche gesteckt hatte.

„Sanna, jetzt müssen wir aber auch den Schnee von unsern Kleidern tun", sagte der Knabe, „daß wir nicht naß werden."

„Ja, Konrad", erwiderte Sanna.

Die Kinder gingen aus ihrem Häuschen, und zuerst reinigte Konrad das Schwesterlein von Schnee. Er nahm die Kleiderzipfel, schüttelte sie, nahm ihr den Hut ab, den er ihr aufgesetzt hatte, entleerte ihn von Schnee, und was noch zurückgeblieben war, das stäubte er mit einem Tuche ab. Dann entledigte er auch sich, so gut es ging, des auf ihm liegenden Schnees.

Der Schneefall hatte zu dieser Stunde ganz aufgehört. Die Kinder spürten keine Flocke.

Sie gingen wieder in die Steinhütte und setzten sich nieder. Das Aufstehen hatte ihnen ihre Müdigkeit erst recht gezeigt, und sie freuten sich auf das Sitzen. Konrad legte die Tasche aus Kalbfell ab. Er nahm das Tuch heraus, in welches die Großmutter eine Schachtel und mehrere Papierpäckchen gewickelt hatte, und tat es zu größerer Wärme um seine Schultern. Auch die zwei Weißbrote nahm er aus dem Ränzchen und reichte sie beide an Sanna: das Kind aß begierig. Es aß eines der Brote und von dem zweiten auch noch einen Teil.

down quite close beside him and was as quiet as a mouse.

"Mother won't be angry," said Conrad; "we'll tell her about the heavy snow which held us up and she won't say anything; nor will father. If we get cold, you know, you must slap your hands against your body, the way the woodcutters did, and then you'll feel warmer."

"Yes, Conrad," said the girl.

Sanna was not so utterly disconsolate as he thought because they couldn't go down the mountain today and go home; for the enormous strain, the extent of which the children had not even realized, made sitting appear sweet, indescribably sweet, to them and they abandoned themselves to it.

But now hunger made itself felt, too. Both of them took their bread out of their pockets almost at the same time and ate it. They also ate the things—little pieces of cake, almonds and nuts and other trifles—which their grandmother had put into their pockets.

"Sanna, but now we must also remove the snow from our clothes," said the boy, "so that we don't get wet."

"Yes, Conrad," replied Sanna.

The children left their little house and Conrad first cleaned the snow off his little sister. He held the clothes by their corners, shook them, took off the hat he had put on her head, emptied it of snow, and what had remained, he dusted off with a cloth. Then he also removed the snow that was on him as best he could.

By this time the snow had ceased falling altogether. The children could not feel a single flake.

They went back into the stone hut and sat down. Getting up had proved to them how tired they really were and they looked forward to sitting down. Conrad put down his calfskin bag. He took out the cloth in which their grandmother had wrapped a box and several paper packages and put it about his shoulders for greater warmth. He also took the two white rolls from the satchel and handed them both to Sanna; the child ate them eagerly, first the one and then part of the second. The rest she handed to Conrad, since she saw that

Den Rest reichte es aber Konrad, da es sah, daß er nich aß.
Er nahm es und verzehrte es.

Von da an saßen die Kinder und schauten.

So weit sie in der Dämmerung zu sehen vermochten, lag
überall der flimmernde Schnee hinab, dessen einzelne winzige
Täfelchen hie und da in der Finsternis seltsam zu funkeln
begannen, als hätte er bei Tag das Licht eingesogen und gäbe
es jetzt von sich.

Die Nacht brach mit der in großen Höhen gewöhnlichen
Schnelligkeit herein. Bald war es rings herum finster, nur der
Schnee fuhr fort, mit seinem bleichen Lichte zu leuchten. Der
Schneefall hatte nicht nur aufgehört, sondern der Schleier an
dem Himmel fing auch an, sich zu verdünnen und zu verteilen;
denn die Kinder sahen ein Sternlein blitzen. Weil der Schnee
wirklich gleichsam ein Licht von sich gab und weil von den
Wolken kein Schleier mehr herabhing, so konnten die Kinder
von ihrer Höhle aus die Schneehügel sehen, wie sie sich in
Linien von dem dunklen Himmel abschnitten. Weil es in der
Höhle viel wärmer war, als es an jedem andern Platze im
ganzen Tage gewesen war, so ruhten die Kinder, enge
aneinander sitzend, und vergaßen sogar die Finsternis zu
fürchten. Bald vermehrten sich auch die Sterne, jetzt kam
hier einer zum Vorscheine, jetzt dort, bis es schien, als wäre
am ganzen Himmel keine Wolke mehr.

Das war der Zeitpunkt, in welchem man in den Tälern die
Lichter anzuzünden pflegte. Zuerst wird eines angezündet
und auf den Tisch gestellt, um die Stube zu erleuchten, oder
es brennt auch nur ein Span, oder es brennt das Feuer auf
der Leuchte, und es erhellen sich alle Fenster von bewohnten
Stuben und glänzen in die Schneenacht hinaus—aber heute
erst [48]—am Heiligen Abende—, da wurden viel mehrere angezündet, um die Gaben zu beleuchten, welche für die Kinder
auf den Tischen lagen oder an den Bäumen hingen, es wurden
wohl unzählige angezündet; denn beinahe in jedem Hause, in
jeder Hütte, jedem Zimmer war eines oder mehrere Kinder,
denen der Heilige Christ etwas gebracht hatte, und wozu man
Lichter stellen mußte. Der Knabe hatte geglaubt, daß man
sehr bald von dem Berge hinabkommen könne, und doch, von
den vielen Lichtern, die heute in dem Tale brannten, kam
nicht ein einziges zu ihnen herauf; sie sahen nichts als den

he wasn't eating. He took it and ate it.

From then on the children sat and looked.
As far as they were able to see in the half light, the glimmering snow lay around everywhere; and its individual tiny flakes began to sparkle strangely in the darkness as if it had absorbed the light by day and were now giving it off.

The night descended with the speed that is characteristic of great heights. Soon it was dark all around; only the snow continued to shine with its pale light. Not only had the snowfall ceased, but the veil in the sky began to grow thinner and to divide; for the children saw a little star flash. Because the snow really gave off a sort of light, and because there was no longer a veil hanging down from the clouds, the children could see from their cave the hills of snow and how they stood out in lines against the dark sky. Because it was much warmer in the cave than it had been in any other place that day, the children rested, sitting close beside each other, and they even forgot to be afraid of the dark. Soon the stars increased in number, now one appeared here, now another there, until it seemed as if there were not a cloud left in the whole sky.

This was the time when people in the valleys are accustomed to put on the lights. First one candle is lit and put on the table to light the room, or maybe it is only a chip of wood burning, or the fire burns in the lamp and all the windows of inhabited rooms light up and shine out into the snowy night. But today especially, on Christmas Eve, far more lights were lit to illuminate the gifts which lay on the tables for the children or hung on the trees. Countless lights would be lit, for in almost every house, in every hut, in every room there were one or more children to whom the Holy Christ had brought something and for this purpose the lights had to be set out. The boy had thought that they could get down the mountain very soon, and yet not one of the many lights that shone below in the valley reached up to them. They saw nothing but the pale snow and the dark sky; everything else had moved down into an invisible distance for them. In

blassen Schnee und den dunkeln Himmel, alles andere war ihnen in unsichtbare Ferne hinabgerückt. In allen Tälern bekommen die Kinder in dieser Stunde die Geschenke des Heiligen Christ: nur die zwei saßen oben am Rande des Eises, und die vorzüglichsten Geschenke, die sie heute hätten bekommen sollen, lagen in versiegelten Päckchen in der Kalbfelltasche im Hintergrunde der Höhle.

Die Schneewolken waren ringsum hinter die Berge hinabgesunken, und ein ganz dunkelblaues, fast schwarzes Gewölbe spannte sich um die Kinder voll von dichten brennenden Sternen, und mitten durch diese Sterne war ein schimmerndes breites milchiges Band gewoben, das sie wohl auch unten im Tale, aber nie so deutlich gesehen hatten. Die Nacht rückte vor. Die Kinder wußten nicht, daß die Sterne gegen Westen rücken und weiter wandeln, sonst hätten sie an ihrem Vorschreiten den Stand der Nacht erkennen können; aber es kamen neue und gingen die alten, sie aber glaubten, es seien immer dieselben. Es wurde von dem Scheine der Sterne auch lichter um die Kinder; aber sie sahen kein Tal, keine Gegend, sondern überall nur Weiß—lauter Weiß. Bloß ein dunkles Horn, ein dunkles Haupt, ein dunkler Arm wurde sichtbar und ragte dort und hier aus dem Schimmer empor. Der Mond war nirgends am Himmel zu erblicken, vielleicht war er schon frühe mit der Sonne untergegangen, oder er ist noch nicht erschienen.

Als eine lange Zeit vergangen war, sagte der Knabe: „Sanna, du mußt nicht schlafen; denn weißt du, wie der Vater gesagt hat, wenn man im Gebirge schläft, muß man erfrieren, so wie der alte Eschenjäger auch geschlafen hat und vier Monate tot auf dem Steine gesessen ist,[49] ohne daß jemand gewußt hatte, wo er sei."

„Nein, ich werde nicht schlafen", sagte das Mädchen matt.

Konrad hatte es an dem Zipfel des Kleides geschüttelt, um es zu jenen Worten zu erwecken.

Nun war es wieder stille.

Nach einer Zeit empfand der Knabe ein sanftes Drücken gegen seinen Arm, das immer schwerer wurde. Sanna war eingeschlafen und war gegen ihn herübergesunken.

„Sanna, schlafe nicht, ich bitte dich, schlafe nicht", sagte er.

all the valleys the children were at this time receiving the gifts from the Holy Christ; only these two sat up there at the edge of the ice, and the most excellent gifts which they were to have received today lay in sealed little packages in the calfskin satchel at the back of the cave.

The clouds of snow had sunk down round about behind the mountains and a very dark blue, almost black, vault stretched about the children, full of dense burning stars; and in the midst of these stars a shimmering, broad, milky band was woven, which they had of course seen down in the valley too, but never so clearly. The night advanced. The children did not know that the stars move westward and go on, or they might have gauged the time of night by their progress; but new stars came and old ones went, and they thought they were always the same ones. It also became brighter around the children because of the starlight; but they saw no valley, no countryside, only whiteness everywhere, nothing but whiteness. Only a dark horn, a dark head, a dark arm became visible and jutted out of the faint light here and there. The moon was nowhere to be seen in the sky; perhaps it had gone down early with the sun or it had not appeared yet.

After a long time had passed the boy said: "Sanna, you mustn't sleep, for you know, as father said, if you sleep in the mountains you're sure to freeze to death, just as old Eschenjäger slept and sat dead on a stone for four months without anyone knowing where he was."

"No, I'm not going to sleep," said the girl faintly.

Conrad had shaken her by the corner of her dress, to wake her so that she could hear his words.

Now it was quiet again.

After a while the boy felt a gentle pressure against his arm, getting heavier all the time. Sanna had fallen asleep and had settled against him.

"Sanna, don't sleep, please, don't sleep," he said.

„Nein", lallte sie schlaftrunken, „ich schlafe nicht."

Er rückte weiter von ihr, um sie in Bewegung zu bringen, allein sie sank um und hätte auf der Erde liegend fortgeschlafen. Er nahm sie an der Schulter und rüttelte sie. Da er sich dabei selber etwas stärker bewegte, merkte er, daß ihn friere und daß sein Arm schwerer sei. Er erschrak und sprang auf.

Er ergriff die Schwester, schüttelte sie stärker und sagte: „Sanna, stehe ein wenig auf, wir wollen eine Zeit stehen, daß es besser wird."

„Mich friert nicht, Konrad", antwortete sie.

„Ja, ja, es friert dich, Sanna, stehe auf", rief er.

„Die Pelzjacke ist warm", sagte sie.

„Ich werde dir emporhelfen", sagte er.

„Nein", erwiderte sie und war stille.

Da fiel dem Knaben etwas anderes ein. Die Großmutter hatte gesagt: Nur ein Schlückchen wärmt den Magen so, daß es den Körper in den kältesten Wintertagen nicht frieren kann.

Er nahm das Kalbfellränzchen, öffnete es und griff so lange, bis er das Fläschchen fand, in welchem die Großmutter der Mutter einen schwarzen Kaffeeabsud schicken wollte. Er nahm das Fläschchen heraus, tat den Verband weg und öffnete mit Anstrengung den Kork. Dann bückte er sich zu Sanna und sagte: „Da ist der Kaffee, den die Großmutter der Mutter schickt, koste ihn ein wenig, er wird dir warm machen. Die Mutter gibt ihn uns, wenn sie nur weiß, wozu wir ihn nötig gehabt haben."

Das Mädchen, dessen Natur zur Ruhe zog,[50] antwortete: „Mich friert nicht."

„Nimm nur etwas", sagte der Knabe, „dann darfst du schlafen."

Diese Aussicht verlockte Sanna, sie bewältigte sich so weit, daß sie fast das eingegossene Getränk verschluckte. Hierauf trank der Knabe auch etwas.

Der ungemein starke Auszug wirkte sogleich, und zwar um so heftiger, da die Kinder in ihrem Leben keinen Kaffee gekostet hatten. Statt zu schlafen, wurde Sanna nun lebhafter und sagte selber, daß sie friere, daß es aber von innen recht warm sei und auch schon so in die Hände und Füße gehe.

"No," she mumbled, drunk with sleep, "I'm not sleeping."

He moved away from her to get her to move, but she fell over and would have continued to sleep lying on the earth. He took her by the shoulder and shook her. Since he moved a little more energetically as he did so, he noticed that he was cold, and that his arm was numb. He was alarmed and jumped up. He seized his sister, shook her more strongly and said: "Sanna, wake up for a while, we'll stand up a bit so that we'll feel better."

"I don't feel cold, Conrad," she replied.

"Yes, yes, you are cold, Sanna, get up," he cried.

"The fur jacket is warm," she said.

"I'll help you up," he said.

"No," she replied and was quiet.

Then the boy had another idea. Grandmother had said, one little sip warms the stomach so, that the body can't freeze even on the coldest winter days.

He took the calfskin satchel, opened it and searched until he found the little flask in which their grandmother was sending mother the black liquid coffee. He took out the little bottle, removed the wrappings and pulled out the cork with an effort. Then he bent down to Sanna and said: "There's the coffee which grandmother is sending to mother, taste a little of it, it will warm you. Mother will let us have it if she only knows why we needed it."

The girl, whose constitution demanded rest, replied: "I'm not cold."

"Just take a little," said the boy, "then you may sleep."

This prospect tempted Sanna; she made enough of an effort to swallow the drink, almost all he had poured out for her. Then the boy drank some, too.

The unusually powerful extract produced an immediate effect which was all the more violent because the children had never tasted coffee in their lives. Instead of sleeping, Sanna now became more animated and admitted that she was cold but that she felt really warm inside and that the warmth was

Die Kinder redeten sogar eine Weile miteinander.

So tranken sie trotz der Bitterkeit immer wieder von dem
Getränke, sobald die Wirkung nachzulassen begann, und
steigerten ihre unschuldigen Nerven zu einem Fieber, das
imstande war, den zum Schlummer ziehenden Gewichten
entgegenzuwirken.

Es war nun Mitternacht gekommen. Weil sie noch so jung
waren und an jedem Heiligen Abende in höchstem Drange
der Freude stets erst sehr spät entschlummerten, wenn sie
nämlich der körperliche Drang übermannt hatte, so hatten
sie nie das mitternächtliche Läuten der Glocken, nie die Orgel
der Kirche gehört, wenn das Fest [51] gefeiert wurde, obwohl
sie nahe an der Kirche wohnten. In diesem Augenblicke der
heutigen Nacht wurde nun mit allen Glocken geläutet, es
läuteten die Glocken in Millsdorf, es läuteten die Glocken
in Gschaid, und hinter dem Berge war noch ein Kirchlein
mit drei hellen klingenden Glocken, die läuteten. In den
fernen Ländern draußen waren unzählige Kirchen und
Glocken, und mit allen wurde zu dieser Zeit geläutet, von
Dorf zu Dorf ging die Tonwelle, ja man konnte wohl zuweilen
von einem Dorfe zum andern durch die blätterlosen Zweige
das Läuten hören: nur zu den Kindern herauf kam kein Laut,
hier wurde nichts vernommen; denn hier war nichts zu verkündigen. In den Talkrümmen gingen jetzt an den Berg-
hängen die Lichter der Laternen hin, und von manchem Hofe
tönte das Hausglöcklein, um die Leute zu erinnern; aber
dieses konnte um so weniger herauf gesehen und gehört
werden, es glänzten nur die Sterne, und sie leuchteten und
funkelten ruhig fort.

Wenn auch Konrad sich das Schicksal des erfrornen Eschen-
jägers vor Augen hielt, wenn auch die Kinder das Fläschchen
mit dem schwarzen Kaffee fast ausgeleert hatten, wodurch sie
ihr Blut zu größerer Tätigkeit brachten, aber gerade dadurch
eine folgende Ermattung herbeizogen: so würden sie den
Schlaf nicht haben überwinden können, dessen verführende
Süßigkeit alle Gründe überwiegt, wenn nicht die Natur in
ihrer Größe ihnen beigestanden wäre und in ihrem Innern
eine Kraft aufgerufen hätte, welche imstande war, dem
Schlafe zu widerstehen.

already spreading to her hands and feet. The children even talked to each other for a while.

So, in spite of its bitterness, they kept drinking the beverage whenever its effect began to wear off and they stimulated their innocent nerves to fever pitch, which was able to counteract the weight that drew them toward slumber.

Midnight had now come. Because they were still so young and, in their ecstasy of joy, always fell asleep very late on Christmas Eve—that is, when physical weariness had overcome them—they had never heard the midnight pealing of the bells, nor the organ in church when Mass was celebrated, though they lived close to the church. At this moment tonight all the bells rang: the bells in Millsdorf rang, the bells in Gschaid rang, and behind the mountain there was another little church with three clear, resonant bells, which rang too. In the distant countryside beyond there were countless churches and bells, and they were all ringing at this time; from village to village the wave of sound went; at times one could even hear the chiming from one village to the next through the leafless branches. But no sound reached the children; they heard nothing, for there was nothing to herald here. In the windings of the valley and on the mountain slopes the lantern lights were now moving, and on many a farmyard the little house bell was ringing to remind the folk; but all this could scarcely be seen or heard up here; the stars alone shone and they calmly went on shining and twinkling.

Even though Conrad kept the fate of the frozen Eschenjäger in mind, even though the children had almost emptied the little flask of black coffee—thus causing their blood to circulate more vigorously, but by this very act bringing on a subsequent weariness—they could not have conquered sleep, whose seductive sweetness outweighs all reasoning, if Nature in her grandeur had not helped them and summoned up in their minds a power that was able to resist sleep.

In der ungeheueren Stille, die herrschte, in der Stille, in der sich kein Schneespitzchen zu rühren schien, hörten die Kinder dreimal das Krachen des Eises. Was das Starrste scheint und doch das Regsamste und Lebendigste ist, der Gletscher, hatte die Töne hervorgebracht. Dreimal hörten sie hinter sich den Schall, der entsetzlich war, also ob die Erde entzweigesprungen wäre, der sich nach allen Richtungen im Eise verbreitete und gleichsam durch alle Äderchen des Eises lief. Die Kinder blieben mit offenen Augen sitzen und schauten in die Sterne hinaus.

Auch für die Augen begann sich etwas zu entwickeln. Wie die Kinder so saßen, erblühte am Himmel vor ihnen ein bleiches Licht mitten unter den Sternen und spannte einen schwachen Bogen durch dieselben. Es hatte einen grünlichen Schimmer, der sich sachte nach unten zog. Aber der Bogen wurde immer heller und heller, bis sich die Sterne vor ihm zurückzogen und erblaßten. Auch in andere Gegenden des Himmels sandte er einen Schein, der schimmergrün sachte und lebendig unter die Sterne floß. Dann standen Garben verschiedenen Lichtes auf der Höhe des Bogens wie Zacken einer Krone und brannten. Es floß helle durch die benachbarten Himmelsgegenden, es sprühte leise und ging in sanftem Zucken durch lange Räume. Hatte sich nun der Gewitterstoff des Himmels durch den unerhörten Schneefall so gespannt, daß er in diesen stummen, herrlichen Strömen des Lichtes ausfloß, oder war es eine andere Ursache der unergründlichen Natur? Nach und nach wurde es schwächer und immer schwächer, die Garben erloschen zuerst, bis es allmählich und unmerklich immer geringer wurde und wieder nichts am Himmel war als die tausend und tausend einfachen Sterne.

Die Kinder sagten keines zu dem andern ein Wort, sie blieben fort und fort sitzen und schauten mit offenen Augen in den Himmel.

Es geschah nun nichts Besonderes mehr. Die Sterne glänzten, funkelten und zitterten, nur manche schießende Schnuppe [52] fuhr durch sie.

Endlich, nachdem die Sterne lange allein geschienen hatten und nie ein Stückchen Mond an dem Himmel zu erblicken gewesen war, geschah etwas anderes. Es fing der Himmel an, heller zu werden, langsam heller, aber doch zu erkennen; [53]

In the vast stillness that prevailed, in the stillness in which not even a speck of snow seemed to stir, the children heard the ice crack three times. What seems to be the most rigid and is yet the most active and living of things, the glacier, had produced the sounds. Three times they heard behind them the sound that was horrifying, as if the earth had broken apart, spreading in the ice in all directions and running, as it were, through all the little veins of the ice. The children sat there with open eyes, looking out at the stars.

Something now began to unfold for their eyes too. As the children were sitting there, a pale light bloomed before them in the sky among the stars and stretched a weak arc through them. It had a greenish shimmer, which gently spread downward. But the arc became brighter and brighter until the stars withdrew before it and paled. It also sent a light into other regions of the sky, flowing gently and alive among the stars in a shimmering green. Then sheaves of varied light stood on the top of the arc like the jagged points of a crown, and were aflame. A brightness flowed through the adjacent celestial regions, it gave off a soft spray and went with a gentle quivering through the vast spaces. Had the electricity in the sky been so charged by the unprecedented snowfall that it discharged itself in these mute, glorious streams of light, or was it the result of some other cause in unfathomable nature? Gradually it grew weaker and ever weaker, the sheaves died out first, until it gradually and imperceptibly became slighter and once more there was nothing in the sky except the thousands upon thousands of simple stars.

The children did not say a word to each other, they kept sitting there, looking at the sky with wide open eyes.

Nothing special happened after this. The stars glittered, sparkled and quivered, occasionally a shooting star went through them.

Finally, after the stars had shone alone for a long time without even a piece of the moon being visible in the sky, something else happened. The sky began to become brighter, slowly but still perceptibly brighter; its color became visible,

es wurde seine Farbe sichtbar, die bleichsten Sterne erloschen, und die anderen standen nicht mehr so dicht. Endlich wichen auch die stärkeren, und der Schnee vor den Höhen wurde deutlicher sichtbar. Zuletzt färbte sich eine Himmelsgegend gelb, und ein Wolkenstreifen, der in derselben war, wurde zu einem leuchtenden Faden entzündet. Alle Dinge waren klar zu sehen, und die entfernten Schneehügel zeichneten sich scharf in die Luft.

„Sanna, der Tag bricht an", sagte der Knabe.

„Ja, Konrad", antwortete das Mädchen.

„Wenn es nur noch ein bißchen heller wird, dann gehen wir aus der Höhle und laufen über den Berg hinunter."

Es wurde heller, an dem ganzen Himmel war kein Stern mehr sichtbar, und alle Gegenstände standen in der Morgendämmerung da.

„Nun, jetzt gehen wir", sagte der Knabe.

„Ja, wir gehen", antwortete Sanna.

Die Kinder standen auf und versuchten ihre erst heute recht müden Glieder. Obwohl sie nicht geschlafen hatten, waren sie doch durch den Morgen gestärkt, wie das immer so ist. Der Knabe hing sich das Kalbfellränzchen um und machte das Pelzjäckchen an Sanna fester zu. Dann führte er sie aus der Höhle.

Weil sie nach ihrer Meinung nur über den Berg hinabzulaufen hatten, dachten sie an kein Essen und untersuchten das Ränzchen nicht, ob noch Weißbrote oder andere Eßwaren darinnen seien.

Von dem Berge wollte nun Konrad, weil der Himmel ganz heiter war, in die Täler hinabschauen, um das Gschaider Tal zu erkennen und in dasselbe hinunterzugehen. Aber er sah gar keine Täler. Es war nicht, als ob sie sich auf einem Berge befänden, von dem man hinabsieht, sondern in einer fremden, seltsamen Gegend, in der lauter unbekannte Gegenstände sind. Sie sahen auch heute in größerer [54] Entfernung furchtbare Felsen aus dem Schnee emporstehen, die sie gestern nicht gesehen hatten, sie sahen das Eis, sie sahen Hügel und Schneelehnen emporstarren, und hinter diesen war entweder der Himmel, oder es ragte die blaue Spitze eines sehr fernen Berges am Schneerande hervor.

In diesem Augenblicke ging die Sonne auf.

the palest stars died away and the others no longer stood so close together. At last even the stronger ones vanished, and the snow in front of the heights became more clearly visible. Finally a region of the sky turned yellow and a strip of cloud in it was kindled into a glowing thread. Everything could be seen clearly and the distant hills of snow stood out sharply in the air.

"Sanna, day is breaking," said the boy.

"Yes, Conrad," the girl replied.

"When it gets just a bit lighter, we'll leave the cave and run down the mountain."

It became lighter; not a star was visible any longer in the whole sky and every object stood out in the faint morning light.

"Well, let's go now," said the boy.

"Yes, we'll go," answered Sanna.

The children stood up and tried their limbs, which felt really tired today. Although they had not slept at all, they were strengthened by the morning, as is always the case. The boy hung the calfskin satchel over his shoulder and drew Sanna's little fur jacket tighter. Then he led her out of the cave.

Because they thought they need only run down the mountain, they did not think of food and did not examine the satchel to see whether there were rolls or other food in it.

As the sky was now quite clear, Conrad wanted to look down from the mountain into the valleys, to make out the Gschaid valley and go down to it. But he saw no valleys at all. They did not seem to be on a mountain from which one can look down, but in a foreign strange region in which there are nothing but unfamiliar objects. Today again they saw at some distance fearful rocks standing out from the snow, rocks they had not seen yesterday. They saw the ice, they saw hills and snow-covered slopes stand up rigidly, and behind these was either the sky or the blue point of a very distant mountain jutted out at the edge of the snow.

At this moment the sun rose.

Eine riesengroße blutrote Scheibe erhob sich an dem Schneesaume in den Himmel, und in dem Augenblicke errötete der Schnee um die Kinder, als wäre er mit Millionen Rosen überstreut worden. Die Kuppen und die Hörner warfen sehr lange grünliche Schatten längs des Schnees.

„Sanna, wir werden jetzt da weiter vorwärts gehen, bis wir an den Rand des Berges kommen und hinuntersehen", sagte der Knabe.

Sie gingen nun in den Schnee hinaus. Er war in der heiteren Nacht noch trockener geworden und wich den Tritten noch besser aus. Sie wateten rüstig fort. Ihre Glieder wurden sogar geschmeidiger und stärker, da sie gingen. Allein sie kamen an keinen Rand und sahen nicht hinunter. Schneefeld entwickelte sich aus Schneefeld, und am Saume eines jeden stand alle Male [55] wieder der Himmel.

Sie gingen desohngeachtet fort.

Da kamen sie wieder in das Eis. Sie wußten nicht, wie das Eis daher gekommen sei, aber unter den Füßen empfanden sie den glatten Boden, und waren gleich nicht [56] die fürchterlichen Trümmer, wie an jenem Rande, an dem sie die Nacht zugebracht hatten, so sahen sie doch, daß sie auf glattem Eise fortgingen, sie sahen hie und da Stücke, die immer mehr wurden, die sich näher an sie drängten und die sie wieder zu klettern zwangen.

Aber sie verfolgten doch ihre Richtung.

Sie kletterten neuerdings an Blöcken empor. Da standen sie wieder auf dem Eisfelde. Heute bei der hellen Sonne konnten sie es erst erblicken, was es ist. Es war ungeheuer groß, und jenseits standen wieder schwarze Felsen empor, es ragte gleichsam Welle hinter Welle auf, das beschneite Eis war gedrängt, gequollen, emporgehoben, gleichsam als schöbe es sich noch vorwärts und flösse gegen die Brust der Kinder heran. In dem Weiß sahen sie unzählige vorwärtsgehende geschlängelte blaue Linien. Zwischen jenen Stellen, wo die Eiskörper gleichsam wie aneinandergeschmettert starrten, gingen auch Linien wie Wege, aber sie waren weiß und waren Streifen, wo sich fester Eisboden vorfand oder die Stücke doch nicht gar so sehr verschoben waren. In diese Pfade gingen die Kinder hinein, weil sie doch einen Teil des Eises überschreiten wollten, um an den Bergrand zu gelangen und

A gigantic, blood-red disk rose up at the edge of the snow into the sky, and at that moment the snow about the children turned red, as if it had been strewn with millions of roses. The knobs and horns cast very long, greenish shadows along the snow.

"Sanna, we will now go on there some more until we come to the edge of the mountain and can look down," said the boy.

They now went out into the snow. It had become even drier in the clear night and yielded even more to their steps. They waded on briskly. Their limbs became even more supple and strong as they walked. But they came to no edge and could not look down. Snowfield developed from snowfield, and at the edge of each they found the sky every time.

They went on nevertheless.

Then they came to the ice again. They did not know where the ice had come from, but under their feet they felt the smooth ground, and even though there was none of the fearful debris they had found at the rim where they had spent the night, they saw nevertheless that they were walking on smooth ice; here and there they saw chunks which kept increasing in number, which pressed closer to them and which compelled them to climb once more.

But they still pursued their direction.

They again climbed up blocks. There they were standing on the ice field again. Only today, in the bright sun, were they able to see what it was. It was enormously big, and on the other side black rocks stood out again, wave upon wave towered up as it were, the snow-covered ice was squeezed, swollen, lifted up as if it were still thrusting forward and flowing towards the children's chests. In the whiteness they saw countless serpentine blue lines advancing. Between those places where the ice blocks stood rigid, as if they had been smashed against each other, lines went like roads; but they were white and were stripes formed by a solid ice floor underneath where the chunks were not too far out of place. The children entered these paths because they really wanted to cross a part of the ice to reach the edge of the mountain and to look down at long last. They did not speak a word. The

endlich einmal hinunterzusehen. Sie sagten kein Wörtlein.
Das Mädchen folgte dem Knaben. Aber es war auch heute
wieder Eis, lauter Eis. Wo sie hinübergelangen wollten, wurde
es gleichsam immer breiter und breiter. Da schlugen sie, ihre
Richtung aufgebend, den Rückweg ein. Wo sie nicht gehen
konnten, griffen sie sich durch die Mengen des Schnees
hindurch, der oft dicht vor ihrem Auge wegbrach und den
sehr blauen Streifen einer Eisspalte zeigte, wo doch früher
alles weiß gewesen war; aber sie kümmerten sich nicht darum,
sie arbeiteten sich fort, bis sie wieder irgendwo aus dem Eise
herauskamen.

„Sanna", sagte der Knabe, „wir werden gar nicht mehr in
das Eis hineingehen, weil wir in demselben nicht fortkommen.
Und weil wir schon in unser Tal gar nicht hinabsehen können,
so werden wir gerade über den Berg hinabgehen. Wir müssen
in ein Tal kommen, dort werden wir den Leuten sagen, daß
wir aus Gschaid sind, die werden uns einen Wegweiser nach
Hause mitgeben."

„Ja, Konrad", sagte das Mädchen.

So begannen sie nun in dem Schnee nach jener Richtung
abwärts zu gehen, welche sich ihnen eben darbot. Der Knabe
führte das Mädchen an der Hand. Allein nachdem sie eine
Weile abwärts gegangen waren, hörte in dieser Richtung das
Gehänge auf, der Schnee stieg wieder empor. Also änderten
die Kinder die Richtung und gingen nach der Länge einer
Mulde hinab. Aber da fanden sie wieder Eis. Sie stiegen also
an der Seite der Mulde empor, um nach einer andern
Richtung ein Abwärts zu suchen. Es führte sie eine Fläche
hinab, allein die wurde nach und nach so steil, daß sie kaum
noch einen Fuß einsetzen konnten und abwärts zu gleiten fürchteten. Sie klommen also wieder empor, um wieder einen andern
Weg nach abwärts zu suchen. Nachdem sie lange im Schnee
emporgeklommen und dann auf einem ebenen Rücken fort-
gelaufen waren, war es wie früher: entweder ging der Schnee
so steil ab, daß sie gestürzt wären, oder er stieg wieder hinan,
daß sie auf den Berggipfel zu kommen fürchteten. Und so
ging es immerfort.

Da wollten sie die Richtung suchen, in der sie gekommen
waren, und zur roten Unglücksäule hinabgehen. Weil es nicht
schneit und der Himmel so helle ist, so würden sie, dachte

girl followed the boy. But today too there was ice, nothing but ice. Where they wanted to cross, it seemed to become broader and broader. So, abandoning their direction, they turned back. Where they could not walk, they crawled through the masses of snow, which often broke away close before their eyes, showing the very blue stripe of a crevasse where everything had been white before; but they did not concern themselves about it, they worked their way forward, until they once more came out of the ice somewhere.

"Sanna," said the boy, "we won't go into the ice any more, because we aren't getting anywhere in it. And since we can't look down into our valley at all, we will go straight down over the mountain. We must get into a valley, there we'll tell the people that we're from Gschaid, and they'll give us a guide to take us home."

"Yes, Conrad," said the girl.

So they now began to walk down in the snow in the direction that happened to lie before them. The boy led the girl by the hand. But after they had gone downhill a while, the slope stopped in this direction and the snow began to rise again. So the children changed their direction and went down the full length of a hollow. But there they found ice again. So they climbed up the side of the hollow to seek another road downhill. A flat surface led them down, but this gradually became so steep that they could hardly find footing and feared they would slip down. So they climbed up again, to seek another way down. After they had climbed in the snow for a long time and had then walked along a level ridge it was as it had been before: either the snow descended so steeply that they would have fallen, or it rose again so that they were afraid they would get to the top of the mountain. And so it went, on and on.

Then they wanted to look for the direction from which they had come, and go down to the red accident pillar. Because it isn't snowing, the boy thought, and the sky is so clear, they

der Knabe, die Stelle schon erkennen, wo die Säule sein solle, und würden von dort nach Gschaid hinabgehen können.

Der Knabe sagte diesen Gedanken dem Schwesterchen, und diese folgte.

Allein auch der Weg auf den Hals hinab war nicht zu finden.

So [57] klar die Sonne schien, so schön die Schneehöhen dastanden und die Schneefelder dalagen, so konnten sie doch die Gegenden nicht erkennen, durch die sie gestern heraufgegangen waren. Gestern war alles durch den fürchterlichen Schneefall verhängt gewesen, daß sie kaum einige Schritte von sich gesehen hatten, und da war alles ein einziges Weiß und Grau durcheinander gewesen. Nur die Felsen hatten sie gesehen, an denen und zwischen denen sie gegangen waren: allein auch heute hatten sie bereits viele Felsen gesehen, die alle den nämlichen Anschein gehabt hatten wie die gestern gesehenen. Heute ließen sie frische Spuren in dem Schnee zurück; aber gestern sind alle Spuren von dem fallenden Schnee verdeckt worden. Auch aus dem bloßen Anblicke konnten sie nicht erraten, welche Gegend auf den Hals führe, da alle Gegenden gleich waren. Schnee, lauter Schnee. Sie gingen aber doch immerfort und meinten, es zu erringen. Sie wichen den steilen Abstürzen aus und kletterten keine steilen Anhöhen hinauf.

Auch heute blieben sie öfter stehen, um zu horchen; aber sie vernahmen auch heute nichts, nicht den geringsten Laut. Zu sehen war auch nichts als der Schnee, der helle weiße Schnee, aus dem hie und da die schwarzen Hörner und die schwarzen Steinrippen emporstanden.

Endlich war es [58] dem Knaben, als sähe er auf einem fernen schiefen Schneefelde ein hüpfendes Feuer. Es tauchte auf, es tauchte nieder. Jetzt sahen sie es, jetzt sahen sie es nicht. Sie blieben stehen und blickten unverwandt auf jene Gegend hin. Das Feuer hüpfte immerfort, und es schien, als ob es näher käme; denn sie sahen es größer und sahen das Hüpfen deutlicher. Es verschwand nicht mehr so oft und nicht mehr auf so lange Zeit wie früher. Nach einer Weile vernahmen sie in der stillen blauen Luft schwach, sehr schwach, etwas wie einen lange anhaltenden Ton aus einem Hirtenhorne. Wie aus Instinkt schrien beide Kinder laut. Nach einer Zeit

would easily recognize the spot where the pillar ought to be
and would be able to go down to Gschaid from there.

The boy communicated this thought to his sister and she
followed him.

But the road down the neck could not be found either.

Though the sun shone clearly, though the snowy heights
stood and the fields of snow lay there so beautifully, they
could not recognize the regions through which they had gone
up yesterday. Yesterday everything had been obscured by the
fearful snowfall, so that they had scarcely been able to see a
few paces ahead of them, and everything had been a single
confused mass of white and gray. They had seen only the
rocks past and between which they had walked; but today,
too, they had already seen many rocks, all of which had had
the same appearance as those they had seen yesterday. Today
they left fresh tracks behind them in the snow; but yesterday
all their tracks were covered by the falling snow. Moreover
they could not tell from merely looking which region led to
the neck, since all the regions were alike. Snow, nothing but
snow. But they kept going forward and thought they would
make it. They avoided the steep drops and climbed up no
steep slopes.

Today, too, they often stopped to listen; but they heard
nothing today either, not the slightest sound. Nor could they
see anything but the snow, the bright, white snow, from
which the black horns and the black stone ribs stood out
here and there.

Finally it seemed to the boy that he saw a skipping fire on
a distant slanting snowfield. It bobbed up and it bobbed
down. Now they saw it, now they didn't see it. They stopped
and looked fixedly at that region. The fire kept skipping and
it seemed to be coming nearer; for they saw it grow larger
and saw the skipping more distinctly. It no longer vanished
so often nor for so long a time as before. After a while they
heard, in the silent blue air, faintly, very faintly, something
like a long steady note from a shepherd's horn. As though by
instinct both children cried aloud. After a while they heard
the note again. They shouted again and stopped where they

hörten sie den Ton wieder. Sie schrien wieder und blieben auf der nämlichen Stelle stehen. Das Feuer näherte sich auch. Der Ton wurde zum dritten Male vernommen und dieses Mal deutlicher. Die Kinder antworteten wieder durch lautes Schreien. Nach einer geraumen Weile erkannten sie auch das Feuer. Es war kein Feuer, es war eine rote Fahne, die geschwungen wurde. Zugleich ertönte das Hirtenhorn näher, und die Kinder antworteten.

„Sanna", rief der Knabe, „da kommen Leute aus Gschaid, ich kenne die Fahne, es ist die rote Fahne, welche der fremde Herr, der mit dem jungen Eschenjäger den Gars bestiegen hatte, auf dem Gipfel aufpflanzte, daß sie der Herr Pfarrer mit dem Fernrohre sähe, was als Zeichen gälte, daß sie oben seien, und welche Fahne damals der fremde Herr dem Herrn Pfarrer geschenkt hat. Du warst noch ein recht kleines Kind."

„Ja, Konrad."

Nach einer Zeit sahen die Kinder auch die Menschen, die bei der Fahne waren, kleine schwarze Stellen, die sich zu bewegen schienen. Der Ruf des Hornes wiederholte sich von Zeit zu Zeit und kam immer näher.

Die Kinder antworteten jedesmal.

Endlich sahen sie über den Schneehang gegen sich her mehrere Männer mit ihren Stöcken herabfahren, die die Fahne in ihrer Mitte hatten. Da sie näher kamen, erkannten sie dieselben. Es war der Hirt Philipp mit dem Horne, seine zwei Söhne, dann der junge Eschenjäger und mehrere Bewohner von Gschaid.

„Gebenedeit sei Gott", schrie Philipp, „da seid ihr ja. Der ganze Berg ist voll Leute. Laufe doch einer gleich in die Sideralpe hinab und läute die Glocke, daß die dort hören, daß wir sie gefunden haben, und einer muß auf den Krebsstein gehen und die Fahne dort aufpflanzen, daß sie dieselbe in dem Tale sehen und die Pöller abschießen, damit die es wissen, die im Millsdorfer Walde suchen, und damit sie in Gschaid die Rauchfeuer anzünden, die in der Luft gesehen werden, und alle, die noch auf dem Berge sind, in die Sideralpe hinabbedeuten. Das sind Weihnachten!" [59]

„Ich laufe in die Alpe hinab", sagte einer.

„Ich trage die Fahne auf den Krebsstein", sagte ein anderer.

„Und wir werden die Kinder in die Sideralpe hinabbringen,

were. The fire was coming closer too. They heard the note a third time and this time more distinctly. The children replied again with a loud shout. After some time they recognized the fire. It wasn't fire, it was a red flag that was being swung. At the same time the shepherd's horn sounded closer and the children replied.

"Sanna," cried the boy, "there are people coming from Gschaid, I know that flag, it's the red flag which the foreign gentleman who had climbed the Gars with young Eschenjäger planted on the peak so that the pastor might see it with his telescope as a sign that they were at the top. The foreign gentleman gave the flag to the pastor at that time. You were still quite a little child."

"Yes, Conrad."

After a while the children also saw the people who were with the flag, little black spots which seemed to be moving. The call of the horn was repeated from time to time and came closer all the time.

The children answered it every time.

Finally they saw several men with sticks sliding down the snowy slope towards them, carrying the flag in their midst. When they came nearer they recognized them. It was Shepherd Philip with his horn, his two sons, then young Eschenjäger and several natives of Gschaid.

"God be praised!" cried Philip, "why, there you are. The whole mountain is full of people. One of you run down to the Sider meadow and ring the bell, so that they may hear that we've found them, and one of you must go to the Krebsstein and plant the flag there, so that they'll see it in the valley and fire the small mortars, so that the people who are searching in the Millsdorf forest may know and so that the people in Gschaid may light the smoke signals that will be seen in the air and bring all those who are still in the mountain down to the Sider meadow. What a Christmas!"

"I'll run down to the meadow," one said.

"I'll carry the flag to the Krebsstein," said another.

"And we'll bring the children down into the Sider meadow

so gut wir es vermögen, und so gut uns Gott helfe", sagte Philipp.

Ein Sohn Philipps schlug den Weg nach abwärts ein, und der andere ging mit der Fahne durch den Schnee dahin.

Der Eschenjäger nahm das Mädchen bei der Hand, der Hirt Philipp den Knaben. Die andern halfen, wie sie konnten. So begann man den Weg. Er ging in Windungen. Bald gingen sie nach einer Richtung, bald schlugen sie die entgegengesetzte ein, bald gingen sie abwärts, bald aufwärts. Immer ging es durch Schnee, immer durch Schnee, und die Gegend blieb sich beständig gleich. Über sehr schiefe Flächen taten sie Steigeisen an die Füße und trugen die Kinder. Endlich nach langer Zeit hörten sie ein Glöcklein, das sanft und fein zu ihnen heraufkam und das erste Zeichen war, das ihnen die niederen Gegenden wieder zusandten. Sie mußten wirklich sehr tief herabgekommen sein, denn sie sahen ein Schneehaupt recht hoch und recht blau über sich ragen. Das Glöcklein aber, das sie hörten, war das der Sideralpe, das geläutet wurde, weil dort die Zusammenkunft verabredet war. Da sie noch weiter kamen, hörten sie auch schwach in die stille Luft die Böllerschüsse herauf, die infolge der ausgesteckten Fahne abgefeuert wurden, und sahen dann in die Luft feine Rauchsäulen aufsteigen.

Da sie nach einer Weile über eine sanfte schiefe Fläche abgingen, erblickten sie die Sideralphütte. Sie gingen auf sie zu. In der Hütte brannte ein Feuer, die Mutter der Kinder war da, und mit einem furchtbaren Schrei sank sie in den Schnee zurück, als sie die Kinder mit dem Eschenjäger kommen sah.

Dann lief sie herzu, betrachtete sie überall, wollte ihnen zu essen geben, wollte sie wärmen, wollte sie in vorhandenes Heu legen; aber bald überzeugte sie sich, daß die Kinder durch die Freude stärker seien, als sie gedacht hatte, daß sie nur einiger warmer Speise bedurften, die sie bekamen, und daß sie nur ein wenig ausruhen mußten, was ihnen ebenfalls zuteil werden sollte.

Da nach einer Zeit der Ruhe wieder eine Gruppe Männer über die Schneefläche herabkam, während das Hüttenglöcklein immerfort läutete, liefen die Kinder selber mit den andern hinaus, um zu sehen, wer es sei. Der Schuster war es, der einstige Alpensteiger, mit Alpenstock und Steigeisen, be-

as best we can and with God's help," said Philip.

One of Philip's sons took the way downhill and the other went off through the snow with the flag.

Eschenjäger took the girl by the hand, the shepherd took the boy. The others helped in any way they could. So they started on their way. It led through many turns. Now they went in one direction, now in the opposite, now they went down, now up. Always they were walking through snow, always through snow and the scenery remained constantly the same. On very steep slopes they put climbing irons on their feet and carried the children. Finally, after a long time, they heard a little bell which came up to them softly and delicately and was the first sign sent to them by the lower regions. They must really have come down very far, for they saw a snowy head towering very high and very blue above them. But the little bell they heard was that of the Sider meadow, which was being rung because they had agreed to meet there. When they came further still they faintly heard in the still air the reports of the small mortar; these were being fired because the flag had been hoisted, and then they saw thin columns of smoke rising into the air.

When after a while they descended a gentle, slanting slope, they caught sight of the Sider meadow hut. They went towards it. In the hut a fire was burning, the mother of the children was there, and when she saw the children coming with Eschenjäger, she sank back into the snow with a tearful cry.

Then she ran up to them, examined them from every side, wanted to give them food, wanted to warm them, wanted to bed them in the hay that was there. But she soon convinced herself that joy had kept the children stronger than she imagined, that they only needed some warm food, which they got, and that they only needed a little rest, which they would likewise get.

After a period of quiet another group of men came down over the snowy slope, while the little bell of the hut kept ringing. The children ran out with the others to see who it was. It was the shoemaker, the one-time Alpine climber, with his alpenstock and climbing irons, accompanied by his friends

gleitet von seinen Freunden und Kameraden.

„Sebastian, da sind sie", schrie das Weib.

Er aber war stumm, zitterte und lief auf sie zu. Dann rührte er die Lippen, als wollte er etwas sagen, sagte aber nichts, riß die Kinder an sich und hielt sie lange. Dann wandte er sich gegen sein Weib, schloß es an sich und rief: „Sanna, Sanna!"

Nach einer Weile nahm er den Hut, der ihm in den Schnee gefallen war, auf, trat unter die Männer und wollte reden. Er sagte aber nur: „Nachbarn, Freunde, ich danke euch."

Da man noch gewartet hatte, bis die Kinder sich zur Beruhigung erholt hatten, sagte er: „Wenn wir alle beisammen sind, so können wir in Gottes Namen aufbrechen."

„Es sind wohl noch nicht alle", sagte der Hirt Philipp, „aber die noch abgehen, wissen aus dem Rauche, daß wir die Kinder haben, und sie werden schon nach Hause gehen, wenn sie die Alphütte leer finden."

Man machte sich zum Aufbruche bereit.

Man war auf der Siederalphütte nicht gar weit von Gschaid entfernt, aus dessen Fenstern man im Sommer recht gut die grüne Matte sehen konnte, auf der die graue Hütte mit dem kleinen Glockentürmlein stand; aber es war unterhalb eine fallrechte Wand, die viele Klafter hoch hinabging und auf der man im Sommer nur mit Steigeisen, im Winter gar nicht hinabkommen konnte. Man mußte daher den Umweg zum Halse machen, um von der Unglückssäule aus nach Gschaid hinabzukommen. Auf dem Wege gelangte man über die Siderwiese, die noch näher an Gschaid ist, so daß man die Fenster des Dörfleins zu erblicken meinte.

Als man über die Wiese ging, tönte hell und deutlich das Glöcklein der Gschaider Kirche herauf, die Wandlung [60] des heiligen Hochamtes verkündend.

Der Pfarrer hatte wegen der allgemeinen Bewegung, die am Morgen in Gschaid war, die Abhaltung des Hochamtes verschoben, da er dachte, daß die Kinder zum Vorscheine kommen würden. Allein endlich, da noch immer keine Nachricht eintraf, mußte die heilige Handlung doch vollzogen werden.

Als das Wandlungsglöcklein [61] tönte, sanken alle, die über die Siderwiese gingen, auf die Kniee in den Schnee und beteten.

and comrades.

"Sebastian, they're here," his wife cried.

But he was silent, he trembled and ran up to them. Then he moved his lips as if he wanted to say something, but said nothing, drew the children to him and held them a long time. Then he turned to his wife, locked her in his arms and cried: "Sanna, Sanna!"

After a while he picked up his hat which had fallen into the snow, stepped among the men and wanted to speak. But all he said was: "Neighbors, friends, I thank you."

They waited until the children had recovered their complete calm, then he said: "If we are all here, we may start out in God's name."

"I don't think they're all here," said the shepherd Philip, "but those that are missing know from the smoke that we have found the children and they'll go home when they find the meadow hut empty."

They got ready to depart.

The Sider meadow hut was not very far from Gschaid, from whose windows the green meadow could be seen quite well in summer, with its gray hut and the little bell tower. But below it was a perpendicular wall, which went down many fathoms deep, and which could be descended in summer only with climbing irons and in winter not at all. They therefore had to make the detour to the neck to get down to Gschaid from the accident pillar. On the way they passed the Sider meadow, which is still closer to Gschaid, so that they thought they could see the windows of the little village.

As they were going over this meadow the little bell of the Gschaid church rang up to them bright and clear, announcing the transubstantiation at Holy Mass.

Because of the general commotion prevailing in Gschaid that morning, the pastor had postponed the celebration of High Mass, assuming that the children would be found. But finally, since there was still no news, High Mass had to be celebrated anyway.

When the little bell announcing transubstantiation rang, all those who were walking over the Sider meadow sank to

Als der Klang des Glöckleins aus war, standen sie auf und
gingen weiter.

Der Schuster trug meistens das Mädchen und ließ sich von
ihm alles erzählen.

Als sie schon gegen den Wald des Halses kamen, trafen sie
Spuren, von denen der Schuster sagte: „Das sind keine
Fußstapfen von Schuhen meiner Arbeit."

Die Sache klärte sich bald auf. Wahrscheinlich durch die
vielen Stimmen, die auf dem Platze tönten, angelockt, kam
wieder eine Abteilung Männer auf die Herabgehenden zu.
Es war der aus Angst aschenhaft entfärbte Färber, der an der
Spitze seiner Knechte, seiner Gesellen und mehrerer Millsdorfer bergab kam.

„Sie sind über das Gletschereis und über die Schründe
gegangen, ohne es zu wissen", rief der Schuster seinem
Schwiegervater zu.

„Da sind sie ja—da sind sie ja—Gott sei Dank", antwortete
der Färber, „ich weiß es schon, daß sie oben waren, als dein
Bote in der Nacht zu uns kam und wir mit Lichtern den
ganzen Wald durchsucht und nichts gefunden hatten—und
als dann das Morgengrau anbrach, bemerkte ich an dem
Wege, der von der roten Unglückssäule links gegen den
Schneeberg hinanführt, daß dort, wo man eben von der Säule
weggeht, hin und wieder mehrere Reiserchen und Rütchen
geknickt sind, wie Kinder gerne tun, wo sie eines Weges
gehen—da wußte ich es—die Richtung ließ sie nicht mehr
aus, weil sie in der Höhlung gingen, weil sie zwischen den
Felsen gingen und weil sie dann auf dem Grat gingen, der
rechts und links so steil ist, daß sie nicht hinabkommen
konnten. Sie mußten hinauf. Ich schickte nach dieser Beob-
achtung gleich nach Gschaid, aber der Holzknecht Michael,
der hinüberging, sagte bei der Rückkunft, da er uns fast am
Eise oben traf, daß ihr sie schon habet, weshalb wir wieder
heruntergingen."

„Ja", sagte Michael, „ich habe es gesagt, weil die rote
Fahne schon auf dem Krebssteine steckt und die Gschaider
dieses als Zeichen erkannten, das verabredet worden war. Ich
sagte euch, daß auf diesem Wege da alle herabkommen
müssen, weil man über die Wand nicht gehen kann."

„Und kniee nieder und danke Gott auf den Knieen, mein

their knees in the snow and prayed. When the bell stopped ringing, they stood up and went on.

The shoemaker carried the girl most of the way and had her tell him everything.

When they reached the forest of the neck, they met tracks of which the shoemaker remarked: "These footprints are not from shoes of my make."

The matter was soon cleared up. Probably attracted by the many voices that were heard on the square, another group of men came to meet those who were descending. It was the dyer, his face ashen white with anxiety, who was coming down the mountain at the head of his servants, his journeymen and several people from Millsdorf.

"They went over the ice of the glacier and across the crevasses, without knowing it," the shoemaker called to his father-in-law.

"Why, there they are, there they are, thank God," the dyer replied, "I know already that they were up there. When your messenger came to us during the night and we hunted with lights through the whole forest and found nothing, and when dawn came I noticed by the road that leads from the red accident pillar to the left toward the snow mountain, that at the spot where you leave the pillar several twigs and switches were broken here and there, as children are accustomed to do when they walk along a road. Then I knew that this direction left them no way out, because they were walking in the hollow between the rocks, and then on the ridge which is so steep both to the right and to the left that they could not get down. They had to go up. After noticing this I at once sent to Gschaid, but Michael the lumberman, who went across, told me on returning when he met us up there almost at the ice, that you already had them, so we went down again."

"Yes," said Michael, "I said so because the red flag was already planted on the Krebsstein and the people of Gschaid recognized this as the sign that had been agreed on. I told you that they all had to come down this way because you can't go over the wall."

"And kneel down and thank God on your knees, my son-

Schwiegersohn", fuhr der Färber fort, „daß kein Wind gegangen ist. Hundert Jahre werden wieder vergehen, daß ein so wunderbarer Schneefall niederfällt und daß er gerade niederfällt, wie nasse Schnüre von einer Stange hängen. Wäre ein Wind gegangen, so wären die Kinder verloren gewesen."

„Ja, danken wir Gott, danken wir Gott", sagte der Schuster.

Der Färber, der seit der Ehe seiner Tochter nie in Gschaid gewesen war, beschloß, die Leute nach Gschaid zu begleiten.

Da man schon gegen die rote Unglücksäule zu kam, wo der Holzweg begann, wartete ein Schlitten, den der Schuster auf alle Fälle [62] dahin bestellt hatte. Man tat [63] die Mutter und die Kinder hinein, versah sie hinreichend mit Decken und Pelzen, die im Schlitten waren, und ließ sie nach Gschaid vorausfahren.

Die andern folgten und kamen am Nachmittag in Gschaid an.

Die, welche noch auf dem Berge gewesen waren und erst durch den Rauch das Rückzugszeichen erfahren hatten, fanden sich auch nach und nach ein. Der letzte, welcher erst am Abend kam, war der Sohn des Hirten Philipp, der die rote Fahne auf den Krebsstein getragen und sie dort aufgepflanzt hatte.

In Gschaid wartete die Großmutter, welche herübergefahren war.

„Nie, nie", rief sie aus, „dürfen die Kinder in ihrem ganzen Leben mehr im Winter über den Hals gehen."

Die Kinder waren von dem Getriebe betäubt. Sie hatten noch etwas zu essen bekommen, und man hatte sie in das Bett gebracht. Spät gegen Abend, da sie sich ein wenig erholt hatten, da einige Nachbarn und Freunde sich in der Stube eingefunden hatten und dort von dem Ereignisse redeten, die Mutter aber in der Kammer an dem Bettchen Sannas saß und sie streichelte, sagte das Mädchen: „Mutter, ich habe heute nachts, als wir auf dem Berge saßen, den Heiligen Christ gesehen."

„O du mein geduldiges, du mein liebes, du mein herziges Kind", antwortete die Mutter, „er hat dir auch Gaben gesendet, die du bald bekommen wirst."

Die Schachteln waren ausgepackt worden, die Lichter

in-law," the dyer continued, "that there was no wind stirring. It will be a hundred years before another such strange snowfall will come down, straight down as wet ropes hang down from a pole. If there had been a wind the children would have been lost."

"Yes, let us thank God, let us thank God," said the shoemaker.

The dyer, who had never been in Gschaid since his daughter's marriage, decided to accompany the people to Gschaid.

When they were already approaching the red accident pillar where the lumber road began, a sleigh was waiting which the shoemaker had ordered to be sent there in case of emergency. The mother and children were put into it, they were provided with sufficient blankets and furs, which were in the sleigh, and were sent ahead to Gschaid.

The others followed and arrived in Gschaid in the afternoon.

Those who had been on the mountain and had learned the signal for retreat from the smoke, turned up gradually, too. The last man, who came only in the evening, was the son of Shepherd Philip, who had carried the red flag to the Krebsstein and planted it there.

In Gschaid the grandmother, who had driven over, was waiting.

"Never, never in their whole lives," she exclaimed, "may the children again go over the neck in winter."

The children were bewildered by all the bustle. They had gotten something to eat and had been put to bed. Late towards evening, when they had somewhat recovered, a few neighbors and friends came into the living room and talked there about the event. The mother, however, was sitting in the bedroom beside Sanna's little bed, fondling her, and the girl said: "Mother, last night when we sat on the mountain, I saw the Holy Christ."

"Oh you patient, dear, beloved child," the mother replied, "He has also sent you gifts, which you will soon get."

The boxes had been unpacked, the lights were lit, the door

waren angezündet, die Tür in die Stube wurde geöffnet, und die Kinder sahen von dem Bette auf den verspäteten, hell leuchtenden freundlichen Christbaum hinaus. Trotz der Erschöpfung mußte man sie noch ein wenig ankleiden, daß sie hinausgingen, die Gaben empfingen, bewunderten und endlich mit ihnen entschliefen.

In dem Wirtshause in Gschaid war es an diesem Abende lebhafter als je. Alle, die nicht in der Kirche gewesen waren, waren jetzt dort, und die andern auch. Jeder erzählte, was er gesehen und gehört, was er getan, was er geraten und was für Begegnisse und Gefahren er erlebt hatte. Besonders aber wurde hervorgehoben, wie man alles hätte anders und besser machen können.

Das Ereignis hat einen Abschnitt in die Geschichte von Gschaid gebracht, es hat auf lange den Stoff zu Gesprächen gegeben, und man wird noch nach Jahren davon reden, wenn man den Berg an heitern Tagen besonders deutlich sieht oder wenn man den Fremden von seinen Merkwürdigkeiten erzählt.

Die Kinder waren von dem Tage an erst recht das Eigentum des Dorfes geworden, sie wurden von nun an nicht mehr als Auswärtige, sondern als Eingeborne betrachtet, die man sich von dem Berge herabgeholt hatte.

Auch ihre Mutter Sanna war nun eine Eingeborne von Gschaid.

Die Kinder aber werden den Berg nicht vergessen und werden ihn jetzt noch ernster betrachten, wenn sie in dem Garten sind, wenn wie in der Vergangenheit die Sonne sehr schön scheint, der Lindenbaum duftet, die Bienen summen und er so schön und so blau wie das sanfte Firmament auf sie herniederschaut.

to the living room was opened and the children looked from their beds on the belated, brightly-lit, friendly Christmas tree. In spite of their exhaustion they had to be partially dressed, so that they might go out, receive their gifts, admire them and finally fall asleep with them.

In the inn at Gschaid it was livelier than ever this evening. All those who had not been in church were there now, and the others too. Everyone told what he had seen and heard, what he had done, what he had advised and what events and dangers he had experienced. But it was especially emphasized how everything could have been done differently and better.

The event created a chapter in Gschaid's history, it provided the material for conversation for a long time, and they will be talking about it for years to come, when the mountain is seen especially clearly on bright days, or when strangers are told about its peculiarities.

The children had only from that day on really become the property of the village, from now on they were no longer regarded as outsiders but as natives who had been fetched down from the mountain.

Their mother Sanna too was now a native of Gschaid.

But the children will not forget the mountain and will now study it still more seriously when they are in the garden, when, as in the past, the sun shines very beautifully, the linden tree gives off its fragrance, the bees hum, and it looks down upon them, as beautiful and as blue as the gentle firmament.

# Gottfried Keller

(1819–1890)

KELLER WAS born in Zurich, Switzerland, the son of an artisan. He was brought up by his widowed mother. Unjustly
expelled from high school for an offense he did not commit, he
gave up his formal education and embarked on the career of a
painter. At twenty-one he went to Munich to paint, supported
by a meager allowance from his poor mother, but gave up after
two unsuccessful years of study. The political events of the
forties stirred the poet in him. The publication of a volume of
verse earned him a Government scholarship which permitted
him further study in Germany. At this time he began work on
his great autobiographical novel *Der grüne Heinrich*, wrote
more verse and began his novellas.

On his return to Zurich, he lived with his mother and sister,
met literary men and artists, and wrote steadily. For fifteen
years he held the post of secretary for the canton, proving
himself an exemplary civil servant. But his literary work suffered during these years; only shortly before his retirement
did he resume publication of his stories and novels. He died a
bachelor.

Keller's principal writings include, besides several volumes
of verse, two substantial novels and four collections of stories:
*Die Leute von Seldwyla* (two cycles), *Sieben Legenden,
Züricher Novellen* and *Das Sinngedicht*.

The spirit of his life work is that of a critical but joyous
optimism, which recognizes the potentiality for evil that lies
within us all, but which refuses to draw pessimistic conclu-

sions from it. Keller is the finest exemplar of that *Bürgertum* which Thomas Mann finds to be the spirit of the nineteenth century: a belief in the solid goods of this earth, checked by a strong ethical and social sense, which forestalls the danger of crass materialism.

This is one of seven legends (*Sieben Legenden*, published in 1872, although begun nearly twenty years earlier), which Keller recreated from Kosegarten's *Legenden* (1804), a rather naïve collection of saints' tales designed to glorify the ideal of medieval asceticism. By making slight changes in detail and shifts in motivation, Keller transformed these legends into a panegyric in homage to earthly life and love. In Keller's tale the Virgin Mary Herself appears as the protectress of love and marriage and the enjoyment of a natural existence. Keller, the disciple of Feuerbach, thus emerges as a member of that coterie of German thinkers and artists (including Winckelmann, Goethe, Schiller, Hölderlin, Heine, Nietzsche, Stefan George, Hauptmann) who have emphasized a pagan neo-Hellenism as a way of life. As Heine summed up this vast Christian-pagan conflict in his brief poem *Psyche*, so Keller has given his classic formulation of it in the *Tanzlegendchen*.

# DAS TANZLEGENDCHEN

## von Gottfried Keller

> „Du Jungfrau Israel, du sollst noch
> fröhlich pauken, und herausgehen an
> den Tanz.—Alsdann werden die Jung-
> frauen fröhlich am Reigen sein, dazu
> die junge Mannschaft, und die Alten
> miteinander."
>
> —Jeremia 31, 4, 13

NACH DER Aufzeichnung des heiligen Gregorius [1] war Musa
die Tänzerin unter den Heiligen. Guter Leute Kind, war sie
ein anmutvolles Jungfräulein, welches der Mutter Gottes fleißig
diente, nur von *einer* Leidenschaft bewegt, nämlich von einer
unbezwinglichen Tanzlust, dermaßen, daß, wenn das Kind
nicht betete, es unfehlbar tanzte. Und zwar auf jegliche [2]
Weise. Musa tanzte mit ihren Gespielinnen, mit Kindern,
mit den Jünglingen und auch allein; sie tanzte in ihrem
Kämmerchen, im Saale, in den Gärten und auf den Wiesen,
und selbst wenn sie zum Altare ging, so war es mehr ein
liebliches Tanzen als ein Gehen, und auf den glatten Marmor-
platten vor der Kirchentüre versäumte sie nie, schnell ein
Tänzchen zu probieren.

Ja, eines Tages, als sie sich allein in der Kirche befand,
konnte sie sich nicht enthalten, vor dem Altar einige Figuren
auszuführen und gewissermaßen der Jungfrau Maria ein
niedliches Gebet vorzutanzen. Sie vergaß sich dabei so sehr,
daß sie bloß zu träumen wähnte, als sie sah, wie ein ältlicher,
aber schöner Herr ihr entgegentanzte und ihre Figuren so
gewandt ergänzte, daß beide zusammen den kunstgerechtesten
Tanz begingen. Der Herr trug ein purpurnes Königskleid, eine
goldene Krone auf dem Kopf und einen glänzend schwarzen,
gelockten Bart, welcher vom Silberreif der Jahre wie von
einem fernen Sternenschein überhaucht war. Dazu ertönte
eine Musik vom Chore her, weil ein halbes Dutzend kleiner

# THE LITTLE DANCE LEGEND
## by Gottfried Keller

> "O virgin of Israel, thou shalt again be
> adorned with thy tabrets, and shalt go
> forth in the dances of them that make
> merry.—Then shall the virgin rejoice in
> the dance, both young men and old to-
> gether."—Jeremiah 31:4, 13

ACCORDING TO a notation made by Saint Gregory, Musa was
the dancer among the saints. The child of good people, she
was a virgin full of grace, serving the Mother of God dili-
gently, swayed by one sole passion, namely by an irresistible
desire to dance; so much so that when the child was not praying she unfailingly danced. And indeed in every possible
manner. Musa danced with her playmates, with children, with
youths and even by herself; she danced in her little room, in
the large parlor, in gardens and on meadows; and even when
she went to the altar, it was more of a graceful dancing than
a walk, and on the smooth marble blocks in front of the
church door she never failed to try a swift little dance.

Yes, one day, when she found herself alone in the church,
she could not restrain herself from executing several figures
in front of the altar, and, so to speak, dancing a pretty
prayer to the Virgin Mary. In doing this she forgot herself
so completely that she thought she was dreaming when she
saw an elderly but handsome gentleman dancing toward her
and complementing her figures so dexterously that the two
of them carried through the most artistic dance. The gentleman wore a royal cloak of purple, a golden crown on his head
and a shining black curly beard, touched by the silver rime of
the years as by the light of a distant star. They were accompanied by music from the choir, because half a dozen little

Engel auf der Brüstung desselben stand oder saß, die dicken
runden Beinchen darüber hinunterhängen ließ und die verschiedenen Instrumente handhabe oder blies. Dabei waren
die Knirpse ganz gemütlich und praktisch und ließen sich die
Notenhefte von ebensoviel steinernen Engelsbildern halten,
welche sich als Zierat auf dem Chorgeländer fanden; nur der
Kleinste, ein pausbäckiger Pfeifenbläser, machte eine Ausnahme, indem er die Beine übereinanderschlug[3] und das
Notenblatt mit den rosigen Zehen zu halten wußte. Auch war
der am eifrigsten: die übrigen baumelten mit den Füßen,
dehnten, bald dieser, bald jener, knisternd die Schwungfedern
aus, daß die Farben derselben schimmerten wie Taubenhälse,
und neckten einander während des Spieles.

Über alles dies sich zu wundern, fand Musa nicht Zeit, bis
der Tanz beendigt war, der ziemlich lang dauerte; denn der
lustige Herr schien sich dabei so wohl zu gefallen als die
Jungfrau, welche im Himmel herumzuspringen meinte. Allein
als die Musik aufhörte und Musa hochaufatmend dastand,
fing sie erst an, sich ordentlich zu fürchten, und sah erstaunt
auf den Alten, der weder keuchte noch warm hatte[4] und nun
zu reden begann. Er gab sich als David, den königlichen
Ahnherrn der Jungfrau Maria, zu erkennen[5] und als deren
Abgesandten. Und er fragte sie, ob sie wohl Lust hätte, die
ewige Seligkeit in einem unaufhörlichen Freudentanze zu
verbringen, einem Tanze, gegen welchen der soeben beendigte
ein trübseliges Schleichen zu nennen sei?

Worauf sie sogleich erwiderte, sie wüßte sich nichts Besseres
zu wünschen! Worauf der selige König David wiederum sagte:
So habe sie nichts anderes zu tun, als während ihrer irdischen
Lebenstage aller Lust und allem Tanze zu entsagen und sich
lediglich der Buße und den geistlichen[6] Übungen zu weihen,
und zwar ohne Wanken und ohne allen Rückfall.

Diese Bedingung machte das Jungfräulein stutzig,[7] und sie
sagte: Also gänzlich müßte sie auf das Tanzen verzichten?
Und sie zweifelte, ob denn auch im Himmel wirklich getanzt
würde? Denn alles habe seine Zeit; dieser Erdboden schiene
ihr gut und zweckdienlich, um darauf zu tanzen, folglich
würde der Himmel wohl andere Eigenschaften haben, ansonst[8] ja der Tod ein überflüssiges Ding wäre.

Allein David setzte ihr auseinander, wie sehr sie in dieser

angels were standing or sitting on the railing, letting their chubby round little legs dangle down, and fingering or blowing on the various instruments. And the little urchins were quite nonchalant and practical about it all, using the stone angel figures that decorated the railing of the choirloft as supports for their sheet music. Only the smallest of them, a chubby-cheeked flutist, made an exception, crossing his legs and holding the sheet of music between his pink toes. He was, moreover, the most zealous one among them; the rest let their feet dangle, and with a crackling sound, now one, now another stretched his wings so that their colors gleamed like the necks of doves, and they teased each other as they played.

Musa did not find time to wonder at all this until the dance was finished, and it lasted a fairly long time; for the merry gentleman seemed to be as pleased with it as the maiden, who thought she was hopping about in Heaven. But when the music stopped and Musa stood there breathing heavily, she really began to be afraid, and looked in astonishment at the old gentleman, who was neither panting nor feeling warm and now began to talk. He identified himself as David, the royal ancestor of the Virgin Mary, and as her ambassador. And he asked her whether she wished to spend eternal bliss in an unceasing dance of joy, a dance compared with which the one they had just finished could only be called a sad crawl.

To which she replied promptly that she could wish nothing better. Whereupon the blessed King David said: then she need do nothing but renounce all pleasures and all dancing during her life on earth and consecrate herself solely to atonement and to spiritual exercises, and indeed without hesitation or backsliding.

This condition disconcerted the maiden and she said: so she must give up dancing wholly? And she expressed doubt whether there really was dancing in Heaven. For there was a time for everything; this earth seemed to her good and purposeful to dance on, so Heaven would probably have other properties, otherwise death would be a superfluous thing.

But David explained to her, how very wrong she was in this

Beziehung im Irrtum sei, und bewies ihr durch viele Bibel-
stellen sowie durch sein eigenes Beispiel, daß das Tanzen
allerdings eine geheiligte Beschäftigung für Selige sei. Jetzt
aber erfordere es einen raschen Entschluß, ja oder nein, ob sie
durch zeitliche Entsagung zur ewigen Freude eingehen wolle
oder nicht; wolle sie nicht, so gehe er weiter; denn man habe
im Himmel noch einige Tänzerinnen vonnöten.

Musa stand noch immer zweifelhaft und unschlüssig und
spielte ängstlich mit den Fingerspitzen am Munde; es schien
ihr zu hart, von Stund, an nicht mehr zu tanzen um eines
unbekannten Lohnes willen.

Da winkte David, und plötzlich spielte die Musik einige
Takte einer so unerhört glückseligen, überirdischen Tanzweise,
daß dem Mädchen die Seele im Leibe hüpfte und alle Glieder
zuckten; aber sie vermochte nicht eines zum Tanze zu regen,
und sie merkte, daß ihr Leib viel zu schwer und starr sei für
diese Weise. Voll Sehnsucht schlug sie ihre Hand in diejenige
des Königs und gelobte das, was er begehrte.

Auf einmal war er nicht mehr zu sehen, und die musizieren-
den Engel rauschten, flatterten und drängten sich durch ein
offenes Kirchenfenster davon, nachdem sie in mutwilliger
Kinderweise ihre zusammengerollten Notenblätter den ge-
duldigen Steinengeln um die Backen geschlagen hatten, daß
es klatschte.

Aber Musa ging andächtigen Schrittes nach Hause, jene
himmlische Melodie im Ohr tragend, und ließ sich ein grobes
Gewand anfertigen, legte alle Zierkleidung ab und zog jenes
an. Zugleich baute sie sich im Hintergrunde des Gartens
ihrer Eltern, wo ein dichter Schatten von Bäumen lagerte,
eine Zelle, machte ein Bettchen von Moos darin und lebte
dort von nun an abgeschieden von ihren Hausgenossen als
eine Büßerin und Heilige. Alle Zeit brachte sie im Gebete zu,
und öfter schlug sie sich mit einer Geißel; aber ihre härteste
Bußübung bestand darin, die Glieder still und steif zu halten;
sobald nur ein Ton erklang, das Zwitschern eines Vogels oder
das Rauschen der Blätter in der Luft, so zuckten ihre Füße
und meinten, sie müßten tanzen.

Als dies unwillkürliche Zucken sich nicht verlieren wollte,
welches sie zuweilen, ehe sie sich dessen versah,[9] zu einem
kleinen Sprung verleitete, ließ sie sich die feinen Füßchen mit

regard, and proved to her by quoting many Bible passages as well as through his own example that dancing was indeed a consecrated occupation for the blessed. But now a swift decision must be made: yes or no, whether she was willing to enter eternal joy through temporal renunciation or not; if she didn't, he would go on; for several girl dancers were still needed in Heaven.

Musa was still standing in doubt and indecision, with the tips of her fingers playing nervously about her mouth; it seemed too hard to her to stop dancing henceforth for the sake of an unknown reward.

Then David made a sign and suddenly the music played a few bars of a dance tune, so ineffably blissful and ethereal that the girl's soul leaped in her body and all her limbs twitched; but she was unable to move any of them to dance, and she noted that her body was far too heavy and rigid for this tune. Filled with longing she put her hand into that of King David and vowed what he desired of her.

Suddenly he was no more to be seen and the music-making angels rustled, fluttered and thronged out of sight through an open church window—after wrapping their rolled-up sheet music, like the mischievous children they were, about the cheeks of the patient stone angels—making a resounding noise.

But Musa went home with reverent step, hearing that heavenly melody in her ear, and had a coarse gown made for herself, laid aside all her pretty clothing and put on that gown. At the same time she built herself a cell at the back of her parents' garden where a dense shadow was made by the trees; she made a little bed of moss in it and from now on she lived there as a penitent and saint, separated from her housemates. She spent all her time in prayer, and often she scourged herself with a whip; but her hardest act of penitence consisted in holding her limbs still and stiff; as soon as ever a note sounded, the twittering of a bird or the rustling of the leaves in the air, her feet twitched and felt they must dance.

When this involuntary twitching refused to disappear, seducing her at times, before she realized it, into a slight leap, she had her delicate little feet tied together with a light chain.

einer leichten Kette zusammenschmieden. Ihre Verwandten
und Freunde wunderten sich über die Umwandlung Tag und
Nacht, freuten sich über den Besitz einer solchen Heiligen
und hüteten die Einsiedelei unter den Bäumen wie einen
Augapfel. Viele kamen, Rat und Fürbitte zu holen. Vorzüglich brachte man junge Mädchen zu ihr, welche etwas
unbeholfen auf den Füßen waren, da man bemerkt hatte,
daß alle, welche sie berührt, alsobald leichten und anmutvollen
Ganges wurden.

So brachte sie drei Jahre in ihrer Klause zu; aber gegen das
Ende des dritten Jahres war Musa fast so dünn und durchsichtig wie ein Sommerwölklein geworden. Sie lag beständig auf
ihrem Bettchen von Moos und schaute voll Sehnsucht in den
Himmel, und sie glaubte schon die goldenen Sohlen der
Seligen durch das Blau hindurch tanzen und schleifen zu
sehen.

An einem rauhen Herbsttage endlich hieß es,[10] die Heilige
liege im Sterben. Sie hatte sich das dunkle Bußkleid aus-
ziehen und mit blendend weißen Hochzeitsgewändern be-
kleiden lassen. So lag sie mit gefalteten Händen und erwartete
lächelnd die Todesstunde. Der ganze Garten war mit andächtigen Menschen angefüllt, die Lüfte rauschten, und die Blätter
der Bäume sanken von allen Seiten hernieder. Aber unversehens
wandelte sich das Wehen des Windes in Musik, in allen
Baumkronen schien dieselbe zu spielen, und als die Leute em-
porsahen, siehe, da waren alle Zweige mit jungem Grün be-
kleidet, die Myrten und Granaten blühten und dufteten, der
Boden bedeckte sich mit Blumen, und ein rosenfarbiger
Schein lagerte sich auf die weiße zarte Gestalt der Sterbenden.

In diesem Augenblicke gab sie ihren Geist auf, die Kette an
ihren Füßen sprang mit einem hellen Klange entzwei, der
Himmel tat sich auf weit in der Runde, voll unendlichen
Glanzes, und jedermann konnte hineinsehen. Da sah man viel
tausend schöne Jungfern und junge Herren im höchsten
Schein, tanzend im unabsehbaren Reigen. Ein herrlicher
König fuhr auf einer Wolke, auf deren Rand eine kleine
Extramusik von sechs Engelchen stand, ein wenig gegen die
Erde und empfing die Gestalt der seligen Musa vor den Augen
aller Anwesenden, die den Garten füllten. Man sah noch, wie
sie in den offenen Himmel sprang und augenblicklich tanzend

Her relatives and friends were astonished day and night at this transformation, rejoiced in the possession of such a saint, and kept guard over the hermitage under the trees as over the apple of their eye. Many came to obtain counsel and intercession. Young girls especially were brought to her, girls who were somewhat clumsy on their feet, since it had been noticed that all whom she touched at once became light and graceful in their walk.

In this way she spent three years in her cell; but towards the end of the third year Musa had become almost as thin and transparent as a little summer cloud. She lay constantly on her little bed of moss and, full of longing, looked into the sky; and she already thought she saw the golden soles of the blessed spirits dance and glide through the blue.

On a raw autumn day the news finally came that the saint lay dying. She had had her dark penitential gown taken off and dazzling white wedding clothes put on her. Thus she lay with folded hands awaiting the hour of her death with a smile. The whole garden was filled with devout people, there was a rustle in the air, and the leaves fell from the trees in all directions. But suddenly the blowing of the wind turned into music, which seemed to be playing in all the treetops; and when the people looked up, behold—all the branches were clothed in young green, the myrtle and the pomegranates bloomed and gave off a fragrance, the ground was covered with flowers, and a pink halo settled on the white, delicate form of the dying woman.

At this moment she gave up the ghost, the chain at her feet burst in two with a shrill sound, the sky opened for a wide area, full of infinite radiance and everyone was able to look into it. There one saw many thousands of beautiful virgins and young gentlemen in the brightest splendor, dancing a round-dance as far as eye could reach. On a cloud, at the rim of which a special orchestra of six little angels stood, a glorious king rode a short distance towards earth and received the form of the blessed Musa before the eyes of all who filled the garden. She was even seen leaping into the open sky and was lost as she danced in the singing and resplendent

sich in den tönenden und leuchtenden Reihen verlor.

Im Himmel war eben hoher Festtag; an Festtagen aber war es, was zwar vom heiligen Gregor von Nyssa bestritten, von demjenigen von Nazianz aber aufrechtgehalten wird, Sitte, die neun Musen, die sonst in der Hölle saßen, einzuladen und in den Himmel zu laden, daß sie da Aushilfe leisteten.[11] Sie bekamen gute Zehrung, mußten aber nach verrichteter Sache [12] wieder an den andern Ort gehen.

Als nun die Tänze und Gesänge und alle Zeremonien zu Ende und die himmlischen Heerscharen sich zu Tische setzten, da wurde Musa an den Tisch gebracht, an welchem die neun Musen bedient wurden. Sie saßen fast verschüchtert zusammengedrängt und blickten mit den feurigen schwarzen oder tiefblauen Augen um sich. Die emsige Martha [13] aus dem Evangelium sorgte in eigener Person für sie, hatte ihre schönste Küchenschürze umgebunden und einen zierlichen kleinen Rußfleck an dem weißen Kinn und nötigte den Musen alles Gute freundlich auf. Aber erst als Musa und auch die heilige Cäcilia [14] und noch andere kunsterfahrene Frauen herbeikamen und die scheuen Pierinnen [15] heiter begrüßten und sich zu ihnen gesellten, da tauten sie auf, wurden zutraulich, und es entfaltete sich ein anmutig fröhliches Dasein in dem Frauenkreise. Musa saß neben Terpsichore,[16] und Cäcilia zwischen Polyhymnien und Euterpen, und alle hielten sich bei den Händen. Nun kamen auch die kleinen Musikbübchen und schmeichelten den schönen Frauen, um von den glänzenden Früchten zu bekommen, die auf dem ambrosischen Tische strahlten. König David selbst kam und brachte einen goldenen Becher, aus dem alle tranken, daß holde Freude sie erwärmte; er ging wohlgefällig um den Tisch herum, nicht ohne der lieblichen Erato [17] einen Augenblick das Kinn zu streicheln im Vorbeigehen. Als es dergestalt hoch herging [18] an dem Musentisch, erschien sogar Unsere liebe Frau in all ihrer Schönheit und Güte, setzte sich auf ein Stündchen [19] zu den Musen und küßte die hehre Urania [20] unter ihrem Sternenkranze zärtlich auf den Mund, als sie ihr beim Abschiede zuflüsterte, sie werde nicht ruhen, bis die Musen für immer im Paradiese bleiben könnten.

Es ist freilich nicht so gekommen. Um sich für die erwiesene Güte und Freundlichkeit dankbar zu erweisen und ihren guten

ranks.

It happened to be a high holiday in Heaven; and on holi-days it was the custom—this is disputed by Saint Gregory of Nyssa but maintained by Saint Gregory of Nazianzus—to invite the nine Muses, who ordinarily lived in Hell, and admit them to Heaven to give assistance. They got good food to eat, but after they had done their stint had to go back to the other place.

Now when the dances and songs and all the ceremonies were over and the Heavenly Host sat down to dinner, Musa was brought to the table at which the nine Muses were being served. They sat squeezed together almost timidly, looking about with their fiery black or deep blue eyes. The eager Martha from the Gospel cared for them personally; she had put on her finest kitchen apron and showed a cute little soot spot on her white chin, and she amiably pressed all the deli-cacies on the Muses. But it was only when Musa and Saint Cecilia and other aesthetically experienced women came over and gaily greeted the shy Pierians and joined their company that they thawed out, became confidential, and a charming, cheerful social life developed among the ladies. Musa sat beside Terpsichore, Cecilia between Polyhymnia and Euterpe, and they all held hands. And now the little music boys came too and flattered the beautiful ladies in order to get some of the shining fruit which lay in radiance on the ambrosial tables. King David himself came and brought a golden cup out of which they all drank, so that they were warmed with lovely joy. He walked around the table with satisfaction, and did not fail to stroke the lovely Erato's chin for a moment as he passed. When things were at their height at the Muses' table even Our Dear Lady, in all Her Beauty and Goodness ap-peared and sat down beside the Muses for a short while and tenderly kissed the sublime Urania on the lips beneath her crown of stars, whispering to her as She went, that She would not rest until the Muses could remain in Paradise for ever.

To be sure it did not turn out so. In order to show their gratitude for the kindness and friendliness which had been

Willen zu zeigen, ratschlagten die Musen untereinander und übten in einem abgelegenen Winkel der Unterwelt einen Lobgesang ein, dem sie die Form der im Himmel üblichen feierlichen Choräle zu geben suchten. Sie teilten sich in zwei Hälften von je vier Stimmen, über welche Urania eine Art Oberstimme führte, und brachten so eine merkwürdige Vokalmusik zuwege.

Als nun der nächste Festtag im Himmel gefeiert wurde und die Musen wieder ihren Dienst taten, nahmen sie einen für ihr Vorhaben günstig scheinenden Augenblick wahr, stellten sich zusammen auf und begannen sänftlich ihren Gesang, der bald gar mächtig anschwellte. Aber in diesen Räumen klang er so düster, ja fast trotzig und rauh, und dabei so sehnsuchtsschwer und klagend, daß erst eine erschrockene Stille waltete, dann aber alles Volk von Erdenleid und Heimweh ergriffen wurde und in ein allgemeines Weinen ausbrach.

Ein unendliches Seufzen rauschte durch die Himmel, bestürzt eilten alle Ältesten und Propheten herbei, indessen die Musen in ihrer guten Meinung immer lauter und melancholischer sangen und das ganze Paradies mit allen Erzvätern, Ältesten und Propheten, alles, was je auf grüner Wiese gegangen oder gelegen, außer Fassung geriet.[21] Endlich aber kam die allhöchste Trinität selber heran, um zum Rechten zu sehen und die eifrigen Musen mit einem lang hinrollenden Donnerschlage zum Schweigen zu bringen.

Da kehrten Ruhe und Gleichmut in den Himmel zurück; aber die armen neun Schwestern mußten ihn verlassen und durften ihn seither nicht wieder betreten.

shown them and to demonstrate their good will the Muses held counsel among themselves and rehearsed, in a remote corner of the underworld, a hymn of praise to which they sought to give the form of those solemn chorales which were usual in Heaven. They divided into two groups of four voices each, with Urania acting as a kind of Overvoice, and thus produced a strange vocal music.

Now when the next holiday was celebrated in Heaven and the Muses once more performed their service, they seized a moment which seemed propitious for their plan, stood together and softly began their song, which soon swelled to mighty volume. But in these halls it sounded so gloomy, indeed almost defiant and coarse, and at the same time so plaintive and heavy with longing, that at first a frightened silence prevailed; but then all the people were seized by an earthly sorrow and nostalgia and broke into a general weeping.

An infinite sighing rustled through the Heavens; in dismay the elders and the prophets hurried over, while the Muses, with the best of intentions, sang louder and with more melancholy all the time; and the whole of Paradise, with all the patriarchs, elders and prophets, everyone who had ever walked or lain on a green meadow, lost control of themselves. But finally the All-highest Trinity Itself appeared, to set things right and bring the eager Muses to silence with a long rolling thunderclap.

Then peace and equanimity returned to Heaven; but the poor nine sisters had to leave it and were not permitted to enter it since.

# Arthur Schnitzler

(1862–1931)

ARTHUR SCHNITZLER was born in Vienna, the son of a prominent throat specialist. He studied medicine himself and for a while practiced in his father's clinic. But he became interested in psychiatry and psychic phenomena and resolved to cultivate the literary talent which nature had given him. He began to publish about 1890 and his literary success led him to devote all his time to writing. His life was uneventful; he lived in Vienna until his death, enjoying a fine reputation as one of the leading literary figures in the German-speaking world.

Schnitzler's work is equally divided between drama and fiction. In both genres he was most successful in the shorter forms: the one-act play and the novella. His playlets are exquisite in their charm and wit, while his novellas are remarkable for their atmosphere of urbanity or melancholy or irony or mystery, or just for their baffling play upon the reader's senses and sensibility.

Schnitzler's world is charming, gracious Vienna with its coffee houses, opera, Strauss waltzes, psychoanalysis and sex. But behind this façade of gaiety there lurks melancholy and the fear of nothingness. The terrifying loneliness which twentieth-century man has discovered as the signature of existence—the trauma of birth, anxiety and dread, care, absurdity, nothingness, nausea—all this atmosphere of disintegration is adumbrated in Schnitzler's work, not in a tragic vein, but hidden beneath an unmatched grace of style. Schnitzler, it might be said, leads us along the existentialist

abyss without letting us suspect it because he is artistically too well bred to make a fuss about it.

The story reprinted here was written in 1899 after a summer spent in the Tyrol and published in the following year. It is rightly famous for its classical simplicity of theme and treatment and its perfection of style. It deals with the central theme of twentieth-century literature: man's essential loneliness even from those who are closest to him and for whom he sacrifices himself to the utmost. But, surprisingly for Schnitzler, it ends on a positive, optimistic note: understanding and true love can exist, men can be brothers. There is an irony in the events described; the mischievous remark made by the tourist about the twenty-franc piece in the long run re-establishes true love between the two brothers, in fact creates that love for the first time in their lives. This is a most unorthodox use of irony; it proves that Schnitzler, like any other great artist, cannot be reduced to a formula.

# DER BLINDE GERONIMO
## UND SEIN BRUDER

von Arthur Schnitzler

DER BLINDE Geronimo stand von der Bank auf und nahm
die Gitarre zur Hand, die auf dem Tisch neben dem Wein-
glase bereit gelegen war.[1] Er hatte das ferne Rollen der ersten
Wagen vernommen. Nun tastete er sich den wohlbekannten
Weg bis zur offenen Türe hin, und dann ging er die schmalen
Holzstufen hinab, die frei in den gedeckten Hofraum hin-
unterliefen. Sein Bruder folgte ihm, und beide stellten sich
gleich neben der Treppe auf, den Rücken zur Wand gekehrt,
um gegen den naßkalten Wind geschützt zu sein, der über
den feuchtschmutzigen Boden durch die offenen Tore strich.

Unter dem düsteren Bogen des alten Wirtshauses mußten
alle Wagen passieren, die den Weg über das Stilfser Joch [2]
nahmen. Für die Reisenden, welche von Italien her nach
Tirol wollten, war es die letzte Rast vor der Höhe. Zu langem
Aufenthalte lud es nicht ein, denn gerade hier lief die Straße
ziemlich eben, ohne Ausblicke, zwischen kahlen Erhebungen
hin. Der blinde Italiener und sein Bruder Carlo waren in den
Sommermonaten hier so gut wie zu Hause.

Die Post fuhr ein, bald darauf kamen andere Wagen. Die
meisten Reisenden blieben sitzen, in Plaids und Mäntel wohl
eingehüllt, andere stiegen aus und spazierten zwischen den
Toren ungeduldig hin und her. Das Wetter wurde immer
schlechter, ein kalter Regen klatschte herab. Nach einer
Reihe schöner Tage schien der Herbst plötzlich und allzu
früh hereinzubrechen.

# THE BLIND GERONIMO
# AND HIS BROTHER

## by Arthur Schnitzler

THE BLIND Geronimo got up from the bench and took his guitar, which had been lying ready on the table near his wine glass, in his hand. He had heard the distant roll of the first carriages. Now he groped his way along the well-known path to the open door, and then he went down the narrow wooden steps which ran down in the open air to the covered courtyard. His brother followed him, and both at once took their position near the staircase, their backs turned to the wall, in order to be protected from the cold, wet wind which was blowing through the open gates over the moist, dirty ground.

All the carriages which took the road over the Stelvio Pass had to pass under the gloomy archway of the old inn. For the travelers who wanted to go from Italy to the Tirol, it was the last resting place before the heights. It did not invite one to stay long, for just at this spot the road was fairly level, without views, between bleak elevations. The blind Italian and his brother Carlo were practically at home here in the summer months.

The stagecoach drove in; soon after that other carriages came. Most of the travelers kept their seats, well wrapped in their plaids and coats; others got out and strolled impatiently back and forth between the gates. The weather became worse and worse; a cold rain splashed down. After a series of beaut' ful days autumn seemed to set in suddenly and all too early.

Der Blinde sang und begleitete sich dazu auf der Gitarre;
er sang mit einer ungleichmäßigen, manchmal plötzlich auf-
kreischenden Stimme, wie immer, wenn er getrunken hatte.
Zuweilen wandte er den Kopf wie mit einem Ausdruck vergeb-
lichen Flehens nach oben. Aber die Züge seines Gesichtes
mit den schwarzen Bartstoppeln und den bläulichen Lippen
blieben vollkommen unbeweglich. Der ältere Bruder stand
neben ihm, beinahe regungslos. Wenn ihm jemand eine
Münze in den Hut fallen ließ, nickte er Dank und sah dem
Spender mit einem raschen, wie irren Blick ins Gesicht. Aber
gleich, beinahe ängstlich, wandte er den Blick wieder fort und
starrte gleich dem Bruder ins Leere. Es war, als schämten
sich seine Augen des Lichts, das ihnen gewährt war, und von
dem sie dem blinden Bruder keinen Strahl schenken konnten.

„Bring mir Wein," sagte Geronimo, und Carlo ging, gehorsam wie immer. Während er die Stufen aufwärts schritt,
begann Geronimo wieder zu singen. Er hörte längst nicht
mehr auf seine eigene Stimme, und so konnte er auf das
merken, was in seiner Nähe vorging. Jetzt vernahm er ganz
nahe zwei flüsternde Stimmen, die eines jungen Mannes und
einer jungen Frau. Er dachte, wie oft diese beiden schon den
gleichen Weg hin und her gegangen sein mochten; denn in
seiner Blindheit und in seinem Rausch war ihm [3] manchmal,
als kämen Tag für Tag dieselben Menschen über das Joch
gewandert, bald von Norden gegen Süden, bald von Süden
gegen Norden. Und so kannte er auch dieses junge Paar seit
langer Zeit.

Carlo kam herab und reichte Geronimo ein Glas Wein.
Der Blinde schwenkte es dem jungen Paare zu und sagte:
„Ihr Wohl, meine Herrschaften!"

„Danke," sagte der junge Mann; aber die junge Frau zog
ihn fort, denn ihr war dieser Blinde unheimlich.

Jetzt fuhr ein Wagen mit einer ziemlich lärmenden Gesellschaft ein: Vater, Mutter, drei Kinder, eine Bonne.

„Deutsche Familie," sagte Geronimo leise zu Carlo.

Der Vater gab jedem der Kinder ein Geldstück, und jedes
durfte das seine in den Hut des Bettlers werfen. Geronimo
neigte jedesmal den Kopf zum Dank. Der älteste Knabe sah
dem Blinden mit ängstlicher Neugier ins Gesicht. Carlo
betrachtete den Knaben. Er mußte, wie immer beim Anblick

The blind man sang and accompanied himself on the guitar; he sang in an uneven voice, which sometimes suddenly turned into a shriek, as always when he had been drinking. At times he turned his head upward as though with an expression of futile pleading. But the features of his face, with its black beard-stubble and its bluish lips, remained completely immobile. His older brother stood beside him, almost motionless. When anyone dropped a coin into his hat he nodded thanks and looked into the face of the giver with a swift, almost wild look. But promptly, almost anxiously, he turned his eyes away again and, like his brother, stared into space. It was as if his eyes felt ashamed of the light that was granted them, and of which they could offer no ray to the blind brother.

"Bring me wine," said Geronimo, and Carlo went, obedient as always. While he went up the steps Geronimo began to sing again. He had long stopped listening to his own voice and so he was able to notice what was going on about him. Now he heard two whispering voices quite near him—those of a young man and a young woman. He thought how often these two might have walked back and forth the same way; for in his blindness and in his intoxication it sometimes seemed to him that the same people came over the pass day after day, now from north to south, again from south to north. And so he had known this young couple, too, for a long time.

Carlo came down and handed Geronimo a glass of wine. The blind man raised it to the young couple and said: "To your health, ladies and gentlemen!"

"Thanks," said the young man; but the young woman drew him away, for the blind man made her feel uncomfortable.

Now a carriage with a fairly noisy company drove in: a father, mother, three children, a maid.

"A German family," said Geronimo softly to Carlo.

The father gave each child a coin and each one was allowed to throw his coin into the beggar's hat. Each time Geronimo bowed his head in thanks. The oldest boy looked into the blind man's face with anxious curiosity. Carlo looked at the boy. As always when he saw such children, he had to think

solcher Kinder, daran denken, daß Geronimo gerade so alt
gewesen war, als das Unglück geschah, durch das er das Augen-
licht verloren hatte. Denn er erinnerte sich jenes Tages auch
heute noch, nach beinahe zwanzig Jahren, mit vollkommener
Deutlichkeit. Noch heute klang ihm der grelle Kinderschrei
ins Ohr, mit dem der kleine Geronimo auf den Rasen hinge-
sunken war, noch heute sah er die Sonne auf der weißen
Gartenmauer spielen und kringeln und hörte die Sonntags-
glocken wieder, die gerade in jenem Augenblick getönt hatten.
Er hatte wie oftmals mit dem Bolzen nach der Esche an der
Mauer geschossen, und als er den Schrei hörte, dachte er
gleich, daß er den kleinen Bruder verletzt haben mußte, der
eben vorbeigelaufen war. Er ließ das Blasrohr aus den Händen gleiten, sprang durchs Fenster in den Garten und
stürzte zu dem kleinen Bruder hin, der auf dem Grase lag,
die Hände vors Gesicht geschlagen, und jammerte. Über die
rechte Wange und den Hals floß ihm Blut herunter. In
derselben Minute kam der Vater vom Felde heim, durch die
kleine Gartentür, und nun knieten beide ratlos neben dem
jammernden Kinde. Nachbarn eilten herbei; die alte Vanetti
war die erste, der es gelang, dem Kleinen die Hände vom Gesicht zu entfernen. Dann kam auch der Schmied, bei dem
Carlo damals in der Lehre war und der sich ein bißchen aufs
Kurieren verstand; und der sah gleich, daß das rechte Auge
verloren war. Der Arzt, der abends aus Poschiavo kam, konnte
auch nicht mehr helfen. Ja, er deutete schon die Gefahr an,
in der das andere Auge schwebte. Und er behielt recht. Ein
Jahr später war die Welt für Geronimo in Nacht versunken.
Anfangs versuchte man, ihm einzureden, daß er später geheilt
werden könnte, und er schien es zu glauben. Carlo, der die
Wahrheit wußte, irrte damals tage- und nächtelang auf der
Landstraße, zwischen den Weinbergen und in den Wäldern
umher, und war nahe daran, sich umzubringen. Aber der
geistliche Herr, dem er sich anvertraute, klärte ihn auf, daß
es seine Pflicht war, zu leben und sein Leben dem Bruder zu
widmen. Carlo sah es ein. Ein ungeheures Mitleid ergriff ihn.
Nur wenn er bei dem blinden Jungen war, wenn er ihm die
Haare streicheln, seine Stirne küssen durfte, ihm Geschichten
erzählte, ihn auf den Feldern hinter dem Hause und zwischen
den Rebengeländen spazieren führte, milderte sich seine Pein.

that Geronimo had been the same age when the accident through which he had lost his eyesight had happened. For even today, after almost twenty years, he remembered that day with perfect clarity. To this day he could hear in his ear the child's shrill scream with which little Geronimo had sunk on the grass; to this day he saw the sun playing and flickering on the white garden wall and again heard the Sunday bells which had sounded at that very moment. As he had often done, he had been shooting at the ash tree by the wall with his dart; and when he heard the scream he thought at once that he must have hurt his little brother who had just run past. He let the blowpipe slip from his hands, jumped through the window into the garden and rushed over to his little brother, who was lying in the grass, his hands clapped to his face, wailing. The blood was flowing down his right cheek and neck. At the same moment their father came home from the field, through the little garden door, and now both of them kneeled helplessly beside the wailing child. Neighbors hurried over; old woman Vanetti was the first person who succeeded in removing the little boy's hands from his face. Then came the smith, to whom Carlo was apprenticed at that time; he was somewhat adept at medicine, and he saw at once that the right eye was lost. The doctor who came from Poschiavo in the evening couldn't help any more either. In fact he even pointed out the danger for the other eye. And he proved to be right. A year later the world had sunk into night for Geronimo. At first they tried to persuade him that he could be cured later on, and he seemed to believe it. At that time Carlo, who knew the truth, wandered about for days and nights on the highway, between the vineyards, in the forests, and came close to committing suicide. But the ecclesiastic in whom he confided made it clear to him that it was his duty to live and to dedicate his life to his brother. Carlo realized this. He was seized by an immense sympathy. Only when he was with the blind boy, when he could stroke his hair, kiss his forehead, tell him stories, take him for walks in the fields behind the house and between the vineyards did his anguish decrease. Right from the beginning he had neglected his instruction at the smithy because he did not like to be separated from his brother, and later on he could no

Er hatte gleich anfangs die Lehrstunden in der Schmiede vernachlässigt, weil er sich von dem Bruder gar nicht trennen mochte, und konnte sich nachher nicht mehr entschließen, sein Handwerk wieder aufzunehmen, trotzdem der Vater mahnte und in Sorge war. Eines Tages fiel es Carlo auf, daß Geronimo vollkommen aufgehört hatte, von seinem Unglück zu reden. Bald wußte er, warum: der Blinde war zur Einsicht gekommen, daß er nie den Himmel, die Hügel, die Straßen, die Menschen, das Licht wieder sehen würde. Nun litt Carlo noch mehr als früher, so sehr er sich auch selbst damit zu beruhigen suchte, daß er ohne jede Absicht das Unglück herbeigeführt hatte. Und manchmal, wenn er am frühen Morgen den Bruder betrachtete, der neben ihm ruhte, ward er von einer solchen Angst erfaßt, ihn erwachen zu sehen, daß er in den Garten hinauslief, nur um nicht dabei sein zu müssen, wie die toten Augen jeden Tag von neuem das Licht zu suchen schienen, das ihnen für immer erloschen war. Zu jener Zeit war es, daß Carlo auf den Einfall kam, Geronimo, der eine angenehme Stimme hatte, in der Musik weiter ausbilden zu lassen. Der Schullehrer von Tola, der manchmal sonntags herüberkam, lehrte ihn die Gitarre spielen. Damals ahnte der Blinde freilich noch nicht, daß die neuerlernte Kunst einmal zu seinem Lebensunterhalt dienen würde.

Mit jenem traurigen Sommertag schien das Unglück für immer in das Haus des alten Lagardi eingezogen zu sein. Die Ernte mißriet ein Jahr nach dem anderen; um eine kleine Geldsumme, die der Alte erspart hatte, wurde er von einem Verwandten betrogen; und als er an einem schwülen Augusttag auf freiem Felde vom Schlag getroffen hinsank und starb, hinterließ er nichts als Schulden. Das kleine Anwesen wurde verkauft, die beiden Brüder waren obdachlos und arm und verließen das Dorf.

Carlo war zwanzig, Geronimo fünfzehn Jahre alt. Damals begann das Bettel- und Wanderleben, das sie bis heute führten. Anfangs hatte Carlo daran gedacht, irgendeinen Verdienst zu finden, der zugleich ihn und den Bruder ernähren könnte; aber es wollte nicht gelingen. Auch hatte Geronimo nirgends Ruhe; er wollte immer auf dem Wege sein.

Zwangzig Jahre war es nun, daß sie auf Straßen und Pässen herumzogen, im nördlichen Italien und im südlichen Tirol,

longer persuade himself to take up his trade again, in spite of the fact that his father urged him to do so and was concerned about him. One day Carlo noticed that Geronimo had completely stopped talking about his misfortune. He soon knew why: the blind boy had realized that he would never again see the sky, the hills, the streets, people, the light. Now Carlo suffered even more than before, however much he sought to soothe himself with the thought that he had caused the accident quite unintentionally. And sometimes, when he contemplated his brother in the early morning, as he slept beside him, he was seized by such anxiety at the prospect of seeing him awake, that he ran out into the garden, just so that he would not have to be present when the dead eyes seemed, every day, to seek once more the light that was extinguished for them forever. It was at that time that Carlo hit upon the idea of having Geronimo, who had a pleasant voice, continue his musical education. The schoolmaster from Tola, who sometimes came over on Sundays, taught him to play the guitar. At that time, of course, the blind boy had no idea that the newly learned art would one day serve him as a livelihood.

With that sad summer day, misfortune seemed to have moved permanently into old Lagardi's house. The crops failed one year after another; a relative swindled the old man out of a small sum of money which he had saved; and when he fell down with a stroke and died in the open field on a sultry August day, he left nothing but debts. The little property was sold; the two brothers, without a roof and poor, left the village.

Carlo was twenty years old, Geronimo fifteen. At that time the life of begging and wandering began which they had led till today. At first Carlo had thought of finding some occupation which could support both him and his brother; but he did not succeed. Besides Geronimo could find peace nowhere; he always wanted to be on the road.

For twenty years now they had been moving around on the roads and passes, in northern Italy and southern Tirol,

immer dort, wo eben der dichtere [5] Zug der Reisenden vor-
überströmte.

Und wenn auch Carlo nach so vielen Jahren nicht mehr
die brennende Qual verspürte, mit der ihn früher jedes
Leuchten der Sonne, der Anblick jeder freundlichen Land-
schaft erfüllt hatte, es war doch ein stetes nagendes Mitleid
in ihm, beständig und ihm unbewußt, wie der Schlag seines
Herzens und sein Atem. Und er war froh, wenn Geronimo
sich betrank.

Der Wagen mit der deutschen Familie war davongefahren.
Carlo setzte sich, wie er gern tat, auf die untersten Stufen
der Treppe, Geronimo aber blieb stehen, ließ die Arme schlaff
herabhängen und hielt den Kopf nach oben gewandt.

Maria, die Magd, kam aus der Wirtsstube.

„Habt's [6] viel verdient heut?" rief sie herunter.

Carlo wandte sich gar nicht um. Der Blinde bückte sich
nach seinem Glas, hob es vom Boden auf und trank es Maria
zu. Sie saß manchmal abends in der Wirtsstube neben ihm;
er wußte auch, daß sie schön war.

Carlo beugte sich vor und blickte gegen die Straße hinaus.
Der Wind blies, und der Regen prasselte, so daß das Rollen
des nahenden Wagens in den heftigen Geräuschen unterging.
Carlo stand auf und nahm wieder seinen Platz an des Bruders
Seite ein.

Geronimo begann zu singen, schon während der Wagen
einfuhr, in dem nur ein Passagier saß. Der Kutscher spannte
die Pferde eilig aus, dann eilte er hinauf in die Wirtsstube.
Der Reisende blieb eine Weile in seiner Ecke sitzen, ganz
eingewickelt in einen grauen Regenmantel; er schien auf den
Gesang gar nicht zu hören. Nach einer Weile aber sprang er
aus dem Wagen und lief mit großer Hast hin und her, ohne
sich weit vom Wagen zu entfernen. Er rieb immerfort die
Hände aneinander, um sich zu erwärmen. Jetzt erst schien er
die Bettler zu bemerken. Er stellte sich ihnen gegenüber
und sah sie lange wie prüfend an. Carlo neigte leicht den Kopf,
wie zum Gruße. Der Reisende war ein sehr junger Mensch
mit einem hübschen, bartlosen Gesicht und unruhigen Augen.
Nachdem er eine ganze Weile vor den Bettlern gestanden,
eilte er wieder zu dem Tore, durch das er weiterfahren sollte,
und schüttelte bei dem trostlosen Ausblick in Regen und

always in the place where the densest throng of tourists streamed past.

And even though, after so many years, Carlo no longer felt the burning torment with which the shining of the sun, the sight of a pleasant landscape had formerly always filled him, there was still a steady nagging sympathy in him, constant and unknown to him, like the beating of his heart and his breathing. And he was happy when Geronimo got drunk.

The carriage with the German family had driven away. Carlo sat down, as he liked to do, on the lowest steps of the stairway, but Geronimo remained standing, let his arms hang limply and held his head turned upward.

Maria, the maid, came out of the taproom.

"Did you make a lot today?" she called down.

Carlo did not even turn around. The blind man bent down for his glass, picked it up from the ground and drank it to Maria. She sometimes sat beside him in the taproom in the evening; he also knew that she was beautiful.

Carlo bent forward and looked out toward the highway. The wind was blowing and the rain pelted down so that the rumbling of the approaching carriage was lost in the loud noise. Carlo stood up and once more took his place at his brother's side.

Geronimo began to sing while the carriage, with only one passenger in it, was still driving up. The coachman hurriedly unhitched the horses, then hurried up to the taproom. For a while the tourist remained sitting in his corner, all wrapped up in a gray raincoat; he did not seem to be listening to the singing at all. But after a while he jumped out of the carriage and walked back and forth in great haste, without going far from the carriage. He kept rubbing his hands against each other to warm himself. Only now did he seem to notice the beggars. He took his position opposite them and looked at them for a long time as if he were testing them. Carlo bowed his head slightly as if in greeting. The tourist was a very young person with a pretty, beardless face and restless eyes. After he had stood before the beggars for quite a while, he hurried again to the gate through which he was to leave; and he shook his head in vexation at the sad prospect in the

Nebel verdrießlich den Kopf.

„Nun?" fragte Geronimo.

„Noch nichts," erwiderte Carlo. „Er wird wohl geben, wenn er fortfährt."

Der Reisende kam wieder zurück und lehnte sich an die Deichsel des Wagens. Der Blinde begann zu singen. Nun schien der junge Mann plötzlich mit großem Interesse zuzuhören. Der Knecht erschien und spannte die Pferde wieder ein. Und jetzt erst, als besänne er sich eben, griff der junge Mann in die Tasche und gab Carlo einen Frank.

„O danke, danke," sagte dieser.

Der Reisende setzte sich in den Wagen und wickelte sich wieder in seinen Mantel. Carlo nahm das Glas vom Boden auf und ging die Holzstufen hinauf. Geronimo sang weiter. Der Reisende beugte sich zum Wagen heraus und schüttelte den Kopf mit einem Ausdruck von Überlegenheit und Traurigkeit zugleich. Plötzlich schien ihm ein Einfall zu kommen, und er lächelte. Dann sagte er zu dem Blinden, der kaum zwei Schritte weit von ihm stand: „Wie heißt du?"

„Geronimo."

„Nun, Geronimo, laß dich nur nicht betrügen." In diesem Augenblick erschien der Kutscher auf der obersten Stufe der Treppe.

„Wieso, gnädiger Herr,[7] betrügen?"

„Ich habe deinem Begleiter ein Zwanzigfrankstück gegeben."

„O Herr, Dank, Dank!"

„Ja; also paß auf!"

„Er ist mein Bruder, Herr; er betrügt mich nicht."

Der junge Mann stutzte eine Weile, aber während er noch überlegte, war der Kutscher auf den Bock gestiegen und hatte die Pferde angetrieben. Der junge Mann lehnte sich zurück mit einer Bewegung des Kopfes, als wollte er sagen: Schicksal, nimm deinen Lauf! und der Wagen fuhr davon.

Der Blinde winkte mit beiden Händen lebhafte Gebärden des Dankes nach. Jetzt hörte er Carlo, der eben aus der Wirtsstube kam. Der rief herunter: „Komm, Geronimo, es ist warm heroben, Maria hat Feuer gemacht!"

Geronimo nickte, nahm die Gitarre unter den Arm und tastete sich am Geländer die Stufen hinauf. Auf der Treppe

rain and mist.

"Well?" asked Geronimo.

"Nothing yet," replied Carlo. "He'll probably give when he leaves."

The tourist came back again and leaned against the shaft of the carriage. The blind man began to sing. Now the young man seemed suddenly to listen with great interest. The stable hand appeared and hitched the horses up again. And only now, as though he were just remembering, the young man put his hand in his pocket and gave Carlo a franc.

"O thanks, thanks," Carlo said.

The tourist sat down in the carriage and wrapped himself in his coat again. Carlo picked up the glass from the ground and went up the wooden steps. Geronimo went on singing. The tourist leaned out of the carriage and shook his head with an expression that indicated both superiority and sadness. Suddenly something seemed to occur to him and he smiled. Then he said to the blind man, who was standing scarcely two feet from him: "What is your name?"

"Geronimo."

"Well, Geronimo, just don't let anyone cheat you!" At this moment the coachman appeared on the top step of the staircase.

"How do you mean, sir, cheat me?"

"I gave your companion a twenty-franc piece."

"O thank you, thank you, sir."

"Yes; so look out."

"He is my brother sir, he doesn't cheat me."

The young man hesitated for a while, but while he was still considering, the coachman had mounted his box and whipped up his horses. The young man leaned back with a movement of his head as if he wanted to say: Destiny, take thy course! and the carriage drove off.

The blind man waved lively gestures of gratitude after him with both hands. Now he heard Carlo who was just coming out of the taproom. He called down: "Come Geronimo, it's warm up here, Maria has made a fire."

Geronimo nodded, took his guitar under his arm and felt his way up the stairs by the railing. While he was still on

schon rief er: „Laß es mich anfühlen! Wie lang hab' ich
schon kein Goldstück angefühlt!"

„Was gibt's?" fragte Carlo. „Was redest du da?"

Geronimo war oben und griff mit beiden Händen nach dem
Kopf seines Bruders, ein Zeichen, mit dem er stets Freude
oder Zärtlichkeit auszudrücken pflegte. „Carlo, mein lieber
Bruder, es gibt doch gute Menschen!"

„Gewiß," sagte Carlo. „Bis jetzt sind es zwei Lire und
dreißig Centesimi, und hier ist noch österreichisches Geld,
vielleicht eine halbe Lira."

„Und zwanzig Franken—und zwanzig Franken!" rief Geronimo. „Ich weiß es ja!" Er torkelte in die Stube und setzte
sich schwer auf die Bank.

„Was weißt du?" fragte Carlo.

„So laß doch die Späße! Gib es mir in die Hand! Wie lang
hab' ich schon kein Goldstück in der Hand gehabt!"

„Was willst du denn? Woher soll ich ein Goldstück nehmen? Es sind zwei Lire oder drei."

Der Blinde schlug auf den Tisch. „Jetzt ist es aber genug,
genug! Willst du es etwa vor mir verstecken?"

Carlo blickte den Bruder besorgt und verwundert an. Er
setzte sich neben ihn, rückte ganz nahe und faßte wie be-
gütigend seinen Arm: „Ich verstecke nichts vor dir. Wie
kannst du das glauben? Niemandem ist es eingefallen, mir
ein Goldstück zu geben."

„Aber er hat mir's doch gesagt!"

„Wer?"

„Nun, der junge Mensch, der hin- und herlief."

„Wie? Ich versteh' dich nicht!"

„So hat er zu mir gesagt: ‚Wie heißt du?' und dann: ‚Gib
acht, gib acht, laß dich nicht betrügen!' "

„Du mußt geträumt haben, Geronimo—das ist ja Unsinn!"

„Unsinn? Ich hab' es doch gehört, und ich höre gut. ‚Laß
dich nicht betrügen; ich habe ihm ein Goldstück . . .'—nein,
so sagte er: ‚Ich habe ihm ein Zwanzigfrankstück gegeben.' "

Der Wirt kam herein. „Nun, was ist's mit euch? Habt ihr
das Geschäft aufgegeben? Ein Vierspänner ist gerade ange-
fahren."

„Komm!" rief Carlo, „komm!"

the steps he called: "Let me feel it. It's a long time since I've felt a gold piece."

"What's up?" said Carlo. "What are you talking about?"

Geronimo had reached the top and took his brother's head in both hands, a sign with which he had always expressed joy or tenderness. "Carlo, my dear brother, there really are good people."

"Certainly," said Carlo. "So far we have two lire and thirty centesimi, and here is some Austrian money too, perhaps half-a-lire."

"And twenty francs—and twenty francs," cried Geronimo. "I know it's so!" He staggered into the taproom and sat down heavily on the bench.

"What do you know?" asked Carlo.

"Stop your jokes! Give it to me in my hand! What a long time since I've had a gold coin in my hand!"

"What is it you want? Where am I to get a gold coin? There are two or three lire."

The blind man thumped the table. "Now this is enough, enough! Do you mean to hide it from me?"

Carlo looked at his brother anxiously and in astonishment. He sat down beside him, moved quite close to him and took his arm as though to soothe him: "I'm hiding nothing from you. How can you believe that? It didn't occur to anyone to give me a gold piece."

"But he told me so."

"Who?"

"Well, the young man who was pacing back and forth."

"What? I don't understand you."

"That's what he told me: 'What's your name?' and then: 'Look out, look out, don't let anyone cheat you.'"

"You must have been dreaming, Geronimo—why this is nonsense."

"Nonsense? But I heard it and my hearing is good. 'Don't let anyone cheat you; I gave him a gold piece . . .' no, this is what he said: 'I gave him a twenty-franc piece.'"

The landlord came in. "Well, what's up between you? Have you given up your business? A coach and four has just driven up."

"Come!" cried Carlo, "come!"

Geronimo blieb sitzen. „Warum denn? Warum soll ich kommen? Was hilft's mir denn? Du stehst ja dabei und—"

Carlo berührte ihn am Arm. „Still, komm jetzt hinunter!"

Geronimo schwieg und gehorchte dem Bruder. Aber auf den Stufen sagte er: „Wir reden noch, wir reden noch!"

Carlo begriff nicht, was geschehen war. War Geronimo plötzlich verrückt geworden? Denn, wenn er auch leicht in Zorn geriet, in dieser Weise hatte er noch nie gesprochen.

In dem eben angekommenen Wagen saßen zwei Engländer; Carlo lüftete den Hut vor ihnen, und der Blinde sang. Der eine Engländer war ausgestiegen und warf einige Münzen in Carlos Hut. Carlo sagte: „Danke" und dann, wie vor sich hin: „Zwanzig Centesimi." Das Gesicht Geronimos blieb unbewegt; er begann ein neues Lied. Der Wagen mit den zwei Engländern fuhr davon.

Die Brüder gingen schweigend die Stufen hinauf. Geronimo setzte sich auf die Bank, Carlo blieb beim Ofen stehen.

„Warum sprichst du nicht?" fragte Geronimo.

„Nun," erwiderte Carlo, „es kann nur so sein, wie ich dir gesagt habe." Seine Stimme zitterte ein wenig.

„Was hast du gesagt?" fragte Geronimo.

„Es war vielleicht ein Wahnsinniger."

„Ein Wahnsinniger? Das wäre ja vortrefflich! Wenn einer sagt: ,Ich habe deinem Bruder zwanzig Franken gegeben,' so ist er wahnsinnig!—Eh, und warum hat er gesagt: ,Laß dich nicht betrügen'—eh?"

„Vielleicht war er auch nicht wahnsinnig . . . aber es gibt Menschen, die mit uns armen Leuten Späße machen . . ."

„Eh!" schrie Geronimo, „Späße?—Ja, das hast du noch sagen müssen—darauf habe ich gewartet!" Er trank das Glas Wein aus, das vor ihm stand.

„Aber, Geronimo!" rief Carlo, und er fühlte, daß er vor Bestürzung kaum sprechen konnte, „warum sollte ich . . . wie kannst du glauben . . . ?"

„Warum zittert deine Stimme . . . eh . . . warum . . . ?"

„Geronimo, ich versichere dir, ich—"

„Eh—und ich glaube dir nicht! Jetzt lachst du . . . ich weiß ja, daß du jetzt lachst!"

Der Knecht rief von unten: „He, blinder Mann, Leut'

Geronimo sat there. "But why? Why should I come? What use is it to me? When you stand beside me and—"

Carlo touched his arm. "Quiet, come down now!"

Geronimo was silent and obeyed his brother. But on the steps he said: "We'll talk more about this; we'll talk about it."

Carlo did not understand what had happened. Had Geronimo suddenly gone mad? For though he became angry easily, he had never spoken this way before.

Two Englishmen sat in the carriage which had just arrived; Carlo raised his hat to them and the blind man sang. The one Englishman had got out and threw a few coins into Carlo's hat. Carlo said: "Thanks." And then, as though to himself: "Twenty *centesimi*." Geronimo's face remained impassive; he began a new song. The carriage with the two Englishmen drove off.

The brothers went up the stairs silently. Geronimo sat down on the bench; Carlo remained standing by the stove.

"Why don't you speak?" Geronimo asked.

"Well," Carlo replied, "it can only be as I told you." His voice was trembling slightly.

"What did you say?" Geronimo asked.

"Perhaps the man was insane."

"Insane? That would be splendid indeed. If a man says: 'I gave your brother twenty francs,' he's insane.—Eh, and why did he say: 'Don't let anyone cheat you'—eh?"

"Perhaps he wasn't insane either, but there are people who like to make jokes with us poor folk . . ."

"Eh!" Geronimo shrieked, "jokes?—yes, you had to say that too—I've been waiting for it." He finished the glass of wine which stood before him.

"But Geronimo!" cried Carlo—and he found, in his astonishment, that he was hardly able to talk—"why should I . . . how can you believe . . . ?"

"Why does your voice tremble . . . eh . . . why . . . ?"

"Geronimo, I assure you, I . . ."

"Eh—and I don't believe you. Now you're laughing . . . I know for sure that you're laughing now."

The groom called from below: "Hey, blind man, there

sind da!"

Ganz mechanisch standen die Brüder auf und schritten die Stufen hinab. Zwei Wagen waren zugleich gekommen, einer mit drei Herren, ein anderer mit einem alten Ehepaar. Geronimo sang; Carlo stand neben ihm, fassungslos. Was sollte er nur tun? Der Bruder glaubte ihm nicht! Wie war das nur möglich?—Und er betrachtete Geronimo, der mit zerbrochener Stimme seine Lieder sang, angstvoll von der Seite. Es war ihm, als sähe er über diese Stirne Gedanken fliehen, die er früher dort niemals gewahrt hatte.

Die Wagen waren schon fort, aber Geronimo sang weiter. Carlo wagte nicht, ihn zu unterbrechen. Er wußte nicht, was er sagen sollte, er fürchtete, daß seine Stimme wieder zittern würde. Da tönte Lachen von oben, und Maria rief: „Was singst denn noch immer? Von mir kriegst du ja doch nichts!"

Geronimo hielt inne, mitten in einer Melodie; es klang, als wäre [8] seine Stimme und die Saiten zugleich abgerissen. Dann ging er wieder die Stufen hinauf, und Carlo folgte ihm. In der Wirtsstube setzte er sich neben ihn. Was sollte er tun? Es blieb ihm nichts anderes übrig: er mußte noch einmal versuchen, den Bruder aufzuklären.

„Geronimo," sagte er, „ich schwöre dir . . . bedenk' doch, Geronimo, wie kannst du glauben, daß ich—"

Geronimo schwieg, seine toten Augen schienen durch das Fenster in den grauen Nebel hinauszublicken. Carlo redete weiter: „Nun, er braucht ja nicht wahnsinnig gewesen zu sein, er wird sich geirrt haben [9] . . . ja er hat sich geirrt . . ." Aber er fühlte wohl, daß er selbst nicht glaubte, was er sagte.

Geronimo rückte ungeduldig fort. Aber Carlo redete weiter, mit plötzlicher Lebhaftigkeit: „Wozu sollte ich denn—du weißt doch, ich esse und trinke nicht mehr als du, und wenn ich mir einen neuen Rock kaufe, so weißt du's doch . . . wofür brauch' ich denn so viel Geld? Was soll ich denn damit tun?"

Da stieß Geronimo zwischen den Zähnen hervor: „Lüg nicht, ich höre, wie du lügst!"

„Ich lüge nicht, Geronimo, ich lüge nicht!" sagte Carlo erschrocken.

„Eh! hast du ihr's schon gegeben, ja? Oder bekommt sie's erst nachher?" schrie Geronimo.

are people here."

Quite mechanically the brothers stood up and went down the steps. Two carriages had arrived at the same time, one with three gentlemen, another with an old couple. Geronimo sang; Carlo stood near him, distracted. What could he do? His brother did not believe him! How was this even possible?—And he gave Geronimo, who was singing his songs in a broken voice, an anxious, sidelong look. It seemed to him that he saw thoughts crossing this brow that he had never perceived there before.

The carriage had already left but Geronimo kept on singing. Carlo did not dare to interrupt him. He did not know what to say; he feared that his voice would tremble again. Then there was laughter from above and Maria cried: "Why do you keep on singing? You won't get anything from me."

Geronimo stopped in the middle of a tune; it sounded as if his voice and the strings had snapped at the same time. Then he went up the steps again and Carlo followed him. In the taproom he sat down beside him. What should he do? Nothing else was left for him: he must try once more to enlighten his brother.

"Geronimo," he said, "I swear to you . . . just consider, Ceronimo, how can you believe that I . . ."

Geronimo was silent; his dead eyes seemed to look through the window out into the gray mist. Carlo went on: "Well, he needn't have been insane, of course, he may have made a mistake . . . yes, he made a mistake . . ." But he clearly felt that he himself did not believe what he was saying.

Geronimo moved away impatiently. But Carlo kept on talking with sudden animation: "Why should I—you know that I don't eat or drink more than you do, and when I buy a new jacket you know about it . . . what would I need so much money for? What am I to do with it?"

Then Geronimo hissed between his teeth: "Don't lie, I hear how you're lying!"

"I'm not lying, Geronimo, I'm not lying!" said Carlo in fright.

"Eh! have you given it to her already, yes? Or will she get it only later?" Geronimo shrieked.

„Maria?"

„Wer denn, als Maria? Eh, du Lügner, du Dieb!" Und als wollte er nicht mehr neben ihm am Tische sitzen, stieß er mit dem Ellbogen den Bruder in die Seite.

Carlo stand auf. Zuerst starrte er den Bruder an, dann verließ er das Zimmer und ging über die Stiege in den Hof. Er schaute mit weit offenen Augen auf die Straße hinaus, die vor ihm in bräunlichen Nebel versank. Der Regen hatte nachgelassen. Carlo steckte die Hände in die Hosentaschen und ging ins Freie. Es war ihm, als hätte ihn sein Bruder davongejagt. Was war denn nur geschehen? . . . Er konnte es noch immer nicht fassen. Was für ein Mensch mochte das gewesen sein? Einen Franken schenkt er her und sagt, es waren zwanzig! Er mußte doch irgendeinen Grund dazu gehabt haben . . . Und Carlo suchte in seiner Erinnerung, ob er sich nicht irgendwo jemanden zum Feind gemacht, der nun einen anderen hergeschickt hatte, um sich zu rächen . . . Aber soweit er zurückdenken mochte, nie hatte er jemanden beleidigt, nie irgendeinen ernsten Streit mit jemandem vorgehabt. Er hatte ja seit zwanzig Jahren nichts anderes getan, als daß er in Höfen oder an Straßenrändern gestanden war [10] mit dem Hut in der Hand . . . War ihm vielleicht einer wegen eines Frauenzimmers [11] böse? . . . Aber wie lange hatte er schon mit keiner was zu tun gehabt . . . die Kellnerin in La Rosa war die letzte gewesen, im vorigen Frühjahr . . . aber um die war ihm gewiß niemand neidisch . . . Es war nicht zu begreifen! . . . Was mochte es da draußen in der Welt, die er nicht kannte, für Menschen geben? . . . Von überall her kamen sie . . . was wußte er von ihnen? . . . Für diesen Fremden hatte es wohl irgendeinen Sinn gehabt, daß er zu Geronimo sagte: Ich habe deinem Bruder zwanzig Franken gegeben . . . Nun ja . . . Aber was war nun zu tun? . . . Mit einemmal war es offenbar geworden, daß Geronimo ihm mißtraute! . . . Das konnte er nicht ertragen! Irgend etwas mußte er dagegen unternehmen . . . Und er eilte zurück.

Als er wieder in die Wirtsstube trat, lag Geronimo auf der Bank ausgestreckt und schien das Eintreten Carlos nicht zu bemerken. Maria brachte den beiden Essen und Trinken. Sie sprachen während der Mahlzeit kein Wort. Als Maria die

"Maria?"

"Who else but Maria? Eh, you liar, you thief!" And, as though he didn't want to sit beside him at the table any longer, he thrust his elbow into his brother's side.

Carlo stood up. At first he stared at his brother, then he left the room and went into the courtyard by way of the staircase. With wide open eyes, he looked at the highway which faded before him in brownish mist. The rain had abated. Carlo put his hands into his trouser pockets and went out into the open. He felt as though his brother had driven him away. What had really happened? . . . He couldn't grasp it even now. What kind of person could that have been? He offers a franc and says it was twenty. He must surely have had some reason for it . . . And Carlo searched his memory: had he somewhere made an enemy of someone, who had now sent another man here to take revenge . . . But as far back as he could think, he had never insulted anyone, had never had a serious quarrel with anyone. For he had done nothing in the last twenty years except to stand around in courtyards and at curbs with his hat in his hand . . . Could it be that someone was angry with him because of a woman? . . . But how long it was since he had had anything to do with one . . . the waitress in La Rosa had been the last one, the previous spring . . . but certainly no one envied him because of her . . . It was incomprehensible! . . . What sort of people could there be out there in that world which he did not know? . . . They came from everywhere . . . what did he know about them? . . . There must have been some reason why this stranger said to Geronimo: "I gave your brother twenty francs . . ." Well yes . . . But what was to be done now? . . . Suddenly it had become obvious that Geronimo distrusted him! . . . This he could not bear! He must do something against it . . . And he hurried back.

When he entered the taproom again Geronimo lay stretched out on the bench and seemed not to notice Carlo's entrance. Maria brought both of them food and drink. They did not say a word during the meal. When Maria cleared off the dishes,

Teller abräumte, lachte Geronimo plötzlich auf und sagte zu ihr: „Was wirst du dir denn dafür kaufen?"

„Wofür denn?"

„Nun, was? Einen neuen Rock oder Ohrringe?"

„Was will er denn von mir?" wandte sie sich an Carlo.

Indes dröhnte unten der Hof von lastenbeladenen Fuhrwerken, laute Stimmen tönten herauf, und Maria eilte hinunter. Nach ein paar Minuten kamen drei Fuhrleute und nahmen an einem Tische Platz; der Wirt trat zu ihnen und begrüßte sie. Sie schimpften über das schlechte Wetter.

„Heute nacht werdet ihr Schnee haben," sagte der eine.

Der zweite erzählte, wie er vor zehn Jahren Mitte August auf dem Joch eingeschneit und beinahe erfroren war. Maria setzte sich zu ihnen. Auch der Knecht kam herbei und erkundigte sich nach seinen Eltern, die unten in Bormio wohnten.

Jetzt kam wieder ein Wagen mit Reisenden. Geronimo und Carlo gingen hinunter, Geronimo sang, Carlo hielt den Hut hin, und die Reisenden gaben ihr Almosen. Geronimo schien jetzt ganz ruhig. Er fragte manchmal: „Wieviel?" und nickte zu den Antworten Carlos leicht mit dem Kopfe. Indes versuchte Carlo selbst seine Gedanken zu fassen. Aber er hatte immer nur das dumpfe Gefühl, daß etwas Schreckliches geschehen und daß er ganz wehrlos war.

Als die Brüder wieder die Stufen hinaufschritten, hörten sie die Fuhrleute oben wirr durcheinanderreden und lachen. Der jüngste rief dem Geronimo entgegen: „Sing uns doch auch was vor, wir zahlen schon!—Nicht wahr?" wandte er sich an die anderen.

Maria, die eben mit einer Flasche rotem Wein kam, sagte: „Fangt heut nichts mit ihm an, er ist schlechter Laune." [12]

Statt jeder Antwort stellte sich Geronimo mitten ins Zimmer hin und fing an zu singen. Als er geendet, klatschten die Fuhrleute in die Hände.

„Komm her, Carlo!" rief einer, „wir wollen dir unser Geld auch in den Hut werfen wie die Leute unten!" Und er nahm eine kleine Münze und hielt die Hand hoch, als wollte er sie in den Hut fallen lassen, den ihm Carlo entgegenstreckte. Da griff der Blinde nach dem Arm des Fuhrmannes und sagte: „Lieber mir, lieber mir! Es könnte daneben [13] fallen—

Geronimo suddenly gave a laugh and said to her: "What are you going to buy for it?"

"For what?"

"Well, what? A new skirt or earrings?"

"What does he want from me?" she said turning to Carlo.

Meanwhile the courtyard below echoed with heavily loaded vehicles, loud voices reached upstairs, and Maria hurried down. After a few minutes three drivers came and took their places at a table; the landlord went up to them and greeted them. They cursed the bad weather.

"Tonight you'll get snow," one of them said.

The second one told how, ten years ago in the middle of August, he had been snowed in on the pass and had almost been frozen. Maria sat down beside them. The groom came up, too, and inquired about his parents who lived down below, in Bormio.

Now another carriage with passengers came. Geronimo and Carlo went down, Geronimo sang, Carlo held out his hat and the tourists gave their alms. Geronimo now seemed quite calm. He sometimes asked: "How much?" and nodded lightly with his head to Carlo's answers. Meanwhile Carlo himself tried to gather his thoughts together. But he always had the obscure feeling that something terrible had happened and that he was quite helpless.

When the brothers went up the steps again, they heard the drivers upstairs talking at the same time and laughing. The youngest one called out to Geronimo: "Sing something for us too, we'll pay you!—Won't we?" said he turning to the others.

Maria, who was just coming with a bottle of red wine, said: "Don't start anything with him today, he's in a bad mood."

Instead of giving an answer Geronimo took his position in the middle of the room and began to sing. When he had finished the drivers applauded.

"Come here, Carlo!" one of them cried, "We'll throw our money into your hat too, like the people down below." And he took a small coin and held up his hand as though he would drop it into the hat which Carlo stretched out to him. At that point the blind man seized the driver's arm and said: "Better give it to me, better to me. It might fall outside."

daneben!"

„Wieso daneben?"

„Eh, nun! zwischen die Beine Marias!"

Alle lachten, der Wirt und Maria auch, nur Carlo stand regungslos da. Nie hatte Geronimo solche Späße gemacht! ...

„Setz' dich zu uns!" riefen die Fuhrleute. „Du bist ein lustiger Kerl!" Und sie rückten zusammen, um Geronimo Platz zu machen. Immer lauter und wirrer war das Durcheinanderreden; Geronimo redete mit, lauter und lustiger als sonst, und hörte nicht auf zu trinken. Als Maria eben wieder hereinkam, wollte er sie an sich ziehen; da sagte der eine von den Fuhrleuten lachend: „Meinst du vielleicht, sie ist schön? Sie ist ja ein altes häßliches Weib!"

Aber der Blinde zog Maria auf seinen Schoß. „Ihr seid alle Dummköpfe," sagte er. „Glaubt ihr, ich brauche meine Augen, um zu sehen? Ich weiß auch, wo Carlo jetzt ist—eh!— dort am Ofen steht er, hat die Hände in den Hosentaschen und lacht."

Alle schauten auf Carlo, der mit offenem Munde am Ofen lehnte und nun wirklich das Gesicht zu einem Grinsen verzog, als dürfte er seinen Bruder nicht Lügen strafen.[14]

Der Knecht kam herein; wenn die Fuhrleute noch vor Dunkelheit in Bormio sein wollten, mußten sie sich beeilen. Sie standen auf und verabschiedeten sich lärmend. Die beiden Brüder waren wieder allein in der Wirtsstube. Es war die Stunde, um die sie sonst manchmal zu schlafen pflegten. Das ganze Wirtshaus versank in Ruhe wie immer um diese Zeit der ersten Nachmittagsstunden. Geronimo, den Kopf auf dem Tisch, schien zu schlafen. Carlo ging anfangs hin und her, dann setzte er sich auf die Bank. Er war sehr müde. Es schien ihm, als wäre er in einem schweren Traum befangen. Er mußte an allerlei denken, an gestern, vorgestern und alle Tage, die früher waren, und besonders an warme Sommertage und an weiße Landstraßen, über die er mit seinem Bruder zu wandern pflegte, und alles war so weit und unbegreiflich, als wenn es nie wieder so sein könnte.

Am späten Nachmittage kam die Post aus Tirol und bald darauf in kleinen Zwischenpausen Wagen, die den gleichen Weg nach dem Süden nahmen. Noch viermal mußten die

"How do you mean outside?"

"Well, between Maria's legs."

They all laughed, the landlord and Maria too, only Carlo stood there motionless. Geronimo had never made such jokes before . . .

"Sit down with us," the drivers cried. "You're a merry fellow." And they moved closer together, to make room for Geronimo. The general talk grew louder and louder and more and more confused. Geronimo joined in, louder and merrier than usual, and did not stop drinking. When Maria came in again, he wanted to draw her to him; one of the drivers said laughing: "Can you possibly think she's beautiful? Why she's an old, ugly woman."

But the blind man drew Maria down on his lap. "You're all stupid," he said. "Do you think I need my eyes to see? I even know where Carlo is now—eh—he's standing there by the stove, has his hands in his pants pockets and is laughing."

They all looked at Carlo, who was leaning against the stove with his mouth open, and now really twisted his face into a grin, as if he mustn't make a liar out of his brother.

The groom came in; if the drivers wanted to reach Bormio before dark, they had to hurry. They stood up and took a noisy leave. The two brothers were alone again in the tap-room. It was the hour when they sometimes took a nap. The whole inn fell into a calm, as always at this time during the first afternoon hours. Geronimo, with his head on the table, seemed to be sleeping. At first Carlo walked back and forth, then he sat down on the bench. He was very tired. It seemed to him that he was experiencing a heavy dream. He had to think of all sorts of things—of yesterday, the day before yesterday and all the days that came before, and especially of warm summer days and white highways over which he was accustomed to walk with his brother—and it was all so far away and unintelligible, as if it could never be the same again.

In the late afternoon the stagecoach from Tirol came and soon afterward, at brief intervals, carriages which were taking the same road to the south. The brothers had to go down into

Brüder in den Hof hinab. Als sie das letztemal heraufgingen, war die Dämmerung hereingebrochen, und das Öllämpchen, das von der Holzdecke herunterhing, fauchte. Arbeiter kamen, die in einem nahen Steinbruche beschäftigt waren und ein paar hundert Schritte unterhalb des Wirtshauses ihre Holzhütten aufgeschlagen hatten. Geronimo setzte sich zu ihnen; Carlo blieb allein an seinem Tische. Es war ihm, als dauerte seine Einsamkeit schon sehr lange. Er hörte, wie Geronimo drüben laut, beinahe schreiend, von seiner Kindheit erzählte: daß er sich noch ganz gut an allerlei erinnerte, was er mit seinen Augen gesehen, Personen und Dinge: an den Vater, wie er auf dem Felde arbeitete, an den kleinen Garten mit der Esche an der Mauer, an das niedrige Häuschen, das ihnen gehörte, an die zwei kleinen Töchter des Schusters, an den Weinberg hinter der Kirche, ja an sein eigenes Kindergesicht, wie es ihm aus dem Spiegel entgegengeblickt hatte. Wie oft hatte Carlo das alles gehört. Heute ertrug er es nicht. Es klang anders als sonst: jedes Wort, das Geronimo sprach, bekam einen neuen Sinn und schien sich gegen ihn zu richten. Er schlich hinaus und ging wieder auf die Landstraße, die nun ganz im Dunkel lag. Der Regen hatte aufgehört, die Luft war sehr kalt, und der Gedanke erschien Carlo beinahe verlockend, weiterzugehen, immer weiter, tief in die Finsternis hinein, sich am Ende irgendwohin in den Straßengraben zu legen, einzuschlafen, nicht mehr zu erwachen.—Plötzlich hörte er das Rollen eines Wagens und erblickte den Lichtschimmer von zwei Laternen, die immer näher kamen. In dem Wagen, der vorüberfuhr, saßen zwei Herren. Einer von ihnen mit einem schmalen, bartlosen Gesichte fuhr erschrocken zusammen, als Carlos Gestalt im Lichte der Laternen aus dem Dunkel hervortauchte. Carlo, der stehengeblieben war, lüftete den Hut. Der Wagen und die Lichter verschwanden. Carlo stand wieder in tiefer Finsternis. Plötzlich schrak er zusammen. Das erstemal in seinem Leben machte ihm das Dunkel Angst. Es war ihm, als könnte er es keine Minute länger ertragen. In einer sonderbaren Art vermengten sich in seinem dumpfen Sinnen die Schauer, die er für sich selbst empfand, mit einem quälenden Mitleid für den blinden Bruder und jagten ihn nach Hause.

Als er in die Wirtsstube trat, sah er die beiden Reisenden,

the courtyard four more times. When they went up for the
last time twilight had fallen and the little oil lamp which
hung down from the wooden ceiling was sputtering. In came
some laborers who worked in a nearby stone quarry and had
put up their wooden huts a few hundred feet below the inn.
Geronimo sat down beside them; Carlo remained at his table
alone. He felt as if his loneliness had already lasted a long
time. He heard Geronimo over there telling about his childhood, talking loudly, almost shouting: that he still remembered everything quite well; persons and things that he had
seen with his eyes: his father working in the field, the little
garden with the ash tree beside the wall, the low little house
that belonged to them, the shoemaker's two little daughters,
the vineyard behind the church, in fact, even his own child's
face looking back at him from the mirror. How often Carlo
had heard all this. Today he could not bear it. It sounded
different than usual: every word that Geronimo spoke acquired a new sense and seemed to turn against him. He stole
out and returned to the highway, which was now quite dark.
The rain had stopped, the air was very cold, and the idea of
going on appeared almost enticing to Carlo—to go on and
on, deep into the darkness, and in the end to lie down somewhere in a ditch, fall asleep, not to awake again. Suddenly
he heard the rumbling of a carriage and caught sight of the
gleam of light from two lamps which came nearer and nearer.
In the carriage that rode by were two gentlemen. One of
them, with a narrow, beardless face, started back in fright as
Carlo's face emerged out of the darkness in the light of the
lamps. Carlo, who had stopped, raised his hat. The carriage
and lights vanished. Carlo stood in deep darkness again.
Suddenly he started. For the first time in his life he was
afraid of the dark. He felt as if he couldn't bear it one minute
longer. In his dulled senses, the horror he felt with himself
mingled strangely with a tormented sympathy for his blind
brother and drove him home.

When he entered the taproom he saw the two tourists who

die vorher an ihm vorbeigefahren waren, bei einer Flasche Rotwein an einem Tische sitzen und sehr angelegentlich miteinander reden. Sie blickten kaum auf, als er eintrat.

An dem anderen Tische saß Geronimo wie früher unter den Arbeitern.

„Wo steckst du denn, Carlo?“ sagte ihm der Wirt schon an der Tür. „Warum läßt du deinen Bruder allein?“

„Was gibt's denn?“ fragte Carlo erschrocken.

„Geronimo traktiert die Leute. Mir kann's ja egal sein, aber ihr solltet doch denken, daß bald wieder schlechtere Zeiten kommen.“

Carlo trat rasch zu dem Bruder und faßte ihn am Arme. „Komm!“ sagte er.

„Was willst du?“ schrie Geronimo.

„Komm zu Bett,“ sagte Carlo.

„Laß mich, laß mich! I c h verdiene das Geld, ich kann mit meinem Gelde tun, was ich will—eh!—alles kannst du ja doch nicht einstecken! Ihr meint wohl, er gibt mir alles! O nein! Ich bin ja ein blinder Mann! Aber es gibt Leute—es gibt gute Leute, die sagen mir: ‚Ich habe deinem Bruder zwanzig Franken gegeben!‘ “

Die Arbeiter lachten auf.

„Es ist genug,“ sagte Carlo, „komm!“ Und er zog den Bruder mit sich, schleppte ihn beinahe die Treppe hinauf bis in den kahlen Bodenraum, wo sie ihr Lager hatten. Auf dem ganzen Wege schrie Geronimo: „Ja, nun ist es an den Tag gekommen, ja, nun weiß ich's! Ah, wartet nur! Wo ist sie? Wo ist Maria? Oder legst du's ihr in die Sparkassa? [15]— Eh, ich singe für dich, ich spiele Gitarre, von mir lebst du—und du bist ein Dieb!“ Er fiel auf den Strohsack hin.

Vom Gang her schimmerte ein schwaches Licht herein; drüben stand die Tür zu dem einzigen Fremdenzimmer des Wirtshauses offen, und Maria richtete die Betten für die Nachtruhe her. Carlo stand vor seinem Bruder und sah ihn daliegen mit dem gedunsenen Gesicht, mit den bläulichen Lippen, das feuchte Haar an der Stirne klebend, um viele Jahre älter aussehend, als er war. Und langsam begann er zu verstehen. Nicht von heute konnte das Mißtrauen des Blinden sein, längst mußte es in ihm geschlummert haben,

had driven past him before, sitting at a table over a bottle of red wine and talking with each other very earnestly. They scarcely looked up when he entered.

At the other table Geronimo sat among the workers as before.

"Where have you been, Carlo?" the landlord said to him when he was still at the door. "Why do you leave your brother alone?"

"Why, what's wrong?" asked Carlo in fright.

"Geronimo is treating people. It makes no difference to me, of course, but you should consider that bad times will soon be coming again."

Carlo quickly stepped up to his brother and grasped his arm. "Come," he said.

"What do you want?" Geronimo shrieked.

"Come to bed," said Carlo.

"Leave me, leave me! I earn the money, I can do what I want with my money—eh—you certainly can't pocket it all. I suppose you think he gives it all to me. Oh no. I'm only a blind man. But there are people—there are people who tell me: 'I gave your brother twenty francs.' "

The laborers laughed loudly.

"It's enough," said Carlo, "come." And he drew his brother to him, almost dragged him up the steps to the bleak attic room where they had their bed. All the way up Geronimo shrieked: "Yes, now it's come to light, yes, now I know it! Oh, just wait. Where is she? Where's Maria? Or are you putting it in her bank account?—Eh, I sing for you, I play the guitar, you live on me—and you're a thief!" He fell down on his straw sack.

From the hall a weak light shone in; over there the door to the only guest room in the inn stood open, and Maria was preparing the beds for the night. Carlo stood before his brother and saw him lying there with his bloated face, his bluish lips, his damp hair clinging to his forehead, looking many years older than he was. And he slowly began to understand. The blind man's distrust could not date from today; it must have slumbered in him for a long time, and he had only lacked the occasion, perhaps the courage, to express it.

und nur der Anlaß, vielleicht der Mut hatte ihm gefehlt, es auszusprechen. Und alles, was Carlo für ihn getan, war vergeblich gewesen; vergeblich die Reue, vergeblich das Opfer seines ganzen Lebens. Was sollte er nun tun?—Sollte er noch weiterhin Tag für Tag, wer weiß wie lange noch, ihn durch die ewige Nacht führen, ihn betreuen, für ihn betteln und keinen anderen Lohn dafür haben als Mißtrauen und Schimpf? Wenn ihn der Bruder für einen Dieb hielt, so konnte ihm ja jeder Fremde dasselbe oder Besseres leisten als er. Wahrhaftig, ihn allein lassen, sich für immer von ihm trennen, das wäre das klügste. Dann mußte Geronimo wohl sein Unrecht einsehen, denn dann erst würde er erfahren, was es heißt, betrogen und bestohlen werden, einsam und elend sein. Und er selbst, was sollte er beginnen? Nun, er war ja noch nicht alt; wenn er für sich allein war, konnte er noch mancherlei anfangen. Als Knecht zum mindesten fand er überall sein Unterkommen. Aber während diese Gedanken durch seinen Kopf zogen, blieben seine Augen immer auf den Bruder geheftet. Und er sah ihn plötzlich vor sich, allein am Rande einer sonnbeglänzten Straße auf einem Stein sitzen, mit den weit offenen, weißen Augen zum Himmel starrend, der ihn nicht blenden konnte, und mit den Händen in die Nacht greifend, die immer um ihn war. Und er fühlte, so wie der Blinde niemand anderen auf der Welt hatte als ihn, so hatte auch er niemand anderen als diesen Bruder. Er verstand, daß die Liebe zu diesem Bruder der ganze Inhalt seines Lebens war, und wußte zum ersten Male mit völliger Deutlichkeit: nur der Glaube, daß der Blinde diese Liebe erwiderte und ihm verziehen, hatte ihn alles Elend so geduldig tragen lassen. Er konnte auf diese Hoffnung nicht mit einem Male verzichten. Er fühlte, daß er den Bruder gerade so notwendig brauchte als der Bruder ihn. Er konnte nicht, er wollte ihn nicht verlassen. Er mußte entweder das Mißtrauen erdulden oder ein Mittel finden, um den Blinden von der Grundlosigkeit seines Verdachtes zu überzeugen . . . Ja, wenn er sich irgendwie das Goldstück verschaffen könnte! Wenn er dem Blinden morgen früh sagen könnte: „Ich habe es nur aufbewahrt, damit du's nicht mit den Arbeitern vertrinkst, damit es dir die Leute nicht stehlen" . . . oder sonst irgend etwas . . .

And everything that Carlo had done for him had been in vain; in vain the remorse, in vain the sacrifice of his whole life. What was he to do now? Should he continue to lead him through the eternal night, on and on, day after day, who knows for how long, caring for him, begging for him, and having no other reward for it except distrust and abuse? If his brother took him for a thief, then any stranger could serve him as well or even better. Truly, to leave him alone, to separate from him forever—that would be the wisest thing. Then Geronimo would indeed have to realize his injustice, for he would learn only then what it means to be cheated and robbed, to be lonely and wretched. And he himself—what should he do? Well, he really wasn't old yet; if he was by himself, he could still do many sorts of things. As a hired hand, at least he would get his keep anywhere. But while these thoughts went through his head, his eyes were fixed steadily on his brother. And suddenly he saw him before him sitting alone on a stone at the side of a road bathed in sunlight, staring with his wide open, white eyes at the sky which could not blind him, stretching his hands out into the night that was always about him. And he felt that, just as the blind man had no one else in the world except him, so he too had no one else except this brother. He understood that the love for this brother was the whole content of his life, and knew for the first time with complete clarity: only the belief that the blind man returned this love and had forgiven him had permitted him to bear all the misery so patiently. He could not renounce this hope all at once. He felt that he needed his brother just as much as his brother him. He could not, he did not want to abandon him. He either had to endure his distrust or find a means of convincing the blind man of the baseless nature of his suspicion . . . Yes, if he could somewhere procure the gold coin! If he could tell the blind man tomorrow morning: "I only kept it so that you wouldn't spend it on drink with the laborers—so that people wouldn't steal it from you" . . . or anything else at all . . .

Schritte näherten sich auf der Holztreppe; die Reisenden gingen zur Ruhe. Plötzlich durchzuckte seinen Kopf der Einfall, drüben anzuklopfen, den Fremden wahrheitsgetreu den heutigen Vorfall zu erzählen und sie um die zwanzig Franken zu bitten. Aber er wußte auch gleich: das war vollkommen aussichtslos! Sie würden ihm die ganze Geschichte nicht einmal glauben. Und er erinnerte sich jetzt, wie erschrocken der eine blasse zusammengefahren war, als er, Carlo, plötzlich im Dunkel vor dem Wagen aufgetaucht war.

Er streckte sich auf den Strohsack hin. Es war ganz finster im Zimmer. Jetzt hörte er, wie die Arbeiter laut redend und mit schweren Schritten über die Holzstufen hinabgingen. Bald darauf wurden beide Tore geschlossen. Der Knecht ging noch einmal die Treppe auf und ab, dann war es ganz still. Carlo hörte nur mehr das Schnarchen Geronimos. Bald verwirrten sich seine Gedanken in beginnenden Träumen. Als er erwachte, war noch tiefe Dunkelheit um ihn. Er sah nach der Stelle, wo das Fenster war; wenn er die Augen anstrengte, gewahrte er dort mitten in dem undurchdringlichen Schwarz ein tiefgraues Viereck. Geronimo schlief noch immer den schweren Schlaf des Betrunkenen. Und Carlo dachte an den Tag, der morgen war; und ihn schauderte. Er dachte an die Nacht nach diesem Tage, an den Tag nach dieser Nacht, an die Zukunft, die vor ihm lag, und Grauen erfüllte ihn vor der Einsamkeit, die ihm bevorstand. Warum war er abends nicht mutiger gewesen? Warum war er nicht zu den Fremden gegangen und hatte sie um die zwanzig Franken gebeten? Vielleicht hätten sie doch Erbarmen mit ihm gehabt. Und doch—vielleicht war es gut, daß er sie nicht gebeten hatte. Ja, warum war es gut? . . . Er setzte sich jäh auf und fühlte sein Herz klopfen. Er wußte, warum es gut war: Wenn sie ihn abgewiesen hätten, so wäre er ihnen jedenfalls verdächtig geblieben —so aber . . . Er starrte auf den grauen Fleck, der matt zu leuchten begann . . . Das, was ihm gegen seinen eigenen Willen durch den Kopf gefahren, war ja unmöglich, vollkommen unmöglich! . . . Die Tür drüben war versperrt— und überdies: sie konnten aufwachen . . . Ja, dort—der graue leuchtende Fleck mitten im Dunkel war der neue Tag—

Carlo stand auf, als zöge es ihn dorthin, und berührte mit der Stirn die kalte Scheibe. Warum war er denn aufgestanden?

Steps were approaching on the wooden staircase; the tourists were going to bed. Suddenly the idea flashed through his mind: to knock at their door, tell the strangers the true story of today's occurrences and to ask them for the twenty francs. But he knew at once: that was completely hopeless! They wouldn't even believe the whole story. And he now remembered how the pale man had shrunk away in fright when he, Carlo, had suddenly appeared in the darkness in front of the carriage.

He stretched out on the straw sack. It was quite dark in the room. Now he heard the laborers going down the wooden steps with heavy tread, talking loudly. Soon after that both gates were locked. The servant went up and down the stairs once more, then all was quite still. Carlo now heard only Geronimo's snoring. Soon his thoughts became confused in incipient dreams. When he awoke, there was still deep darkness about him. He looked at the spot where the window was; when he strained his eyes, he perceived there, in the center of the impenetrable black, a deep gray rectangle. Geronimo was still sleeping the heavy sleep of the intoxicated. And Carlo thought of the day that was tomorrow; and he shuddered. He thought of the night after this day, of the day after this night, of the future which lay before him, and horror filled him at the loneliness that faced him. Why had he not been more courageous in the evening? Why had he not gone to the strangers and asked them for the twenty francs? Perhaps they might have had pity on him after all. And yet— perhaps it was good that he had not asked them. Yes, why was it good? . . . He sat up suddenly and he felt his heart beating. He knew why it was good: if they had refused him, he would have remained an object of suspicion to them all the same—but now . . . He stared at the gray spot, which began to shine faintly . . . What had gone through his head against his own will, was impossible of course, completely impossible! . . . The door over there was locked—and besides: they could wake up . . . Yes, there—the gray, shining spot in the middle of the darkness was the new day—

Carlo stood up, as if he were drawn to that place, and touched the cold window pane with his forehead. Why had

Um zu überlegen? . . . Um es zu versuchen? . . . Was denn? . . . Es war ja unmöglich—und überdies war es ein Verbrechen. Ein Verbrechen? Was bedeuten zwanzig Franken für solche Leute, die zum Vergnügen tausend Meilen weit reisen? Sie würden ja gar nicht merken, daß sie ihnen fehlten . . . Er ging zur Türe und öffnete sie leise. Gegenüber war die andere, mit zwei Schritten zu erreichen, geschlossen. An einem Nagel im Pfosten hingen Kleidungsstücke. Carlo fuhr mit der Hand über sie . . . Ja, wenn die Leute ihre Börsen in der Tasche ließen, dann wäre das Leben sehr einfach, dann brauchte bald niemand mehr betteln zu gehen . . . Aber die Taschen waren leer. Nun, was blieb übrig? Wieder zurück ins Zimmer, auf den Strohsack. Es gab vielleicht doch eine bessere Art, sich zwanzig Franken zu verschaffen—eine weniger gefährliche und rechtlichere. Wenn er wirklich jedesmal einige Centesimi von den Almosen zurückbehielte, bis er zwanzig Franken zusammengespart, und dann das Goldstück kaufte . . . Aber wie lang konnte das dauern—Monate, vielleicht ein Jahr. Ah, wenn er nur Mut hätte! Noch immer stand er auf dem Gang. Er blickte zur Tür hinüber . . . Was war das für ein Streif, der senkrecht von oben auf den Fußboden fiel? War es möglich? Die Tür war nur angelehnt, nicht versperrt? . . . Warum staunte er denn darüber? Seit Monaten schon schloß die Tür nicht. Wozu auch? Er erinnerte sich: nur dreimal hatten hier in diesem Sommer Leute geschlafen, zweimal Handwerksburschen und einmal ein Tourist, der sich den Fuß verletzt hatte. Die Tür schließt nicht—er braucht jetzt nur Mut—ja, und Glück! Mut? Das Schlimmste, was ihm geschehen kann, ist, daß die beiden aufwachen, und da kann er noch immer eine Ausrede finden. Er lugt durch den Spalt ins Zimmer. Es ist noch so dunkel, daß er eben nur die Umrisse von zwei auf den Betten lagernden Gestalten gewahren kann. Er horcht auf: sie atmen ruhig und gleichmäßig. Carlo öffnet die Tür leicht und tritt mit seinen nackten Füßen völlig geräuschlos ins Zimmer. Die beiden Betten stehen der Länge nach an der gleichen Wand dem Fenster gegenüber. In der Mitte des Zimmers ist ein Tisch; Carlo schleicht bis hin. Er fährt mit der Hand über die Fläche und fühlt einen Schlüsselbund, ein Federmesser, ein kleines Buch—weiter nichts . . . Nun natürlich! . . . Daß

he really got up? To think it over? . . . To try it? . . . Try
what? . . . It was impossible, of course—and besides it was
a crime. A crime? What do twenty francs mean to such people who travel a thousand miles for their pleasure? They
wouldn't even notice that it was missing . . . He went to the
door and opened it softly. Facing him was the other door, to
be reached by taking two steps, locked. On a nail in the jamb,
articles of clothing were hanging. Carlo moved his hand over
them . . . Yes, if people left their wallets in their pockets,
life would be very simple; then, soon, no one would have to
go begging any more . . . But the pockets were empty. Well,
what was there left to do? Back to his room again, on the
straw sack. Perhaps there really was a better way of procuring
twenty francs—less dangerous and more honest. If he really
held back a few centesimi from the alms every time, until he
had saved up twenty francs, and then bought the gold coin
. . . But how long would that take—months, perhaps a year.
Oh, if only he had courage! He was still standing in the hall.
He looked over toward the door . . . What sort of line was
that which fell vertically to the floor from above? Was it
possible? The door was ajar, not locked? . . . but why was he
astonished at that? The door had not been locked for months.
And why should it? He remembered: this summer people had
slept here only three times—artisans twice, and once a tourist
who had hurt his foot. The door doesn't lock—now he only
needs courage—yes, and luck. Courage? The worst that can
happen to him is that the two men will wake up, and then
he can always find an excuse. He peers through the crack into
the room. It is still so dark that he can just perceive the mere
outlines of two figures lying on the beds. He listens: they are
breathing calmly and evenly. Carlo opens the door lightly
and, without a sound, walks into the room in his bare feet.
The two beds stand lengthwise against the same wall opposite
the window. In the center of the room is a table; Carlo steals
up to it. He runs his hand over its surface and feels a bunch
of keys, a pen knife, a little book—nothing more . . . Well,
of course! . . . That he could even imagine they would lay
their money on the table! Ah, now he can get out at once!
. . . And yet, perhaps all that is needed is one good snatch
and it's done . . . And he approaches the bed near the door;

er nur daran denken konnte, sie würden ihr Geld auf den Tisch legen! Ah, nun kann er gleich wieder fort! . . . Und doch, vielleicht braucht es nur einen guten Griff, und es ist geglückt . . . Und er nähert sich dem Bett neben der Tür; hier auf dem Sessel liegt etwas—er fühlt danach—es ist ein Revolver . . . Carlo zuckt zusammen . . . Ob er ihn nicht lieber gleich behalten sollte? Denn warum hat dieser Mensch den Revolver bereitliegen? Wenn er erwacht und ihn bemerkt . . . Doch nein, er würde ja sagen: Es ist drei Uhr, gnädiger Herr, aufstehn! . . . Und er läßt den Revolver liegen.

Und er schleicht tiefer ins Zimmer. Hier auf dem anderen Sessel unter den Wäschestücken . . . Himmel! das ist sie . . . das ist eine Börse—er hält sie in der Hand! . . . In diesem Moment hört er ein leises Krachen. Mit einer raschen Bewegung streckt er sich der Länge nach zu Füßen des Bettes hin . . . Noch einmal dieses Krachen—ein schweres Aufatmen—ein Räuspern—dann wieder Stille, tiefe Stille. Carlo bleibt auf dem Boden liegen, die Börse in der Hand, und wartet. Es rührt sich nichts mehr. Schon fällt der Dämmer blaß ins Zimmer herein. Carlo wagt nicht aufzustehen, sondern kriecht auf dem Boden vorwärts bis zur Tür, die weit genug offen steht, um ihn durchzulassen, kriecht weiter bis auf den Gang hinaus, und hier erst erhebt er sich langsam, mit einem tiefen Atemzug. Er öffnet die Börse; sie ist dreifach geteilt: links und rechts nur kleine Silberstücke. Nun öffnet Carlo den mittleren Teil, der durch einen Schieber nochmals verschlossen ist, und fühlt drei Zwangzigfrankenstücke. Einen Augenblick denkt er daran, zwei davon zu nehmen, aber rasch weist er diese Versuchung von sich, nimmt nur ein Goldstück heraus und schließt die Börse zu. Dann kniet er nieder, blickt durch die Spalte in die Kammer, in der es wieder völlig still ist, und dann gibt er der Börse einen Stoß, so daß sie bis unter das zweite Bett gleitet. Wenn der Fremde aufwacht, wird er glauben müssen, daß sie vom Sessel heruntergefallen ist. Carlo erhebt sich langsam. Da knarrt der Boden leise, und im gleichen Augenblick hört er eine Stimme von drinnen: „Was ist's? Was gibt's denn?" Carlo macht rasch zwei Schritte rückwärts, mit verhaltenem Atem, und gleitet in seine eigene Kammer. Er ist in Sicherheit und lauscht . . .

here on the easy chair something is lying—he feels for it—it's a revolver . . . Carlo starts . . . Wouldn't it be better to take possession of it right now? Why does this man have a revolver lying in readiness? If he wakes up and notices him . . . But no, he would just say: It's three o'clock, sir, time to get up . . . And he lets the revolver lie there.

And he steals deeper into the room. Here on the other easy chair, among the linen . . . Heavens! that's it . . . that is a wallet—he holds it in his hand . . . At this moment he hears a slight creaking. With a swift movement he stretches out full length at the foot of the bed . . . Again this creaking—heavy breathing—clearing of the throat—then silence again, deep silence. Carlo remains lying on the floor, the wallet in his hand, waiting. Nothing stirs any more. The dawn is already casting its pale light into the room. Carlo does not dare to stand up, but crawls forward on the floor to the door which is open far enough to let him through; he crawls on, out into the hall, and only here does he slowly get to his feet, taking a deep breath. He opens the wallet; it is divided into three compartments: at the left and right there are only small silver coins. Now Carlo opens the middle part, which is also closed by a clasp, and feels three twenty-franc pieces. For a moment he thinks of taking two of them, but he quickly rejects this temptation, takes out only one gold piece and closes the wallet. Then he kneels down, looks through the crack into the room in which there is complete silence again, and then he shoves the wallet forward so that it glides under the second bed. When the stranger awakes he will have to believe that it fell down from the chair. Carlo rises slowly. Then the floor creaks slightly and at the same moment he hears a voice from inside: "What is it? What's up?" Carlo takes two swift steps backwards, holding his breath, and slips into his own room. He is safe and listens . . . Once more the bed over there creaks and then all is silent. Between his fingers he holds the gold piece. He has succeeded

Noch einmal kracht drüben das Bett, und dann ist alles still.
Zwischen seinen Fingern hält er das Goldstück. Es ist gelungen—gelungen! Er hat die zwanzig Franken, und er kann
seinem Bruder sagen: ‚Siehst du nun, daß ich kein Dieb bin!‘
Und sie werden sich noch heute auf die Wanderschaft
machen—gegen den Süden zu, nach Bormio, dann weiter
durchs Veltlin . . . dann nach Tirano . . . nach Edole . . .
nach Breno . . . an den See von Iseo wie voriges Jahr . . .
Das wird durchaus nicht verdächtig sein, denn schon vorgestern hat er selbst zum Wirt gesagt: „In ein paar Tagen
gehen wir hinunter.“

Immer lichter wird es, das ganze Zimmer liegt in grauem
Dämmer da. Ah, wenn Geronimo nur bald aufwachte! Es
wandert sich [16] so gut in der Frühe! Noch vor Sonnenaufgang
werden sie fortgehen. Einen guten Morgen dem Wirt, dem
Knecht und Maria auch, und dann fort, fort . . . Und erst
wenn sie zwei Stunden weit sind, schon nahe dem Tale, wird
er es Geronimo sagen.

Geronimo reckt und dehnt sich. Carlo ruft ihn an: „Geronimo!“

„Nun, was gibt's?“ Und er stützt sich mit beiden Händen
und setzt sich auf.

„Geronimo, wir wollen aufstehen.“

„Warum?“ Und er richtet die toten Augen auf den Bruder.
Carlo weiß, daß Geronimo sich jetzt des gestrigen Vorfalles
besinnt, aber er weiß auch, daß der [17] keine Silbe darüber
reden wird, ehe er wieder betrunken ist.

„Es ist kalt, Geronimo, wir wollen fort. Es wird heuer [18]
nicht mehr besser; ich denke, wir gehen. Zu Mittag können wir
in Boladore sein.“

Geronimo erhob sich. Die Geräusche des erwachenden
Hauses wurden vernehmbar. Unten im Hof sprach der Wirt
mit dem Knecht. Carlo stand auf und begab sich hinunter.
Er war immer früh wach und ging oft schon in der Dämmerung auf die Straße hinaus. Er trat zum Wirt hin und
sagte: „Wir wollen Abschied nehmen.“

„Ah, geht ihr schon heut?“ fragte der Wirt.

„Ja. Es friert schon zu arg, wenn man jetzt im Hof steht,
und der Wind zieht durch.“

„Nun, grüß' mir den Baldetti, wenn du nach Bormio

—succeeded. He has the twenty francs and he can say to his brother: "Do you see now that I'm not a thief?" And they will set out on the road this very day—towards the south, to Bormio, then through the Valtellina . . . then to Tirano . . . to Edolo . . . to Breno . . . to Lake Iseo like last year . . . This will be in no way suspicious, for the day before yesterday he himself had told the landlord: "In a few days we're going down."

It gets brighter all the time; the whole room lies before him in a gray twilight. Ah, if only Geronimo would wake up soon. It's so nice to hike in the early morning. They will set out even before sunrise. A "good morning" to the landlord, to the servant and Maria too, and then off, off . . . And only when they are two hours' distant, near the valley, will he tell Geronimo.

Geronimo stirs and stretches. Carlo calls to him: "Geronimo."

"Well, what's up?" And he supports himself with both his hands and sits up.

"Geronimo, we'll get up."

"Why?" And he fixes his dead eyes on his brother. Carlo knows that Geronimo now remembers the event of yesterday, but he also knows that he will not utter a syllable about it until he is drunk again.

"It's cold, Geronimo, let's leave. It won't improve this year any more; I think we'll go. By noon we can be in Boladore."

Geronimo got up. The sounds of the waking house became audible. Down in the courtyard the landlord was talking to the servant. Carlo got up and went down. He was always up early and often went out on the highway when it was still twilight. He went over to the landlord and said: "We want to take leave."

"Ah, are you leaving today?" asked the landlord.

"Yes. The cold is getting too bad now, when you stand in the yard and the wind blows through it."

"Well, my regards to Baldetti when you get down to

hinunterkommst, und er soll nicht vergessen, mir das Öl zu schicken."

„Ja, ich will ihn grüßen. Im übrigen—das Nachtlager von heut." Er griff in den Sack.

„Laß sein, Carlo," sagte der Wirt. „Die zwanzig Centesimi schenk' ich deinem Bruder; ich hab' ihm ja auch zugehört. Guten Morgen."

„Dank," sagte Carlo. „Im übrigen, so eilig haben wir's nicht. Wir sehen dich noch, wenn du von den Hütten zurückkommst; Bormio bleibt am selben Fleck stehen, nicht wahr?" Er lachte und ging die Holzstufen hinauf.

Geronimo stand mitten im Zimmer und sagte: „Nun, ich bin bereit zu gehen."

„Gleich," sagte Carlo.

Aus einer alten Kommode, die in einem Winkel des Raumes stand, nahm er ihre wenigen Habseligkeiten und packte sie in ein Bündel. Dann sagte er: „Ein schöner Tag, aber sehr kalt."

„Ich weiß," sagte Geronimo. Beide verließen die Kammer.

„Geh leise," sagte Carlo, „hier schlafen die zwei, die gestern abend gekommen sind." Behutsam schritten sie hinunter. „Der Wirt läßt dich grüßen," sagte Carlo; „er hat uns die zwanzig Centesimi für heut nacht geschenkt. Nun ist er bei den Hütten draußen und kommt erst in zwei Stunden wieder. Wir werden ihn ja im nächsten Jahre wiedersehen."

Geronimo antwortete nicht. Sie traten auf die Landstraße, die im Dämmerschein vor ihnen lag. Carlo ergriff den linken Arm seines Bruders, und beide schritten schweigend talabwärts. Schon nach kurzer Wanderung waren sie an der Stelle, wo die Straße in langgezogenen Kehren weiterzulaufen beginnt. Nebel stiegen nach aufwärts, ihnen entgegen, und über ihnen die Höhen schienen von den Wolken wie eingeschlungen. Und Carlo dachte: Nun will ich's ihm sagen.

Carlo sprach aber kein Wort, sondern nahm das Goldstück aus der Tasche und reichte es dem Bruder; dieser nahm es zwischen die Finger der rechten Hand, dann führte er es an die Wange und an die Stirn, endlich nickte er. „Ich hab's ja gewußt," sagte er.

„Nun ja,[19]" erwiderte Carlo und sah Geronimo be-

Bormio, and tell him not to forget to send me the oil."

"Yes, I'll give him your regards. And—for last night's bed."
He put his hand into his bag.

"Never mind, Carlo," said the landlord. "I'll present the
twenty centesimi to your brother; after all, I've listened to him
too. Good morning."

"Thanks," said Carlo. "For that matter, we're not in that
much of a hurry. We'll see you again when you come back
from the huts; Bormio will still be in the same place, won't
it?" He laughed and went up the wooden steps.

Geronimo stood in the middle of the room and said: "Well,
I'm ready to go."

"Right away," said Carlo.

Out of an old chest that stood in a corner of the room he
took their few belongings and packed them into a bundle.
Then he said: "A beautiful day, but very cold."

"I know," said Geronimo. They both left the bedroom.

"Go softly," said Carlo, "the two men who came last night
are sleeping here." They went down cautiously. "The landlord
sends you his regards," said Carlo; "he didn't charge us the
twenty centesimi for tonight. Now he's out by the huts and
won't be back for two hours. But we'll see him again next
year."

Geronimo did not reply. They went out on the highway
which lay in the twilight before them. Carlo took his brother's
left arm and they both went down towards the valley silently.
After a short stroll they were already at the spot where the
road begins to run on in sweeping turns. Mists rose up towards them, and the heights above them seemed as though
swallowed up by the clouds. And Carlo thought: now I'll
tell him.

But Carlo did not say a word; he took the gold coin out of
his pocket and handed it to his brother; the latter took it between the fingers of his right hand, then he touched it to
his cheek and forehead, finally he nodded. "I knew it," he
said.

"Is that so?" Carlo replied, and looked at Geronimo in

fremdet an.

„Auch wenn der Fremde mir nichts gesagt hätte, ich hätte es doch gewußt."

„Nun ja," sagte Carlo ratlos. „Aber du verstehst doch, warum ich da oben vor den anderen—ich habe gefürchtet, daß du das Ganze auf einmal—— Und sieh, Geronimo, es wäre doch an der Zeit, hab' ich mir gedacht, daß du dir einen neuen Rock kaufst und ein Hemd und Schuhe auch, glaube ich; darum habe ich . . ."

Der Blinde schüttelte heftig den Kopf. „Wozu?" Und er strich mit der einen Hand über seinen Rock. „Gut genug, warm genug; jetzt kommen wir nach dem Süden."

Carlo begriff nicht, daß Geronimo sich gar nicht zu freuen schien, daß er sich nicht entschuldigte. Und er redete weiter: „Geronimo, war es denn nicht recht von mir? Warum freust du dich denn nicht? Nun haben wir es doch, nicht wahr? Nun haben wir es ganz. Wenn ich dir's oben gesagt hätte, wer weiß . . . Oh, es ist gut, daß ich dir's nicht gesagt habe—gewiß!"

Da schrie Geronimo: „Hör' auf zu lügen, Carlo, ich habe genug davon!"

Carlo blieb stehen und ließ den Arm des Bruders los. „Ich lüge nicht."

„Ich weiß doch, daß du lügst! . . . Immer lügst du! . . . Schon hundertmal hast du gelogen! . . . Auch das hast du für dich behalten wollen, aber Angst hast du bekommen, das ist es!"

Carlo senkte den Kopf und antwortete nichts. Er faßte wieder den Arm des Blinden und ging mit ihm weiter. Es tat ihm weh, daß Geronimo so sprach; aber er war eigentlich erstaunt, daß er nicht trauriger war.

Die Nebel zerteilten sich. Nach langem Schweigen sprach Geronimo: „Es wird warm." Er sagte es gleichgültig, selbstverständlich, wie er es schon hundertmal gesagt, und Carlo fühlte in diesem Augenblick: für Geronimo hatte sich nichts geändert. Für Geronimo war er immer ein Dieb gewesen.

„Hast du schon Hunger?" fragte er.

Geronimo nickte, zugleich nahm er ein Stück Käse und Brot aus der Rocktasche und aß davon. Und sie gingen weiter.

surprise.

"Even if the stranger had told me nothing, I would have known it anyhow."

"Is that so?" said Carlo helplessly. "But you do understand why up there—before the others—I was afraid that you would spend all of it at once. And see, Geronimo, it is really time, I thought to myself, that you should buy yourself a new coat and a shirt and shoes too, I think; that's why I—"

The blind man shook his head vehemently. "What for?" And he ran his one hand over his coat. "Good enough, warm enough; now we'll get to the south."

Carlo did not understand why Geronimo did not seem to be glad at all, why he did not apologize. And he went on: "Geronimo, didn't I do right? Why aren't you glad? Now we have it, don't we? Now we have the whole of it. If I'd told you about it up there who knows . . . Oh, it's good that I didn't tell you—for sure!"

Then Geronimo shrieked: "Stop lying, Carlo, I have enough of that."

Carlo stopped and released his brother's arm. "I'm not lying."

"I know quite well that you're lying! . . . You're always lying! . . . You've lied a hundred times already! . . . You wanted to keep this one for yourself too, but you got scared, that's what it is."

Carlo lowered his head and did not reply. He took the blind man's arm again and went on with him. It hurt him that Geronimo talked this way; but he was really astonished at not being sadder.

The mists parted. After a long silence Geronimo spoke: "It's getting warm." He said it indifferently, casually, as he had said it a hundred times before, and Carlo felt at this moment: nothing had changed for Geronimo. For Geronimo, he had always been a thief.

"Are you hungry yet?" he asked.

Geronimo nodded; at the same time he took a piece of cheese and bread out of his jacket pocket and ate it. And they went on.

Die Post von Bormio begegnete ihnen; der Kutscher rief sie an: „Schon hinunter?" Dann kamen noch andere Wagen, die alle aufwärts fuhren.

„Luft aus dem Tal," sagte Geronimo, und im gleichen Augenblick, nach einer raschen Wendung, lag das Veltlin zu ihren Füßen.

Wahrhaftig—nichts hat sich geändert, dachte Carlo . . . Nun hab' ich gar für ihn gestohlen—und auch das ist umsonst gewesen.

Die Nebel unter ihnen wurden immer dünner, der Glanz der Sonne riß Löcher hinein. Und Carlo dachte: ‚Vielleicht war es doch nicht klug, so rasch das Wirtshaus zu verlassen . . . Die Börse liegt unter dem Bett, das ist jedenfalls verdächtig.' . . . Aber wie gleichgültig war das alles! Was konnte ihm noch Schlimmes geschehen? Sein Bruder, dem er das Licht der Augen zerstört, glaubte sich von ihm bestohlen und glaubte es schon jahrelang und wird es immer glauben—was konnte ihm noch Schlimmes geschehen?

Da unter ihnen lag das große weiße Hotel wie in Morgenglanz gebadet, und tiefer unten, wo das Tal sich zu weiten beginnt, lang hingestreckt, das Dorf. Schweigend gingen die beiden weiter, und immer lag Carlos Hand auf dem Arm des Blinden. Sie gingen an dem Park des Hotels vorüber, und Carlo sah auf der Terrasse Gäste in lichten Sommergewändern sitzen und frühstücken. „Wo willst du rasten?" fragte Carlo.

„Nun, im ‚Adler', wie immer."

Als sie bei dem kleinen Wirtshause am Ende des Dorfes angelangt waren, kehrten sie ein. Sie setzten sich in die Schenke und ließen sich Wein geben.

„Was macht ihr so früh bei uns?" fragte der Wirt.

Carlo erschrak ein wenig bei dieser Frage. „Ist's denn so früh? Der zehnte oder elfte September—nicht?"

„Im vergangenen Jahr war es gewiß viel später, als ihr herunterkamt."

„Es ist so kalt oben," sagte Carlo. „Heut nacht haben wir gefroren. Ja richtig, ich soll dir bestellen, du möchtest nicht vergessen, das Öl hinaufzuschicken."

Die Luft in der Schenke war dumpf und schwül. Eine sonderbare Unruhe befiel Carlo; er wollte gern wieder im

The stagecoach from Bormio met them; the coachman called to them: "Going down already?" Then other carriages came too, all going up.

"Air from the valley," said Geronimo, and at the same moment, after a sudden turn, the Valtellina lay at their feet.

Truly—nothing has changed, Carlo thought . . . Now I've even stolen for him—and this too has been for nothing.

The mists below them became thinner all the time; the light of the sun tore holes in them. And Carlo thought: "Perhaps it wasn't really wise to leave the inn so quickly . . . The wallet is lying under the bed . . . that is certainly suspicious." But how little all that mattered! What other evil could befall him? His brother, the light of whose eyes he had destroyed, thought himself robbed by him and had thought so for years and will always think so—what other evil could befall him?

There below them the great white hotel lay as though bathed in morning splendor, and deeper below them, where the valley begins to broaden, the village stretched out in a long line. The two went on silently and all the time Carlo's hand lay on the blind man's arm. They went past the park of the hotel, and Carlo saw guests in light summer clothes sitting on the terrace and eating breakfast. "Where do you want to rest?" Carlo asked.

"Well, in the *Eagle*, as always."

When they reached the little inn at the end of the village, they went in. They sat down in the taproom and ordered wine.

"What are you doing here so early?" asked the landlord.

Carlo was a little frightened at this question. "But is it so early? The tenth or eleventh of September, isn't it?"

"Last year it was certainly much later when you came down."

"It's so cold up there," said Carlo. "Last night we froze. Oh yes, I'm to tell you you mustn't forget to send the oil up."

The air in the taproom was heavy and sultry. A strange uneasiness befell Carlo; he very much wanted to be in the open

Freien sein, auf der großen Straße, die nach Tirano, nach Edole, nach dem See von Iseo, überallhin, in die Ferne führt! Plötzlich stand er auf.

„Gehen wir schon?" fragte Geronimo.

„Wir wollen doch heut mittag in Boladore sein, im ‚Hirschen' halten die Wagen Mittagsrast; es ist ein guter Ort."

Und sie gingen. Der Friseur Benozzi stand rauchend vor seinem Laden. „Guten Morgen," rief er. „Nun, wie sieht's da oben aus? Heut nacht hat es wohl geschneit?"

„Ja, ja," sagte Carlo und beschleunigte seine Schritte.

Das Dorf lag hinter ihnen, weiß dehnte sich die Straße zwischen Wiesen und Weinbergen, den rauschenden Fluß entlang. Der Himmel war blau und still. ‚Warum hab' ich's getan?' dachte Carlo. Er blickte den Blinden von der Seite an. ‚Sieht sein Gesicht denn anders aus als sonst? Immer hat er es geglaubt—immer bin ich allein gewesen—und immer hat er mich gehaßt.' Und ihm war, als schritte er unter einer schweren Last weiter, die er doch niemals von den Schultern werfen dürfte, und als könnte er die Nacht sehen, durch die Geronimo an seiner Seite schritt, während die Sonne leuchtend auf allen Wegen lag.

Und sie gingen weiter, gingen, gingen stundenlang. Von Zeit zu Zeit setzte sich Geronimo auf einen Meilenstein, oder sie lehnten beide an einem Brückengeländer, um zu rasten. Wieder kamen sie durch ein Dorf. Vor dem Wirtshause standen Wagen, Reisende waren ausgestiegen und gingen hin und her; aber die beiden Bettler blieben nicht. Wieder hinaus auf die offene Straße. Die Sonne stieg immer höher; Mittag mußte nahe sein. Es war ein Tag wie tausend andere.

„Der Turm von Boladore," sagte Geronimo. Carlo blickte auf. Er wunderte sich, wie genau Geronimo die Entfernungen berechnen konnte: wirklich war der Turm von Boladore am Horizont erschienen. Noch von ziemlich weither kam ihnen jemand entgegen. Es schien Carlo, als sei[20] er am Wege gesessen und plötzlich aufgestanden. Die Gestalt kam näher. Jetzt sah Carlo, daß es ein Gendarm war, wie er ihnen so oft auf der Landstraße begegnete. Trotzdem schrak Carlo leicht zusammen. Aber als der Mann näher kam, erkannte er ihn und war beruhigt. Es war Pietro Tenelli; erst im Mai waren

air again, on the great highway which leads to Tirano, to Edolo, to Lake Iseo, everywhere, far away. Suddenly he stood up.

"Are we going already?" asked Geronimo.

"Don't we want to be in Boladore at noon today? The carriages stop at the *Stag* for their midday rest; it's a good place."

And they went. The barber Benozzi stood in front of his shop smoking. "Good morning," he cried. "Well, how does it look up there? I suppose it snowed last night?"

"Yes, yes," said Carlo, hastening his steps.

The village lay behind them, the road stretched white between meadows and vineyards, along the murmuring river. The sky was blue and still. "Why did I do it?" Carlo thought. He gave the blind man a sidelong glance. "Does his face look any different than usual? He always thought so—I've always been alone—and he has always hated me." And he felt as if he were walking on under a heavy burden which he would never be permitted to throw off his shoulders, and as if he could see the night through which Geronimo walked at his side, while the sun lay shining on all the roads.

And they went on, walked, walked for hours. From time to time Geronimo sat down on a milestone, or they both leaned against the railing of a bridge to rest. Again they walked through a village. In front of the inn stood carriages; tourists had gotten out and were walking back and forth; but the two beggars did not stay. Again, they went out onto the open highway. The sun rose higher and higher; midday must be near. It was a day like a thousand others.

"The tower of Boladore," said Geronimo. Carlo looked up. He was astonished how exactly Geronimo could calculate distances: the tower of Boladore had really appeared on the horizon. Someone was coming toward them from a fairly long distance away. It seemed to Carlo that the man had been sitting by the road and had suddenly stood up. The figure came closer. Now Carlo saw that it was a gendarme, the kind he met so often on the highway. Still, Carlo felt a slight tremor. But when the man came closer he recognized him and was calmed. It was Pietro Tenelli; only last May the two

die beiden Bettler im Wirtshaus des Raggazzi in Morignone
mit ihm zusammen gesessen, und er hatte ihnen eine schauer-
liche Geschichte erzählt, wie er von einem Strolch einmal
beinahe erdolcht worden war.

„Es ist einer [21] stehengeblieben," sagte Geronimo.

„Tenelli, der Gendarm," sagte Carlo.

Nun waren sie an ihn herangekommen.

„Guten Morgen, Herr Tenelli," sagte Carlo und blieb vor
ihm stehen.

„Es ist nun einmal so," [22] sagte der Gendarm, „ich muß
euch vorläufig beide auf den Posten nach Boladore führen."

„Eh!" rief der Blinde.

Carlo wurde blaß. ‚Wie ist das nur möglich?' dachte er.
‚Aber es kann sich nicht darauf beziehen. Man kann es ja
hier unten noch nicht wissen.'

„Es scheint ja euer Weg zu sein," sagte der Gendarm
lachend, „es macht euch wohl nichts, wenn ihr mitgeht."

„Warum redest du nichts, Carlo?" fragte Geronimo.

„O ja, ich rede . . . Ich bitte, Herr Gendarm, wie ist es
denn möglich . . . was sollen wir denn . . . oder vielmehr,
was soll ich . . . wahrhaftig, ich weiß nicht . . ."

„Es ist nun einmal so. Vielleicht bist du auch unschuldig.
Was weiß ich. Jedenfalls haben wir die telegraphische Anzeige ans Kommando bekommen, daß wir euch aufhalten
sollen, weil ihr verdächtig seid, dringend verdächtig, da oben
den Leuten Geld gestohlen zu haben. Nun, es ist auch
möglich, daß ihr unschuldig seid. Also vorwärts!"

„Warum sprichst du nichts, Carlo?" fragte Geronimo.

„Ich rede—o ja, ich rede . . ."

„Nun geht endlich! Was hat es für einen Sinn, auf der
Straße stehenzubleiben! Die Sonne brennt. In einer Stunde
sind wir an Ort und Stelle. Vorwärts!"

Carlo berührte den Arm Geronimos wie immer, und so
gingen sie langsam weiter, der Gendarm hinter ihnen.

„Carlo, warum redest du nicht?" fragte Geronimo wieder.

„Aber was willst du, Geronimo, was soll ich sagen? Es wird
sich alles herausstellen; ich weiß selber nicht . . ."

Und es ging ihm durch den Kopf: Soll ich's ihm erklären,
ehe wir vor Gericht stehen? . . . Es geht wohl nicht. Der

beggars had sat beside him in Ragazzi's inn in Morignone, and he had told them a gruesome story of how he had once almost been stabbed by a tramp.

"Someone has stopped," said Geronimo.

"Tenelli, the gendarme," said Carlo.

Now they had come up to him.

"Good morning, Mr. Tenelli," said Carlo and stopped before him.

"That's the way it is," said the gendarme. "For the present I must take you both to the station at Boladore."

"Eh!" cried the blind man.

Carlo turned pale. "But how is this possible?" he thought. "But it can't have anything to do with this. They can't know about it down here yet."

"It seems to be on your way, doesn't it?" the gendarme laughed. "It doesn't really matter to you if you come along with me."

"Why don't you say anything, Carlo?" Geronimo asked.

"Oh yes, I'm talking . . . Please, gendarme, how is it possible . . . what are we supposed to . . . or rather, what am I supposed to . . . really, I don't know . . ."

"That's the way it is. Perhaps you're really innocent. What do I know? Anyway we got a telegraphic report at the station to stop you because you are suspected, strongly suspected, of having stolen money from the people up there. Well, it's possible, of course, that you're innocent. So come on."

"Why don't you say anything, Carlo?" asked Geronimo.

"I'm talking—oh yes, I'm talking . . ."

"Well, come on! What sense is there of stopping on the road? The sun is burning. In an hour we'll be on the spot. On with you."

Carlo touched Geronimo's arm as always, and so they went on slowly, the gendarme behind them.

"Carlo, why don't you talk?" Geronimo asked again.

"But what do you want, Geronimo, what am I to say? Everything will come to light; I don't know myself . . ."

And it went through his head: shall I explain it to him before we stand before the Court? . . . It won't do, I fear.

Gendarm hört uns zu . . . Nun, was tut's.[23] Vor Gericht
werd' ich ja doch die Wahrheit sagen. „Herr Richter," werd'
ich sagen, „es ist doch kein Diebstahl wie ein anderer. Es war
nämlich so: . . ." Und nun mühte er sich, die Worte zu
finden, um vor Gericht die Sache klar und verständlich darzu-
stellen. „Da fuhr gestern ein Herr über den Paß . . . es mag
ein Irrsinniger gewesen sein—oder am End' hat er sich nur
geirrt . . . und dieser Mann . . ."

Aber was für ein Unsinn! Wer wird es glauben? . . . Man
wird ihn gar nicht so lange reden lassen.—Niemand kann
diese dumme Geschichte glauben . . . nicht einmal Geronimo glaubt sie . . . —Und er sah ihn von der Seite an. Der
Kopf des Blinden bewegte sich nach alter Gewohnheit
während des Gehens wie im Takte auf und ab, aber das
Gesicht war regungslos, und die leeren Augen stierten in die
Luft.—Und Carlo wußte plötzlich, was für Gedanken hinter
dieser Stirne liefen . . . . ‚So also stehen die Dinge,‘ mußte
Geronimo wohl denken.—‚Carlo bestiehlt nicht nur mich,
auch die anderen Leute bestiehlt er . . . Nun, er hat es gut,
er hat Augen, die sehen, und er nützt sie aus . . .‘—Ja, das
denkt Geronimo, ganz gewiß . . . Und auch, daß man kein
Geld bei mir finden wird, kann mir nicht helfen,—nicht vor
Gericht, nicht vor Geronimo. Sie werden mich einsperren
und ihn . . . Ja, ihn geradeso wie mich, denn er hat ja das
Geldstück.—Und er konnte nicht mehr weiter denken, er
fühlte sich so sehr verwirrt. Es schien ihm, als verstünde er
überhaupt nichts mehr von der ganzen Sache, und er wußte
nur eines: daß er sich gern auf ein Jahr in den Arrest setzen
ließe . . . oder auf zehn, wenn nur Geronimo wüßte, daß
er für ihn allein zum Dieb geworden war.

Und plötzlich blieb Geronimo stehen, so daß auch Carlo
innehalten mußte.

„Nun, was ist denn?" sagte der Gendarm ärgerlich. „Vorwärts, vorwärts!" Aber da sah er mit Verwunderung, daß der
Blinde die Gitarre auf den Boden fallen ließ, seine Arme
erhob und mit beiden Händen nach den Wangen des Bruders
tastete. Dann näherte er seine Lippen dem Munde Carlos,
der zuerst nicht wußte, wie [24] ihm geschah, und küßte ihn.

„Seid ihr verrückt?" fragte der Gendarm. „Vorwärts! vorwärts! Ich habe keine Lust zu braten."

The gendarme is listening to us . . . Well, what does it matter? Before the Court I'll tell the truth, of course. "Your Honor," I'll say: "This is no theft like any other. It was this way, you must know . . ." And now he strove to find the words with which he could present the matter to the Court clearly and intelligibly. "Yesterday a gentleman was riding over the pass . . . he may have been a madman—or he was only mistaken after all . . . and this man . . ."

But what nonsense! Who will believe it?. They won't even let him talk that long.—No one can believe this stupid story . . . not even Geronimo believes it . . . —And he gave him a sidelong glance. As usual, the blind man's head was moving rhythmically up and down as he walked, but his face was motionless and his empty eyes stared into the air. And Carlo suddenly knew what sort of thoughts were racing behind this brow . . . "That's the way things are," Geronimo must probably be thinking, "Carlo steals not only from me, he steals from other people, too . . . Well, he's lucky, he has eyes that see and he's making use of them . . ." —Yes, that's what Geronimo is thinking, I'm quite certain . . . And also the fact that they will find no money on me can't help me,—not before the Court, not before Geronimo. They'll lock me up and him, too . . . Yes, him just as much as me, for he has the coin, of course. And he could not think any more, he felt so very confused. It seemed to him that he understood nothing more of the whole matter, and he knew only one thing: that he would be glad to be put under arrest for a year . . . or for ten, if only Geronimo knew that he had become a thief for him alone.

And suddenly Geronimo stopped, so that Carlo, too, had to stop.

"Well, what's wrong?" the gendarme said peevishly. "Go on, go on." But then he saw in astonishment that the blind man dropped his guitar on the ground, raised his two arms and groped for his brother's cheeks with both hands. Then he brought his lips close to Carlo's mouth, who at first didn't know what was happening, and kissed him.

"Are you two crazy?" the gendarme asked. "Keep going, keep going. I have no wish to roast."

Geronimo hob die Gitarre vom Boden auf, ohne ein Wort zu sprechen. Carlo atmete tief auf und legte die Hand wieder auf den Arm des Blinden. War es denn möglich? Der Bruder zürnte ihm nicht mehr? Er begriff am Ende—? Und zweifelnd sah er ihn von der Seite an.

„Vorwärts!" schrie der Gendarm. „Wollt ihr endlich—!" Und er gab Carlo eins [25] zwischen die Rippen.

Und Carlo, mit festem Druck den Arm des Blinden leitend, ging wieder vorwärts. Er schlug einen viel rascheren Schritt ein als früher. Denn er sah Geronimo lächeln in einer milden, glückseligen Art, wie er es seit den Kinderjahren nicht mehr an ihm gesehen hatte. Und Carlo lächelte auch. Ihm war, als könnte ihm jetzt nichts Schlimmes mehr geschehen,—weder vor Gericht, noch sonst irgendwo auf der Welt.—Er hatte seinen Bruder wieder . . . Nein, er hatte ihn zum erstenmal . . .

Geronimo picked up his guitar from the ground, without saying a word. Carlo drew a deep breath and again laid his hand on his blind brother's arm. Was it really possible? His brother was no longer angry with him? He finally realized—? And dubiously he gave him a sidelong glance.

"Go on!" the gendarme roared. "Will you . . . !" And he gave Carlo a punch between the ribs.

And Carlo, guiding the blind man's arm with firm pressure, went forward again. He took a much faster pace than before. For he saw Geronimo smile in that gentle, happy way, which he had not seen in him since his childhood. And Carlo smiled, too. He felt as if nothing bad could happen to him now—neither before the Court, nor anywhere else in the world.—He had found his brother again . . . No, he had him for the first time . . .

# Thomas Mann

(1875–1955)

THOMAS MANN was born in Lübeck, North Germany. On his
father's side he was descended from an old established patri-
cian family of merchants; his mother was of Portuguese-Creole
stock. He gave up his formal education with the secondary
school and entered an insurance office as an unpaid clerk.
He was already writing and publishing and being noticed.
With the appearance of his superb novel *Buddenbrooks*
(1901) he revealed himself as a writer of the first rank. Thereafter his life became synonymous with his successful career
as a writer. He was awarded the Nobel Prize for Literature in
1929. Many honors were showered on him. In 1933, when
the National Socialists seized power in Germany, he left his
native land and settled first in Switzerland, then in the United
States, finally returning to Switzerland, where he died at the
age of eighty.

Thomas Mann is generally acknowledged to be among the
handful of outstanding men of letters of the twentieth century. He has brought to the art of fiction a combination of
qualities equalled only by James Joyce: deep philosophical and
social insight, an understanding of the condition of contemporary man and a subtle mastery of the verbal art which
literature, after all, is.

He is a man of one idea: throughout his vast work he has
wrestled with the problem of *Natur* (the physical, practical,
"instinctive") and *Geist* (spirit, mind) as they appear respec-
tively in the bourgeois philistine and the artist-intellectual.

This conflict has, of course, been known to Western literature and thought from the eighteenth century on; it is the romantic thesis of Rousseau which has haunted literature for two centuries. But Thomas Mann has given it a peculiar relevance to us by bringing his subtle and vastly erudite mind to bear on it.

Stated crudely, this thesis holds that *Geist* or intellectualism leads to weakness, decadence, disease and death, whereas the non-intellectual bourgeois, living instinctively, has health, vigor and robustness. Realizing this, the intellectual develops an ambivalent attitude; he envies the man of nature his adjustment and yet feels superior to him as an intellectual-artist. This basic theme Thomas Mann has presented with many variations in his work: Tonio Kröger the artist envies the average, normal Hans Hansen; Detlev Spinell is made to look ridiculous in his encounter with the crude but vigorous Herr Klöterjahn. Within the realm of spirit itself, the complete intellectual Schiller envies his rival Goethe, who has much of the naïve character of the man of nature.

*Schwere Stunde* was written in 1905, the centennial of Schiller's death. What Thomas Mann has achieved in this brief sketch is a deep probing into Schiller's mind and soul, based on Schiller's famous essay *Über naive und sentimentalische Dichtung*. This study should be supplemented by Thomas Mann's important essay *Goethe und Tolstoy*, in which the polarity between *Natur* and *Geist* is brilliantly illustrated in the antagonism between Goethe and Schiller, and Tolstoy and Dostoevsky.

# SCHWERE STUNDE

## von Thomas Mann

ER STAND vom Schreibtisch auf, von seiner kleinen, gebrech-
lichen Schreibkommode, stand auf wie ein Verzweifelter und
ging mit hängendem Kopfe in den entgegengesetzten Winkel
des Zimmers zum Ofen, der lang und schlank war wie eine
Säule. Er legte die Hände an die Kacheln, aber sie waren
fast ganz erkaltet, denn Mitternacht war lange vorbei, und
so lehnte er, ohne die kleine Wohltat empfangen zu haben,
die er suchte, den Rücken daran, zog hustend die Schöße
seines Schlafrockes zusammen, aus dessen Brustaufschlägen
das verwaschene Spitzenjabot heraushing, und schnob mühsam durch die Nase, um sich ein wenig Luft zu verschaffen;
denn er hatte den Schnupfen wie gewöhnlich.

Das war ein besonderer und unheimlicher Schnupfen, der
ihn fast nie völlig verließ. Seine Augenlider waren entflammt
und die Ränder seiner Nasenlöcher ganz wund davon, und
in Kopf und Gliedern lag dieser Schnupfen ihm wie eine
schwere, schmerzliche Trunkenheit. Oder war an all der
Schlaffheit und Schwere das leidige Zimmergewahrsam schuld,
das der Arzt nun schon wieder seit Wochen über ihn verhängt
hielt? Gott wußte, ob er wohl daran tat. Der ewige Katarrh
und die Krämpfe in Brust und Unterleib mochten es nötig
machen, und schlechtes Wetter war über Jena,[1] seit Wochen,
seit Wochen, das war richtig, ein miserables und hassenswertes
Wetter, das man in allen Nerven spürte, wüst, finster und
kalt, und der Dezemberwind heulte im Ofenrohr, verwahrlost
und gottverlassen, daß es klang nach nächtiger Heide im Sturm
und Irrsal und heillosem Gram der Seele. Aber gut war sie

# THE DIFFICULT HOUR

## by Thomas Mann

HE GOT up from his desk, from his small, fragile secretary, got up like a desperate man and went, with drooping head, to the opposite corner of the room, to the stove which was tall and slender like a pillar. He placed his hands on the tiles but they were now almost cold, for midnight was long past, and so he leaned with his back against them without receiving the small comfort which he sought, coughed and drew the skirts of his dressing gown together, between the lapels of which the faded lace jabot hung out, and puffed with an effort through his nose in order to get a little air; for he had a catarrh as usual.

It was a special and uncanny catarrh, which almost never left him completely. His eyelids were inflamed and the edges of his nostrils were quite sore from it, and this catarrh lay in his head and limbs like a heavy, painful intoxication. Or was this nasty confinement to his room, which the doctor had again held over his head for weeks now, responsible for all the weakness and heaviness? Heaven knew whether he was doing the right thing. The eternal catarrh and the cramps in his chest and abdomen might have made it necessary. And there had been bad weather over Jena for weeks, for weeks, that was true, a miserable and hateful weather which one felt in all one's nerves, desolate, dark and cold. And the December wind howled in the stove pipe, so wild and God-forsaken, that it sounded like a heath in a storm by night—and like straying, hopeless mental grief. But it was not good, this narrow prison,

nicht, diese enge Gefangenschaft, nicht gut für die Gedanken und den Rhythmus des Blutes, aus dem die Gedanken kamen.—

Das sechseckige Zimmer, kahl, nüchtern und unbequem, mit seiner geweißten Decke, unter der Tabaksrauch schwebte, seiner schräg karierten Tapete, auf der oval gerahmte Silhouetten hingen, und seinen vier, fünf dünnbeinigen Möbeln, lag im Lichte der beiden Kerzen, die zu Häupten des Manuskripts auf der Schreibkommode brannten. Rote Vorhänge hingen über den oberen Rahmen der Fenster, Fähnchen nur, symmetrisch geraffte Kattune; aber sie waren rot, von einem warmen, sonoren Rot, und er liebte sie und wollte sie niemals missen, weil sie etwas von Üppigkeit und Wollust in die unsinnlich enthaltsame Dürftigkeit seines Zimmers brachten.—

Er stand am Ofen und blickte mit einem raschen und schmerzlich angestrengten Blinzeln hinüber zu dem Werk, von dem er geflohen war, dieser Last, diesem Druck, dieser Gewissensqual, diesem Meer, das auszutrinken,[2] dieser furchtbaren Aufgabe, die sein Stolz und sein Elend, sein Himmel und seine Verdammnis war. Es schleppte sich, es stockte, es stand—schon wieder, schon wieder! Das Wetter war schuld und sein Katarrh und seine Müdigkeit. Oder das Werk? Die Arbeit selbst? Die eine unglückselige und der Verzweiflung geweihte Empfängnis war?

Er war aufgestanden, um sich ein wenig Distanz davon zu verschaffen, denn oft bewirkte die räumliche Entfernung vom Manuskript, daß man Übersicht gewann, einen weiteren Blick über den Stoff, und Verfügungen zu treffen vermochte. Ja, es gab Fälle, wo das Erleichterungsgefühl, wenn man sich abwendete von der Stätte des Ringens, begeisternd wirkte. Und das war eine unschuldigere Begeisterung, als wenn man Likör nahm oder schwarzen, starken Kaffee.—Die kleine Tasse stand auf dem Tischchen. Wenn sie ihm über das Hemmnis hülfe? Nein, nein, nicht mehr! Nicht der Arzt nur, auch ein zweiter noch, ein Ansehnlicherer, hatte ihm dergleichen behutsam widerraten, der Andere, der dort, in Weimar, den er mit einer sehnsüchtigen Feindschaft liebte. Der war weise. Der wußte zu leben, zu schaffen; mißhandelte sich nicht; war voller Rücksicht gegen sich selbst.—

not good for the thoughts and the rhythm of the blood out of which the thoughts came.

The hexagonal room, bare, plain and uncomfortable, with its white-washed ceiling, under which the tobacco smoke floated, its wall paper with oblique squares, on which hung silhouettes in oval frames, and its four or five spindly-legged pieces of furniture, lay in the light of the two candles, which burned at the head of the manuscript on the secretary. Red drapes hung over the upper window frames, mere tatters, pieces of calico gathered symmetrically; but they were red, of a warm, sonorous red; and he loved them and never wanted to be without them because they brought something of luxury and voluptuousness into the non-sensuous, abstemious meagerness of his room.

He stood at the stove and peered, with a swift and painfully strained blinking of his eyes, at the work from which he had fled, this burden, this pressure, this torment of conscience, this sea which he had to drink up, this terrible task which was his pride and his misery, his heaven and his damnation. It dragged, it got stuck, it stood still—once again, once again! It was the fault of the weather and his catarrh and his weariness. Or was it the work? Was it the labor itself that an unhappy conception doomed to despair?

He had stood up to get some distance, for often a removal in space from the manuscript gave one perspective, a longer view of the material, and enabled one to make decisions. Yes, there were cases where the feeling of relief gained from turning away from the place of struggle produced inspiration. And that was a more innocent inspiration than when one took liquor or black, strong coffee.—The little cup stood on the small table. Suppose it should help him over the obstacle? No, no, no more! Not only the doctor, another person too, a more prominent one, had advised him prudently against such things, that other one, that man there in Weimar, whom he loved with a longing enmity. He was wise. He knew how to live, how to create; did not abuse himself; was full of consideration towards himself.

Stille herrschte im Hause. Nur der Wind war hörbar, der die Schloßgasse hinuntersauste, und der Regen, wenn er prickelnd gegen die Fenster getrieben ward. Alles [3] schlief, der Hauswirt und die Seinen, Lotte und die Kinder. Und er stand einsam wach am erkalteten Ofen und blinzelte gequält zu dem Werk hinüber, an das seine kranke Ungenügsamkeit ihn nicht glauben ließ,—Sein weißer Hals ragte lang aus der Binde hervor, und zwischen den Schößen des Schlafrocks sah man seine nach innen gekrümmten [4] Beine. Sein rotes Haar war aus der hohen und zarten Stirn zurückgestrichen, ließ blaß geäderte Buchten über den Schläfen frei [5] und bedeckte die Ohren in dünnen Locken. An der Wurzel der großen, gebogenen Nase, die unvermittelt in eine weißliche Spitze endete, traten die starken Brauen, dunkler als das Haupthaar, nahe zusammen, was dem Blick der tiefliegenden, wunden Augen etwas tragisch Schauendes gab. Gezwungen, durch den Mund zu atmen, öffnete er die dünnen Lippen, und seine Wangen, sommersprossig und von Stubenluft fahl, erschlafften und fielen ein.—

Nein, es mißlang, und alles war vergebens! Die Armee! Die Armee hätte gezeigt werden müssen! Die Armee war die Basis von allem! Da sie nicht vors Auge gebracht werden konnte— war die ungeheure Kunst denkbar, sie der Einbildung aufzuzwingen? Und der Held war kein Held; er war unedel und kalt! Die Anlage war falsch und die Sprache war falsch, und es war ein trockenes und schwungloses Kolleg in Historie, breit, nüchtern und für die Schaubühne verloren!

Gut, es war also aus. Eine Niederlage. Ein verfehltes Unternehmen. Bankerott. Er wollte es Körnern [6] schreiben, dem guten Körner, der an ihn glaubte, der in kindischem Vertrauen seinem Genius anhing. Er würde höhnen, flehen, poltern—der Freund; würde ihn an den Carlos [7] gemahnen, der auch aus Zweifeln und Mühen und Wandlungen hervorgegangen und sich am Ende, nach aller Qual, als ein weithin Vortreffliches, eine ruhmvolle Tat erwiesen hat. Doch das war anders gewesen. Damals war er der Mann noch, eine Sache mit glücklicher Hand zu packen und sich den Sieg daraus zu gestalten. Skrupel und Kämpfe? O ja. Und krank war er gewesen, wohl kränker als jetzt, ein Darbender, Flüchtiger, mit der Welt Zerfallener, gedrückt und im Menschlichen

Silence reigned in the house. Only the wind could be heard, roaring down the Schlossgasse, and the rain when it was driven and pattered against the windows. Everyone was asleep, the landlord and his family, Lotte and the children. And he stood in solitude and awake at the cold stove, and blinked in torment at the work in which his pathological inadequacy did not permit him to believe. His white neck stood far out of the neckband and between the skirts of his dressing gown one could see his knock-kneed legs. His red hair, brushed back from his high, delicate brow, exposed pale-veined bays above his temples and covered his ears in thin curls. At the base of the large, curved nose, which ended abruptly in a whitish point, the well-marked eyebrows came close together; they were of a darker color than the hair of his head and gave the deep-set, smarting eyes a somewhat tragic appearance. Compelled to breathe through his mouth, he opened his thin lips; and his cheeks, covered with freckles and pale from the air inside the room, grew slack and hollow.

No, it was a failure, and it was all in vain! The army! The army should have been shown. The army was the basis of everything! But since it could not be brought before the eyes, was the tremendous art conceivable that would force it upon the imagination? And the hero was no hero; he was common and cold. The setting was wrong and the diction was wrong and it was a dry and prosaic lecture in history, elaborate, colorless and a total loss for the stage.

Good, so it was over. A defeat. An undertaking that had failed. Bankruptcy. He wanted to write Körner about it, the good Körner who believed in him, who clung to his genius with childish confidence. He would mock, implore, bluster—that friend; would remind him of *Carlos*, which had also emerged from doubts and efforts and changes and in the end, after all the torment, had revealed itself as something really excellent, a meritorious achievement. But that had been different. At that time he had still been the man to take hold of a thing with a lucky hand and to shape it into victory. Scruples and struggles? Oh yes. And he had been ill, probably more so than now, a starving man, a refugee, at odds with the world, oppressed and a beggar in his human sympathy.

bettelarm. Aber jung, ganz jung noch! Jedesmal, wie tief auch gebeugt, war sein Geist geschmeidig emporgeschnellt, und nach den Stunden des Harms waren die anderen des Glaubens und des inneren Triumphes gekommen. Die kamen nicht mehr, kamen kaum noch. Eine Nacht der flammenden Stimmung, da man auf einmal in einem genialisch leidenschaftlichen Lichte sah, was werden könnte, wenn man immer solcher Gnade genießen dürfte, mußte bezahlt werden mit einer Woche der Finsternis und der Lähmung. Müde war er, siebenunddreißig erst alt und schon am Ende. Der Glaube lebte nicht mehr, der an die Zukunft, der im Elend sein Stern gewesen. Und so war es, dies war die verzweifelte Wahrheit: Die Jahre der Not und der Nichtigkeit, die er für Leidens- und Prüfungsjahre gehalten, sie eigentlich waren reiche und fruchtbare Jahre gewesen; und nun, da ein wenig Glück sich herniedergelassen, da er aus dem Freibeutertum des Geistes in einige Rechtlichkeit und bürgerliche Verbindung eingetreten war, Amt und Ehren trug, Weib und Kinder besaß, nun war er erschöpft und fertig. Versagen und verzagen—das war's, was übrigblieb.

Er stöhnte, preßte die Hände vor die Augen und ging wie gehetzt durch das Zimmer. Was er da eben gedacht, war so furchtbar, daß er nicht an der Stelle zu bleiben vermochte, wo ihm der Gedanke gekommen war. Er setzte sich auf einen Stuhl an der Wand, ließ die gefalteten Hände zwischen den Knien hangen und starrte trüb auf die Diele nieder.

Das Gewissen . . . Wie laut sein Gewissen schrie! Er hatte gesündigt, sich versündigt gegen sich selbst in all den Jahren, gegen das zarte Instrument seines Körpers. Die Ausschweifungen seines Jugendmutes, die durchwachten Nächte, die Tage in tabakrauchiger Stubenluft, übergeistig und des Leibes uneingedenk, die Rauschmittel, mit denen er sich zur Arbeit gestachelt—das rächte, rächte sich jetzt!

Und rächte es sich, so wollte er den Göttern trotzen, die Schuld schickten und dann Strafe verhängten. Er hatte gelebt, wie er leben mußte, er hatte nicht Zeit gehabt, weise, nicht Zeit, bedächtig zu sein. Hier, an dieser Stelle der Brust, wenn er atmete, hustete, gähnte, immer am selben Punkt dieser Schmerz, diese kleine, teuflische, stechende, bohrende Mah-

But young, still quite young. Each time his spirit had bobbed up nimbly, however deeply it had been bent; and after the hours of grief, those others of faith and inner triumph had come. These no longer came, scarcely ever came. One night of flaming mood when, in a passionate light of genius, one suddenly saw what could be created, if one were still permitted to enjoy such grace, had to be paid for with a week of darkness and paralysis. He was tired, only thirty-seven years old and already at the end. His faith was no longer alive, his faith in the future, which had been his star in his wretchedness. And so it was; this was the desperate truth: the years of distress and nothingness which he had considered his years of suffering and testing—these had really been rich and fruitful years; and now, when a little good fortune had descended to him, when, from intellectual piracy, he had entered into a certain integrity and bourgeois belonging, had an office and honors, possessed a wife and children, now he was exhausted and finished. To fail and despair—that is what was left for him.

He groaned, pressed his hands to his eyes and walked through the room as if possessed. What he had just thought was so terrible that he could not remain in the spot where the thought had come to him. He sat down on a chair near the wall, let his folded hands hang between his knees and stared down dully at the floor.

His conscience . . . How loudly his conscience was crying! He had sinned, sinned against himself all these years, against the delicate instrument of his body. The excesses of his youthful spirits, the nights spent awake, the days in a room whose confined air was saturated with tobacco smoke, the excessive intellectuality and heedlessness of his body, the intoxicating stimulants with which he had goaded himself to work—this was now avenging itself!

And if it was taking vengeance, he would defy the gods who sent guilt and then imposed a penalty. He had lived as he had to live, he had not had time to be wise, no time to be cautious. Here, at this spot in his chest, when he breathed, coughed, yawned, always at the same point; this pain, this small, devilish, piercing, boring exhortation, which was never

nung, die nicht schwieg, seitdem vor fünf Jahren in Erfurt
das Katarrhfieber, jene hitzige Brustkrankheit, ihn angefallen;
—was wollte sie sagen? In Wahrheit, er wußte es nur zu gut,
was sie meinte,—mochte der Arzt sich stellen [8] wie er konnte
und wollte. Er hatte nicht Zeit, sich mit kluger Schonung zu
begegnen,[9] mit milder Sittlichkeit hauszuhalten. Was er tun
wollte, mußte er bald tun, heute noch, schnell.—Sittlichkeit?
Aber wie kam es zuletzt, daß die Sünde gerade, die Hingabe
an das Schädliche und Verzehrende ihn moralischer dünkte
als alle Weisheit und kühle Zucht? Nicht sie, nicht die
verächtliche Kunst des guten Gewissens waren das Sittliche,
sondern der Kampf und die Not, die Leidenschaft und der
Schmerz!

Der Schmerz . . . Wie das Wort ihm die Brust weitete!
Er reckte sich auf, verschränkte die Arme; und sein Blick,
unter den rötlichen zusammenstehenden Brauen, beseelte sich
mit schöner Klage. Man war noch nicht elend, ganz elend
noch nicht, solange es möglich war, seinem Elend eine stolze
und edle Benennung zu schenken. Eins war not: Der gute
Mut, seinem Leben große und schöne Namen zu geben! Das
Leid nicht auf Stubenluft und Konstipation zurückzuführen!
Gesund genug sein, um pathetisch sein—um über das Körperliche hinwegsehen, hinwegfühlen zu können! Nur hierin naiv
sein, wenn auch sonst wissend in allem! Glauben, an den
Schmerz glauben können . . Aber er glaubte ja an den
Schmerz, so tief, so innig, daß etwas, was unter Schmerzen
geschah, diesem Glauben zufolge weder nutzlos noch schlecht
sein konnte. Sein Blick schwang sich zum Manuskript hinüber,
und seine Arme verschränkten sich fester über der Brust.—
Das Talent selbst—war es nicht Schmerz? Und wenn *das* dort,
das unselige Werk, ihn leiden machte, war es nicht in der
Ordnung so und fast schon ein gutes Zeichen? Es hatte noch
niemals gesprudelt, und sein Mißtrauen würde erst eigentlich
beginnen, wenn es das täte. Nur bei Stümpern und Dilettanten
sprudelte es, bei den Schnellzufriedenen und Unwissenden,
die nicht unter dem Druck und der Zucht des Talentes lebten.
Denn das Talent, meine Damen und Herren dort unten,
weithin im Parterre,[10] das Talent ist nichts Leichtes, nichts
Tändelndes, es ist nicht ohne weiteres [11] ein Können. In der
Wurzel ist es *Bedürfnis*, ein kritisches Wissen um das Ideal,

silent since that time in Erfurt five years ago, when catarrhal fever, that inflammation of his chest had seized him;—what did it mean? In truth he knew only too well what it meant— no matter what his doctor could or might say. He did not have time to act with prudent care towards himself, to be thrifty with a gentle virtue. What he wanted to do he had to do soon, this very day, quickly.—Virtue? But how did it happen, after all, that it was precisely sin, surrender to what was harmful and consuming, which seemed to him more moral than all wisdom and cool discipline? Not this, not the contemptible art of a good conscience was virtue, but struggle and distress, passion and pain!

Pain . . . How the word caused his chest to swell. He stood upright, folded his arms; and his eyes, under the reddish, joined eyebrows, were animated with beautiful lament. One was not wretched yet, not quite wretched yet, as long as it was possible to give one's misery a proud and noble name. One thing was needed: the good courage to give one's life great and beautiful names! Not to attribute one's suffering to the stuffy air in the room and constipation. To be healthy enough to be able to have lofty feelings, to be able to disregard the physical, to cease feeling it. To be naïve in this alone, though sophisticated in everything else. To believe, to be able to believe in pain . . . But he did believe in pain, so deeply, so fervently, that anything which happened under pain could not, according to this faith, be either useless or bad. His eye turned to the manuscript, and his arms folded more tightly over his chest.—Talent itself—was it not pain? And if that thing over there, the unhappy work, caused him suffering, wasn't it proper and almost a good sign in itself? It had never bubbled forth yet, and his distrust would really begin if it should do so. It bubbled only for bunglers and dilettantes, for those who were easily satisfied and ignorant, who did not live under the pressure and discipline of talent. For talent, ladies and gentlemen down there far away in the orchestra, talent is not a facile thing, not a bauble; it is not a mere ability. At its root it is a *need*, a critical knowing of the ideal, a dissatisfaction which only creates and increases its skill; and not without torment. And for the greatest, the least satisfied,

eine Ungenügsamkeit, die sich ihr Können nicht ohne Qual
erst schafft und steigert. Und den Größten, den Ungenüg-
samsten ist ihr Talent die schärfste Geißel.—Nicht klagen!
Nicht prahlen! Bescheiden, geduldig denken von dem, was
man trug! Und wenn nicht ein Tag in der Woche, nicht
eine Stunde von Leiden frei war—was weiter? Die Lasten
und Leistungen, die Anforderungen, Beschwerden, Strapazen
gering achten, *klein* sehen,—das war's, was groß machte!

Er stand auf, zog die Dose und schnupfte gierig, warf dann
die Hände auf den Rücken und schritt so heftig durch das
Zimmer, daß die Flammen der Kerzen im Luftzuge flatterten.
—Größe! Außerordentlichkeit! Welteroberung und Unsterblichkeit des Namens! Was galt alles Glück der ewig Unbekannten gegen dies Ziel? Gekannt sein,—gekannt und geliebt
von den Völkern der Erde! Schwatzet von Ichsucht, die ihr
nichts wißt von der Süßigkeit dieses Traumes und Dranges!
Ichsüchtig ist alles Außerordentliche, sofern es leidet. Mögt
ihr selbst zusehen, spricht es, ihr Sendungslosen, die ihr's auf
Erden so viel leichter habt! Und der Ehrgeiz spricht: Soll
das Leiden umsonst gewesen sein? Groß muß es mich
machen!—

Die Flügel seiner großen Nase waren gespannt, sein Blick
drohte und schweifte. Seine Rechte war heftig und tief in den
Aufschlag seines Schlafrockes geschoben, während die Linke
geballt herniederhing. Eine fliegende Röte war in seine
hageren Wangen getreten, eine Lohe, emporgeschlagen aus
der Glut seines Künstleregoismus, jener Leidenschaft für sein
Ich, die unauslöschlich in seiner Tiefe brannte. Er kannte ihn
wohl, den heimlichen Rausch dieser Liebe. Zuweilen brauchte
er nur seine Hand zu betrachten, um von einer begeisterten
Zärtlichkeit für sich selbst erfüllt zu werden, in deren Dienst
er alles, was ihm an Waffen des Talentes und der Kunst gegeben war, zu stellen beschloß. Er durfte es, nichts war unedel
daran. Denn tiefer noch, als diese Ichsucht, lebte das Bewußtsein, sich dennoch bei alldem im Dienste von irgend
etwas Hohem, ohne Verdienst freilich, sondern unter einer
Notwendigkeit, uneigennützig zu verzehren und aufzuopfern.
Und dies war seine Eifersucht: daß niemand größer werde als
er, der nicht auch tiefer als er um dieses Hohe gelitten.

their talent is the sharpest scourge.—Not to complain! Not to boast! To think modestly, patiently of what one endured! And if there was not a day in the week, not an hour that was free from suffering—what of it? To make light of one's burdens and achievements, of demands, difficulties, hardships, to see them as *petty*—it was that which made one great!

He stood up, took out his snuff-box and sniffed eagerly, then swiftly put his hands behind his back and strode so vehemently through the room, that the candle flames fluttered in the draught.—Greatness! Extraordinariness! World conquest and an immortal name! What value was there in the happiness of the perpetually unknown compared with this goal? To be known—known and loved by the peoples of the earth! Prattle about egotism, you who know nothing of the sweetness of this dream and urge! Everything extraordinary is egotistical, insofar as it suffers. May you observe it yourselves, it speaks, you without a mission, for whom things on earth are so much easier! And ambition speaks: shall the suffering have been in vain? It must make me great!—

The nostrils of his large nose were taut, his eye looked threatening and wild. His right hand was thrust vehemently and deeply into the opening of his dressing gown, while his left hand hung down clenched. A fleeting red had spread over his haggard cheeks, a fire thrown up from the glow of his artist's egoism, that passion for his ego which burned inextinguishably in his depth. He knew it well, the secret intoxication of this love. At times he needed only to look at his hand to be filled with an enthusiastic tenderness for himself, in whose service he resolved to place everything that was given to him as weapons of his talent and art. He was permitted to do so; there was nothing ignoble about it. For even deeper than this egotism lay the consciousness that he was nevertheless, in spite of it all, unselfishly consuming and sacrificing himself in the service of something lofty; without any merit on his part, it is true, merely out of a feeling of necessity. And this was his jealousy: that no one should become greater than he, who had not also suffered more deeply than he for the sake of this lofty thing.

Niemand!—Er blieb stehen, die Hand über den Augen, den Oberkörper halb seitwärts gewandt, ausweichend, fliehend. Aber er fühlte schon den Stachel dieses unvermeidlichen Gedankens in seinem Herzen, des Gedankens an ihn, den anderen, den Hellen, Tatseligen, Sinnlichen, Göttlich-Unbewußten, an *den* dort, in Weimar, den er mit einer sehnsüchtigen Feindschaft liebte.—Und wieder, wie stets, in tiefer Unruhe, mit Hast und Eifer, fühlte er die Arbeit in sich beginnen, die diesem Gedanken folgte: das eigene Wesen und Künstlertum gegen das des anderen zu behaupten und abzugrenzen.—War er denn größer? Worin? Warum? War es ein blutendes Trotzdem, wenn er siegte? Würde je sein Erliegen ein tragisches Schauspiel sein? Ein Gott, vielleicht,—ein Held war er nicht. Aber es war leichter, ein Gott zu sein, als ein Held!—Leichter . . . Der andere hatte es leichter! Mit weiser und glücklicher Hand Erkennen und Schaffen zu scheiden, das mochte heiter und quallos und quellend fruchtbar machen. Aber war Schaffen göttlich, so war Erkenntnis Heldentum, und beides war der, ein Gott und ein Held, welcher erkennend schuf!

Der Wille zum Schweren . . . Ahnte man, wieviel Zucht und Selbstüberwindung ein Satz, ein strenger Gedanke ihn kostete? Denn zuletzt war er unwissend und wenig geschult, ein dumpfer und schwärmender Träumer. Es war schwerer, einen Brief des Julius [12] zu schreiben, als die beste Szene zu machen,—und war es nicht darum auch fast schon das Höhere?—Vom ersten rhythmischen Drange innerer Kunst nach Stoff, Materie, Möglichkeit des Ergusses—bis zum Gedanken, zum Bilde, zum Worte, zur Zeile: welch Ringen! welch Leidensweg! Wunder der Sehnsucht waren seine Werke, der Sehnsucht nach Form, Gestalt, Begrenzung, Körperlichkeit, der Sehnsucht hinüber in die klare Welt des anderen, der unmittelbar und mit göttlichem Mund die besonnten Dinge bei Namen nannte.

Dennoch, und jenem zum Trotz: Wer war ein Künstler, ein Dichter gleich ihm, ihm selbst? Wer schuf, wie er, aus dem Nichts, aus der eigenen Brust? War nicht als Musik,[13] als reines Urbild des Seins ein Gedicht in seiner Seele geboren, lange bevor es sich Gleichnis und Kleid aus der Welt der Erscheinungen lieh? Geschichte, Weltweisheit, Leiden-

No one!—He stopped, his hand over his eyes, his torso turned half sideways, avoiding, fleeing. But he already felt the goad of this unavoidable thought in his heart, the thought of him, the other one, the bright one, happy in doing, sensuous, divinely unconscious—of *that man* there, in Weimar, whom he loved with a yearning enmity. And once again, as always, in deep disquiet, with haste and zeal, he felt stirring within him the labor which followed this thought: to assert and delimit his own essence and artistry against that of the other. Was he really greater? In what? Why? When he triumphed—was it a bloody "despite"? Would his defeat ever be a tragic spectacle? A god, perhaps—he was no hero. But it was easier to be a god than a hero. Easier . . . The other had an easier time of it. To differentiate knowing and creating with a wise and happy hand—that could make one serene and free from torment and gushingly fertile. But if creation was divine, knowledge was heroism and he was both, a god and a hero, who created knowingly.

The will to the difficult . . . Did anyone suspect how much discipline and self-control a sentence, a rigorous thought cost him? For in the final analysis he was ignorant and had little schooling, a muddled, enthusiastic dreamer. It was harder to write a letter of Julius than to produce the best scene—and was it not, for that reason alone, almost the higher achievement? From the first rhythmic impulse of inner art toward matter, material, a potential eruption—to the thought, word, line: what a struggle, what a way of suffering. His works were miracles of yearning, of the yearning for form, shape, limitation, corporeality; yearning for the clear world of the other one, who, directly and with divine lips, named the sunlit things by their names.

And yet, and despite the other: who else was an artist, a poet like himself? Who created, as he did, out of nothing, out of his own breast? Was not a poem born in his soul as music, as a pure archetype of being, long before it borrowed a symbol and dress from the world of phenomena? History, world wisdom, passion: means and pretexts, no more, for

schaft: Mittel und Vorwände, nicht mehr, für etwas, was
wenig mit ihnen zu schaffen, was seine Heimat in or-
phischen [14] Tiefen hatte. Worte, Begriffe: Tasten nur, die sein
Künstlertum schlug, um ein verborgenes Saitenspiel klingen
zu machen.—Wußte man das? Sie priesen ihn sehr, die guten
Leute, für die Kraft der Gesinnung, mit welcher er die oder
jene Taste schlug. Und sein Lieblingswort, sein letztes Pathos,
die große Glocke,[15] mit der er zu den höchsten Festen der
Seele rief, sie lockte viele herbei.—Freiheit . . . Mehr und
weniger, wahrhaftig, begriff er darunter, als sie, wenn sie
jubelten. Freiheit—was hieß das? Ein wenig Bürgerwürde doch
nicht vor Fürstenthronen? [16] Laßt ihr euch träumen, was alles
ein Geist mit dem Worte zu meinen wagt? Freiheit wovon?
Wovon zuletzt noch? Vielleicht sogar noch vom Glücke, vom
Menschenglück, dieser seidenen Fessel, dieser weichen und
holden Verpflichtung.—

Vom Glück . . . Seine Lippen zuckten; es war, als kehrte
sein Blick sich nach innen, und langsam ließ er das Gesicht
in die Hände sinken.—Er war im Nebenzimmer. Bläuliches
Licht floß von der Ampel, und der geblümte Vorhang verhüllte in stillen Falten das Fenster. Er stand am Bette, beugte
sich über das süße Haupt auf dem Kissen . . . Eine schwarze
Locke ringelte sich über die Wange, die von der Blässe der
Perle schien, und die kindlichen Lippen waren im Schlummer
geöffnet . . . Mein Weib! Geliebte! Folgtest du meiner
Sehnsucht und tratest du zu mir, mein Glück zu sein? Du
bist es, sei still! Und schlafe! Schlag jetzt nicht diese süßen,
langschattenden Wimpern auf, um mich anzuschauen, so groß
und dunkel, wie manchmal, als fragtest und suchtest du mich!
Bei Gott, bei Gott, ich liebe dich sehr! Ich kann mein Gefühl
nur zuweilen nicht finden, weil ich oft sehr müde vom Leiden
bin und vom Ringen mit jener Aufgabe, welche mein Selbst
mir stellt. Und ich darf nicht allzusehr dein, nie ganz in dir
glücklich sein, um dessentwillen, was meine Sendung ist.—

Er küßte sie, trennte sich von der lieblichen Wärme ihres
Schlummers, sah um sich, kehrte zurück. Die Glocke mahnte
ihn, wieweit schon die Nacht vorgeschritten, aber es war auch
zugleich, als zeigte sie gütig das Ende einer schweren Stunde
an. Er atmete auf, seine Lippen schlossen sich fest; er ging
und ergriff die Feder.—Nicht grübeln! Er war zu tief, um

something which had little to do with them, which had its
habitat in Orphic depths. Words, concepts: mere keys which
his artistry struck, to draw music out of a hidden instrument.
—Was this known? They praised him highly, the good people,
for the power of emotion with which he struck this or that
key. And his favorite word, his final transport, the great bell
with which he summoned people to the highest banquets of
the soul—these enticed many. Freedom . . . Truly, he understood more and less by it than they when they exulted.
Freedom—what did it mean? Surely not a little civic dignity
before the thrones of princes? Do you even dare dream of all
that a spirit dares to mean by the word? Freedom from what?
And from what after that? Perhaps even from hapiness, from
human happiness, that silken bond, that soft and sweet obligation.

From happiness . . . His lips twitched; it was as if his eye
were turning inward and slowly he let his face sink into his
hands. He was in the next room. A bluish light flowed from
the lamp, and the flowered curtain concealed the window in
silent folds. He stood by the bed, bent over the sweet head on
the pillow . . . A black lock curled over her cheek, which
seemed to have the pallor of the pearl, and the childlike lips
were open in slumber . . . My wife! Beloved! Did you obey
my yearning and did you come to me to be my happiness?
You are that, be still! And sleep. Don't open those sweet, long
shadowy lashes to look at me now with those big and dark
eyes, as you sometimes do, as if you were questioning and
seeking me. By Heaven, by Heaven, I love you very much.
Only at times I can't find my feeling because I'm often very
tired from suffering and from struggling with that task which
my self imposes upon me. And I must not be too much yours,
never wholly happy in you, for the sake of that which is my
mission.

He kissed her, separated himself from the pleasant warmth
of her slumber, looked around and went back. The chiming
clock reminded him how far the night had already progressed;
but at the same time it was as if it kindly announced the end
of a difficult hour. He drew a deep breath, his lips closed
firmly; he went and took his pen. No brooding! He was too

grübeln zu dürfen! Nicht ins Chaos hinabsteigen, sich wenigstens nicht dort aufhalten! Sondern aus dem Chaos, welches die Fülle ist, ans Licht emporheben, was fähig und reif ist, Form zu gewinnen. Nicht grübeln! Arbeiten! Begrenzen, ausschalten, gestalten, fertig werden!—

Und es wurde fertig, das Leidenswerk. Es wurde vielleicht nicht gut, aber es wurde fertig. Und als es fertig war, siehe, da war es auch gut. Und aus seiner Seele, aus Musik und Idee, rangen sich neue Werke hervor, klingende und schimmernde Gebilde, die in heiliger Form die unendliche Heimat wunderbar ahnen ließen, wie in der Muschel das Meer saust, dem sie entfischt ist.

far down to be permitted to brood. No descent into chaos; at least no tarrying there. But raise out of the chaos which is fullness, into the light, what is capable and ripe for winning form. No brooding! Work! Limit, exclude, shape, complete!

And it was completed—that labor of suffering. Perhaps it did not turn out well, but it was completed. And when it was completed, behold, it was good too. And out of his soul, out of music and idea, new works struggled forth, ringing and gleaming structures, which in a sacred form, afforded a wonderful intuition of the infinite source of their being—as the sea roars in the shell that was fished from it.

# Hermann Hesse

## (1877-    )

HERMANN HESSE was born in South Germany of a family of missionaries. He rebelled against the strict parental and school atmosphere by running away from home in his adolescence; worked as a machinist, then as a clerk in a bookstore. He left Germany before the First World War and has lived in Switzerland ever since. He has been awarded a number of literary distinctions, including the Nobel Prize for Literature in 1946, on the occasion of his seventieth birthday, and the Order Pour le Mérite in 1954.

Hesse's emotional life has been difficult, bringing him into conflict with traditional, bourgeois society. He has been all his life a fearless, outspoken individualist, promoting the philosophy of self-realization against the tremendous pressures toward conformity that contemporary society imposes. This return to oneself, Hesse believes, is a lifelong task. Siddharta, the hero of the story by that title, realizes himself only at his death; so does the poet in our little parable. Hesse, too, has searched all his life; he has been open to every stimulus from all the cultural forces at work in our world: Oriental mysticism, psychoanalysis, the German romantics, the medieval mystics, Nietzsche. It is this espousal of the doctrine of truth to oneself and the open mind, as well as his recognition of the conflicting souls that are at war within each of us, that has won him a strong following among the youth of the world.

In the little parable reprinted here we are told that Han Fook "slowly learned the secret art of saying what seems un-

complicated and simple, yet stirs the listener's soul as the wind stirs the surface of the water." There is no better way of describing the quality of Hesse's writing. He has the mysterious faculty of expressing in limpid, untranslatable diction the complex sensibility of modern man. The reader can look into the chaos of the world and his own soul, and gaze at the Gorgon without becoming petrified at the sight. Hesse's art is healing, though it calls for constant effort as the price of recovery. His work is varied in theme and tone. He can be tenderly romantic; he can create a fairy tale mood and atmosphere; he can be caustically satirical; he can be tantalizingly ambiguous. The one thing he cannot do is to be dull or write badly.

# DER DICHTER

von Hermann Hesse

Es WIRD erzählt, daß der chinesische Dichter Han Fook in seiner Jugend von einem wunderbaren Drang beseelt war, alles zu lernen und sich in allem zu vervollkommnen, was zur Dichtkunst irgend [1] gehört. Er war damals, da er noch in seiner Heimat am Gelben Flusse lebte, auf seinen Wunsch und mit Hilfe seiner Eltern, die ihn zärtlich liebten, mit einem Fräulein aus gutem Hause verlobt worden, und die Hochzeit sollte nun bald auf einen glückverheißenden Tag festgesetzt werden. Han Fook war damals etwa zwanzig Jahre alt und ein hübscher Jüngling, bescheiden und von angenehmen Umgangsformen, in den Wissenschaften unterrichtet und trotz seiner Jugend schon durch manche vorzügliche Gedichte unter den Literaten seiner Heimat bekannt. Ohne gerade reich zu sein, hatte er doch ein auskömmliches Vermögen zu erwarten, das durch die Mitgift seiner Braut [2] noch erhöht wurde, und da diese Braut außerdem sehr schön und tugendhaft war, schien an dem Glücke des Jünglings durchaus nichts mehr zu fehlen. Dennoch war er nicht ganz zufrieden, denn sein Herz war von dem Ehrgeiz erfüllt, ein vollkommener Dichter zu werden.

Da geschah es an einem Abend, da ein Lampenfest auf dem Flusse begangen wurde, daß Han Fook allein am jenseitigen Ufer des Flusses wandelte. Er lehnte sich an den Stamm eines Baumes, der sich über das Wasser neigte, und sah im Spiegel des Flusses tausend Lichter schwimmen und zittern, er sah auf den Booten und Flößen Männer und Frauen und

# THE POET

## by Hermann Hesse

It is told that, in his youth, the Chinese poet Han Fook was inspired with a wonderful urge to learn everything and to perfect himself in everything that in any way pertained to the art of poetry. At that time, when he still lived in his native city by the Yellow River, he had become engaged to a young lady of good family, at his own request and with the help of his parents who loved him tenderly. The wedding was soon to be fixed for an auspicious day. At that time Han Fook was about twenty years old, a handsome youth, modest and with pleasant manners, well informed in the sciences and, in spite of his youth, already known for some excellent poems among the literati of his native city. Without being exactly rich, he could nevertheless expect an adequate fortune which was to be further increased by his bride's dowry; and since this bride was very beautiful and virtuous besides, the youth's happiness seemed to lack absolutely nothing. And yet he was not altogether contented, for his heart was filled with the ambition to become a perfect poet.

Then it happened one evening, when a lantern feast was being celebrated on the river, that Han Fook was walking alone on the opposite bank of the river. He leaned against the trunk of a tree that bent over into the water, and saw a thousand lights swimming and trembling on the surface of the river; he saw men and women and young girls greet each other on

junge Mädchen einander begrüßen und in festlichen Gewändern wie schöne Blumen glänzen, er hörte das schwache Gemurmel der beleuchteten Wasser, den Gesang der Sängerinnen, das Schwirren der Zither und die süßen Töne der Flötenbläser, und über dem allem sah er die bläuliche Nacht wie das Gewölbe eines Tempels schweben. Dem Jünglinge schlug das Herz, da er als einsamer Zuschauer, seiner Laune folgend, alle diese Schönheit betrachtete. Aber so sehr ihn verlangte,[3] hinüberzugehen und dabei zu sein und in der Nähe seiner Braut und seiner Freunde das Fest zu genießen, so begehrte er dennoch weit sehnlicher, dies alles als ein feiner [4] Zuschauer aufzunehmen und in einem ganz volkommenen Gedichte widerzuspiegeln: die Bläue der Nacht und das Lichterspiel des Wassers sowohl wie die Lust der Festgäste und die Sehnsucht des stillen Zuschauers, der am Stamm des Baumes über dem Ufer lehnt. Er empfand, daß ihm bei allen Festen und aller Lust dieser Erde doch niemals ganz und gar wohl und heiter ums Herz sein könnte, daß er auch inmitten des Lebens ein Einsamer und gewissermaßen ein Zuschauer und Fremdling bleiben würde, und er empfand, daß seine Seele unter vielen anderen allein so beschaffen sei, daß er zugleich die Schönheit der Erde und das heimliche Verlangen des Fremdlings fühlen mußte. Darüber wurde er traurig und sann dieser Sache nach, und das Ziel seiner Gedanken war dieses, daß ihm ein wahres Glück und eine tiefe Sättigung nur dann zuteil werden könnte, wenn es ihm einmal gelänge, die Welt so vollkommen in Gedichten zu spiegeln, daß er in diesen Spiegelbildern die Welt selbst geläutert und verewigt besäße.

Kaum wußte Han Fook, ob er noch wache oder eingeschlummert sei, als er ein leises Geräusch vernahm und neben dem Baumstamm einen Unbekannten stehen sah, einen alten Mann in einem violetten Gewande und mit ehrwürdigen Mienen. Er richtete sich auf und begrüßte ihn mit dem Gruß, der den Greisen und Vornehmen zukommt, der Fremde aber lächelte und sprach einige Verse, in denen war alles, was der junge Mann soeben empfunden hatte, so vollkommen und schön und nach den Regeln der großen Dichter ausgedrückt, daß dem Jüngling vor Staunen das Herz stillstand.

„O, wer bist du", rief er, indem er sich tief verneigte, „der du [5] in meine Seele sehen kannst und schönere Verse sprichst,

the boats and rafts, resplendent like beautiful flowers in their festive clothes; he heard the faint murmur of the illumined waters, the songs of the girl singers, the vibration of the zithers and the sweet tones of the flutists; and above all this he saw the bluish night suspended like the vault of a temple. The youth's heart beat fast when, as a lonely spectator following his whim, he contemplated all this beauty. But, however much he wanted to cross over, to participate, and to enjoy the festival in the company of his bride and his friends, he yet desired far more ardently to absorb all this as a sensitive spectator and to reflect it in a quite perfect poem: the blue of the night and the play of lights on the water as well as the pleasure of the festival guests and the yearning of the silent spectator who leans against the trunk of the tree above the bank. He felt that, despite all the festivals and pleasures of this earth, his heart could never feel quite comfortable and serene, that even in the midst of life he would remain a lonely man and to a certain extent a spectator and a stranger. And he felt that his soul, alone among many others, was so constituted that he must at the same time feel the beauty of the earth and the secret yearning of the stranger. This saddened him and he pondered on it, and the goal of his thoughts was this: that true happiness and a deep satisfaction could only be his if he once succeeded in mirroring the world so perfectly in a poem that he would possess the world itself, purified and perpetuated in these mirror images.

Han Fook scarcely knew whether he was still awake or had fallen asleep, when he heard a slight rustle and saw an unknown man standing near the tree trunk, an old man of venerable mien, dressed in a violet cloak. Han Fook drew himself up and saluted him with the greeting that is fitting for old and distinguished men. But the stranger smiled and spoke some verses which contained everything that the young man had just felt, expressed so perfectly and beautifully and according to the rules of the great poets that the youth's heart stood still in astonishment.

"Oh, who are you," he cried, bowing deeply, "you who can see into my soul and speak more beautiful verses than

als ich je von allen meinen Lehrern vernommen habe?"

Der Fremde lächelte abermals mit dem Lächeln der Vollendeten und sagte: „Wenn du ein Dichter werden willst, so komm zu mir. Du findest meine Hütte bei der Quelle des großen Flusses in den nordwestlichen Bergen. Mein Name ist Meister des vollkommenen Wortes."

Damit trat der alte Mann in den schmalen Schatten des Baumes und war alsbald verschwunden, und Han Fook, der ihn vergebens suchte und keine Spur von ihm mehr fand, glaubte nun fest, daß alles ein Traum der Müdigkeit gewesen sei. Er eilte zu den Booten hinüber und wohnte dem Feste bei, aber zwischen Gespräch und Flötenklang vernahm er immerzu die geheimnisvolle Stimme des Fremden, und seine Seele schien mit jenem dahingegangen, denn er saß fremd und mit träumenden Augen unter den Fröhlichen, die ihn mit seiner Verliebtheit neckten.

Wenige Tage später wollte Han Fooks Vater seine Freunde und Verwandten berufen, um den Tag der Vermählung zu bestimmen. Da widersetzte sich der Bräutigam und sagte: „Verzeihe mir, wenn ich gegen den Gehorsam zu verstoßen scheine, den der Sohn dem Vater schuldet. Aber du weißt, wie sehr es mein Velangen ist, in der Kunst der Dichter mich auszuzeichnen, und wenn auch einige meiner Freunde meine Gedichte loben, so weiß ich doch wohl, daß ich noch ein Anfänger und noch auf den ersten Stufen des Weges bin. Darum bitte ich dich, laß mich noch eine Weile in die Einsamkeit gehen und meinen Studien nachhängen, denn mir scheint, wenn ich erst eine Frau und ein Haus zu regieren habe, wird dies mich von jenen Dingen abhalten. Jetzt aber bin ich noch jung und ohne andere Pflichten und möchte noch eine Zeit allein für meine Dichtkunst leben, von der ich Freude und Ruhm erhoffe."

Die Rede setzte den Vater in Erstaunen, und er sagte: „Diese Kunst muß dir wohl über alles lieb sein, da du ihretwegen sogar deine Hochzeit verschieben willst. Oder ist etwas zwischen dich und deine Braut gekommen, so sage es mir, daß ich dir helfen kann, sie zu versöhnen oder dir eine andere zu verschaffen."

Der Sohn schwur aber, daß er seine Braut nicht weniger liebe als gestern und immer, und daß nicht der Schatten eines

I have ever heard from all my teachers?"

The stranger smiled again, the smile of the accomplished, and said: "If you want to become a poet, come to me. You will find my hut by the source of the great river in the northwestern mountains. My name is Master of the Perfect Word."

With that the old man stepped into the narrow shadow of the tree and had soon vanished; and Han Fook, who looked for him in vain and found no trace of him, now firmly believed that it had all been a dream born of his weariness. He hurried over to the boats and took part in the feast, but between the conversation and the flute playing he constantly heard the mysterious voice of the stranger; and his soul seemed to have left with the other, for he sat, a stranger and dreamy-eyed, among the cheerful guests who teased him about his lovesickness.

A few days later Han Fook's father wanted to summon his friends and relatives to set the date of the wedding. But the bridegroom objected and said: "Forgive me if I seem to offend against the obedience which the son owes his father. But you know how very much it is my desire to distinguish myself in the art of the poets; and even though some of my friends praise my poems, I know quite well that I am still only a beginner and only on the first steps of the road. Therefore I beg you, let me first go into solitude for a while and pursue my studies, for it seems to me that once I have a wife and a house to manage, they will keep me away from those things. But now I am still young and without other duties and would like to live a little while longer just for my poetry, from which I hope to gain happiness and fame."

This speech astonished his father and he said: "This art must surely be dear to you above everything else, since you even want to postpone your wedding because of it. Or if something has come between your bride and you, tell me about it, so that I may help you to appease her or to find you another."

But the son swore that he loved his bride no less than yesterday and always, and that not even the shadow of a quar-

Streites zwischen ihn und sie gefallen sei. Und zugleich erzählte er seinem Vater, daß ihm durch einen Traum am Tag des Lampenfestes ein Meister kundgeworden sei, dessen Schüler zu werden er sehnlicher wünsche als alles Glück der Welt.

„Wohl", sprach der Vater, „so gebe ich dir ein Jahr. In dieser Zeit magst du deinem Traum nachgehen, der vielleicht von einem Gott zu dir gesandt worden ist."

„Es mögen auch zwei Jahre werden", sagte Han Fook zögernd, „wer will [6] das wissen?"

Da ließ ihn der Vater gehen und war betrübt, der Jüngling aber schrieb seiner Braut einen Brief, verabschiedete sich und zog davon.

Als er sehr lange gewandert war, erreichte er die Quelle des Flusses und fand in großer Einsamkeit eine Bambushütte stehen, und vor der Hütte saß auf einer geflochtenen Matte der alte Mann, den er am Ufer bei dem Baumstamm gesehen hatte. Er saß und spielte die Laute, und als er den Gast sich mit Ehrfurcht nähern sah, erhob er sich nicht, noch grüßte er ihn, sondern lächelte nur und ließ die zarten Finger über die Saiten laufen, und eine zauberhafte Musik floß wie eine silberne Wolke durch das Tal, daß der Jüngling stand und sich verwunderte und in süßem Erstaunen alles andere vergaß, bis der Meister des vollkommenen Wortes seine kleine Laute beiseite legte und in die Hütte trat. Da folgte ihm Han Fook mit Ehrfurcht und blieb bei ihm als sein Diener und Schüler.

Ein Monat verging, da hatte er gelernt, alle Lieder, die er zuvor gedichtet hatte, zu verachten, und er tilgte sie aus seinem Gedächtnisse. Und wieder nach Monaten tilgte er auch die Lieder, die er daheim von seinen Lehrern gelernt hatte, aus seinem Gedächtnis. Der Meister sprach kaum ein Wort mit ihm, er lehrte ihn schweigend die Kunst des Lautenspieles, bis das Wesen [7] des Schülers ganz von Musik durchflossen war. Einst machte Han Fook ein kleines Gedicht, worin er den Flug zweier Vögel am herbstlichen Himmel beschrieb, und das ihm wohlgefiel. Er wagte nicht, es dem Meister zu zeigen, aber er sang es eines Abends abseits von der Hütte, und der Meister hörte es wohl. Er sagte jedoch kein Wort. Er spielte nur leise auf seiner Laute, und alsbald ward die Luft kühl und die Dämmerung beschleunigt, ein scharfer Wind erhob sich,

rel had fallen between him and her. And at the same time he told his father that, in a dream which he had had on the day of the lantern feast, a master had been revealed to him; and that he yearned more ardently to become his pupil than to possess all the happiness of the world.

"Very well," said his father, "then I will give you a year. During this time you may pursue your dream, which was perhaps sent to you by a god."

"It may well be two years," said Han Fook hesitatingly, "who can know?"

So his father let him go and was saddened; but the youth wrote his bride a letter, said good-bye and left.

When he had walked for a very long time, he reached the source of the river and found a bamboo hut standing there in great solitude; and before the hut the old man whom he had seen by the bank near the tree trunk sat on a woven mat. He sat there playing the lute, and when he saw his guest approaching reverently, he did not rise nor did he greet him, but only smiled and let his delicate fingers run over the strings, and an enchanting music floated like a silver cloud through the valley, so that the youth stood and marveled, and in his sweet wonderment he forgot everything else until the Master of the Perfect Word laid his little lute aside and went into the hut. Han Fook followed him in reverence and stayed with him as his servant and pupil.

A month passed and he had learned to despise all the songs which he had composed till now, and he obliterated them from his memory. And after several more months, he also removed from his mind those songs which he had learned from his teachers at home. The master scarcely spoke a word to him; he silently taught him the art of lute playing, until the soul of the pupil was completely saturated with music. Once Han Fook made a little poem in which he described the flight of two birds in the autumnal sky and which he liked well. He did not dare to show it to the master, but he sang it one evening at a little distance from the hut, and the master must have heard it. But he did not say a word. He merely played softly on his lute, and soon the air grew cool and the twilight dimmer; a sharp wind arose although it was

obwohl es mitten im Sommer war, und über den grau gewordenen Himmel flogen zwei Reiher in mächtiger Wandersehnsucht, und alles dies war so viel schöner und vollkommener als des Schülers Verse, daß dieser traurig wurde und schwieg und sich wertlos fühlte. Und so tat der Alte jedesmal, und als ein Jahr vergangen war, da hatte Han Fook das Lautenspiel beinahe vollkommen erlernt, die Kunst der Dichtung aber sah er immer schwerer und erhabener stehen.

Als zwei Jahre vergangen waren, spürte der Jüngling ein heftiges Heimweh nach den Seinigen, nach der Heimat und nach seiner Braut, und er bat den Meister, ihn reisen zu lassen.

Der Meister lächelte und nickte. „Du bist frei", sagte er, „und kannst gehen, wohin du willst. Du magst wiederkommen, du magst wegbleiben, ganz wie es dir gefällt."

Da machte sich der Schüler auf die Reise und wanderte rastlos, bis er eines Morgens in der Dämmerung am heimatlichen Ufer stand und über die gewölbte Brücke nach seiner Vaterstadt hinübersah. Er schlich verstohlen in seines Vaters Garten und hörte durchs Fenster des Schlafzimmers seines Vaters Atem gehen, der noch schlief, und er stahl sich in den Baumgarten beim Hause seiner Braut und sah vom Wipfel eines Birnbaumes, den er erstieg, seine Braut in der Kammer stehen und ihre Haare kämmen. Und indem er dies alles, wie er es mit seinen Augen sah, mit dem Bilde verglich, das er in seinem Heimweh davon gemalt hatte, ward es ihm deutlich, daß er doch zum Dichter bestimmt sei, und er sah, daß in den Träumen der Dichter eine Schönheit und Anmut wohnt, die man in den Dingen der Wirklichkeit vergeblich sucht. Und er stieg von dem Baume herab und floh aus dem Garten und über die Brücke aus seiner Vaterstadt und kehrte in das hohe Tal im Gebirge zurück. Da saß wie einstmals der alte Meister vor seiner Hütte auf der bescheidenen Matte und schlug mit seinen Fingern die Laute, und statt der Begrüßung sprach er zwei Verse von den Beglückungen der Kunst, bei deren Tiefe und Wohllaut dem Jünger die Augen voll Tränen wurden.

Wieder blieb Han Fook bei dem Meister des vollkommenen Wortes, der ihn nun, da er die Laute beherrschte, auf der Zither unterrichtete, und die Monate schwanden hinweg wie Schnee im Westwinde. Noch zweimal geschah es, daß

midsummer, and across the sky, which had turned gray, two
herons flew, driven by a powerful wanderlust; and all this
was so much more beautiful and more perfect than the pupil's
verses that he became sad and fell silent and felt himself to
be worthless. And the old man did this every time; and when
a year had passed, Han Fook had almost completely learned
the art of lute playing; but the art of poetry stood before him
more and more difficult and sublime.

When two years had passed, the youth felt an intense
nostalgia for his family, his native city and his bride, and he
asked the master to let him journey.

The master smiled and nodded. "You are free," he said,
"and may go wherever you will. You may come back, you
may stay away, just as you please."

So the pupil set out on his journey and walked without
resting, until one morning at dawn he stood on his native
shore and looked across the arched bridge toward his home
town. He crept stealthily into his father's garden and heard
his father's breathing through the window of his bedroom,
for he was still sleeping; and he crept into the orchard beside
his bride's house and, from the top of a pear tree which he
climbed, he saw his bride standing in her room, combing her
hair. And when he compared all this that he saw with his
eyes with the picture he had painted of it in his homesickness,
it became clear to him that he was destined, after all, to be
a poet; and he realized that in the dreams of poets there
dwells a beauty and grace which one seeks in vain in the
things of reality. And he climbed down from the tree and
fled from the garden, over the bridge and from his native city,
and returned to the high valley in the mountains. There the
old master sat, as before, in front of his hut on the modest
mat, plucking the lute with his fingers. Instead of a greeting
he spoke two verses on the joys of art, whose depth and
euphony caused the youth's eyes to fill with tears.

Again Han Fook stayed with the Master of the Perfect
Word, who now instructed him on the zither, since he had
mastered the lute, and the months vanished away like snow
in the west wind. Twice more it happened that he was over-

ihn das Heimweh übermannte. Das eine Mal lief er heimlich
in der Nacht davon, aber noch ehe er die letzte Krümmung
des Tales erreicht hatte, lief der Nachtwind über die Zither,
die in der Tür der Hütte hing, und die Töne flohen ihm nach
und riefen ihn zurück, daß er nicht widerstehen konnte. Das
andere Mal aber träumte ihn, er pflanze einen jungen Baum in
seinen Garten, und sein Weib stünde dabei, und seine Kinder
begössen den Baum mit Wein und Milch. Als er erwachte,
schien der Mond in seine Kammer, und er erhob sich verstört
und sah nebenan den Meister im Schlummer liegen und seinen
greisen Bart sachte zittern; da überfiel ihn ein bitterer Haß
gegen diesen Menschen, der, wie ihm schien, sein Leben
zerstört und ihn um seine Zukunft betrogen habe. Er wollte
sich über ihn stürzen und ihn ermorden, da schlug der Greis
die Augen auf und begann alsbald mit einer feinen, traurigen
Sanftmut zu lächeln, die den Schüler entwaffnete.

„Erinnere dich, Han Fook", sagte der Alte leise, „du bist
frei, zu tun, was dir beliebt. Du magst in deine Heimat gehen
und Bäume pflanzen, du magst mich hassen und erschlagen,
es ist wenig daran gelegen." [8]

„Ach, wie könnte ich dich hassen", rief der Dichter in
heftiger Bewegung. „Das ist, als ob ich den Himmel selbst
hassen wollte."

Und er blieb und lernte die Zither spielen, und danach die
Flöte, und später begann er unter des Meisters Anweisung
Gedichte zu machen, und er lernte langsam jene heimliche
Kunst, scheinbar nur das Einfache und Schlichte zu sagen,
damit [9] aber in des Zuhörers Seele zu wühlen wie der Wind in
einem Wasserspiegel. Er beschrieb das Kommen der Sonne,
wie sie am Rand des Gebirges zögert, und das lautlose Huschen der Fische, wenn sie wie Schatten unter dem Wasser
hinfliehen, oder das Wiegen einer jungen Weide im Früh-
lingswind, und wenn man es hörte, so war es nicht die Sonne
und das Spiel der Fische und das Flüstern der Weide allein,
sondern es schien der Himmel und die Welt jedesmal für
einen Augenblick in vollkommener Musik zusammenzu-
klingen, und jeder Hörer dachte dabei mit Lust oder Schmerzen an das, was er liebte oder haßte, der Knabe ans Spiel, der
Jüngling an die Geliebte und der Alte an den Tod.

Han Fook wußte nicht mehr, wie viele Jahre er bei dem

come by homesickness. One time he ran away secretly at night; but even before he had reached the last bend of the valley, the night wind rustled over the zither which hung in the door of the hut, and the tones sped after him and called him back, so that he was unable to resist. The other time, however, he dreamed that he was planting a sapling in his garden, and his wife stood beside him and his children watered the tree with wine and milk. When he awakened, the moon was shining into his room, and he arose in a disturbed state and saw the master lying in slumber nearby, his ancient beard quivering gently. A bitter hatred arose in him against this man who, as it seemed to him, had destroyed his life and cheated him of his future. He wanted to fall upon him and murder him; at that moment the old man opened his eyes and soon began to smile with a subtle, sad gentleness, which disarmed the pupil.

"Remember, Han Fook," the old man said softly, "you are free to do as you please. You may go to your native city and plant trees, or you may hate and slay me, it matters little."

"Ah, how could I hate you," cried the poet deeply moved, "that would be like hating Heaven itself."

And he stayed and learned to play the zither, and then the flute, and later on he began, under the direction of the master, to make poems; and he slowly learned the secret art of saying what seems uncomplicated and simple, yet stirs the listener's soul as the wind stirs the surface of the water. He described the coming of the sun, how it hesitates at the ridge of the mountains, and the noiseless gliding of the fish when they flit by like shadows under the water, or the swaying of a young willow in the spring wind; and when one heard it, it was not merely the sun and the play of the fish and the whispering of the willow, but the sky and the world seemed each time to harmonize for a moment in perfect music; and every listener thought, as he listened with pleasure or pain, of what he loved or hated: the boy thought of his games, the youth of his beloved and the old man of death.

Han Fook no longer knew how many years he had spent

Meister an der Quelle des großen Flusses verweilt habe; oft
schien es ihm, als sei er erst gestern abend in dieses Tal getreten und vom Saitenspiel des Alten empfangen worden,
oft auch war ihm, als [10] seien hinter ihm alle Menschenalter
und Zeiten hinabgefallen und wesenlos geworden.

Da erwachte er eines Morgens allein in der Hütte, und wo
er auch suchte und rief, der Meister war verschwunden. Über
Nacht schien plötzlich der Herbst gekommen, ein rauher
Wind rüttelte an der alten Hütte, und über den Grat des Gebirges flogen große Scharen von Zugvögeln, obwohl es noch
nicht ihre Zeit war.

Da nahm Han Fook die kleine Laute mit sich und stieg in
das Land seiner Heimat hinab, und wo er zu Menschen kam,
begrüßten sie ihn mit dem Gruß, der den Alten und Vornehmen zukommt, und als er in seine Vaterstadt kam, da war [11]
sein Vater und seine Braut und seine Verwandtschaft gestorben, und andere Menschen wohnten in ihren Häusern. Am
Abend aber wurde das Lampenfest auf dem Flusse gefeiert,
und der Dichter Han Fook stand jenseits auf dem dunkleren
Ufer, an den Stamm eines alten Baumes gelehnt, und als er
auf seiner kleinen Laute zu spielen begann, da seufzten die
Frauen und blickten entzückt und beklommen in die Nacht,
und die jungen Männer riefen nach dem Lautenspieler, den
sie nirgends finden konnten, und riefen laut, daß noch keiner
von ihnen jemals solche Töne einer Laute gehört habe. Han
Fook lächelte. Er schaute in den Fluß, wo die Spiegelbilder
der tausend Lampen schwammen; und wie er die Spiegelbilder nicht mehr von den wirklichen zu unterscheiden wußte,
so fand er in seiner Seele keinen Unterschied zwischen
diesem [12] und jenem ersten, da er hier als ein Jüngling gestanden war und die Worte des fremden Meisters vernommen
hatte.

with the master at the source of the great river. Often it seemed to him as if he had entered this valley only last night and had been received by the old man's music. Often, too, he felt as if all human generations and ages had fallen away behind him and become insubstantial.

Then one morning he awoke alone in the hut, and no matter where he looked and called, the master had vanished. Autumn seemed to have come suddenly over night; a raw wind shook the old hut, and over the ridge of the mountains great flocks of migratory birds were flying, although their time had not come yet.

Then Han Fook took his little lute with him and descended into the land of his native city, and wherever he met people they gave him the greeting which is fitting for old and distinguished men. And when he came to his native city, his father and his bride and his relatives had died and other people lived in their houses. In the evening the lantern festival was celebrated on the river, and the poet Han Fook stood on the far side, on the darker shore, leaning against the trunk of an old tree; and when he began to play on his small lute, the women sighed and looked in rapture and uneasiness into the night, and the young men called for the lute player, whom they could find nowhere, and shouted that not one of them had ever heard such lute tones before. But Han Fook smiled. He looked into the river where the mirrored images of the thousand lanterns swam. And just as he was no longer able to distinguish the mirrored images from the real ones, he found no difference in his soul between this feast and that first one, when he had stood here as a youth and had heard the words of the strange master.

# Franz Kafka

## (1883–1924)

KAFKA, RILKE and Thomas Mann are the three German
writers of the twentieth century who have had the greatest
impact on the Western mind. Of the three Kafka has enjoyed
the greatest popularity among the sophisticated, because of
the peculiar fascination which his grotesque world exercises
on contemporary man and because he presents that world
with such consummate artistry. It is a world full of frustra-
tions, absurdities, cruelties and injustices. Kafka's anonymous
"heroes" move through life as in a nightmare; space, time,
causality, our ordinary forms of thinking and perceiving are
distorted or altogether abolished. The intellectuals see in
this crazy world the perfect mirror of what the politicians and
the scientists have made of our earth.

These bewildered, anonymous men of his seek acceptance,
grace, the ideal, God, but do not find them. Sometimes it is
the goal itself that is a mystery to them. Or they see the goal
and make for it, but are prevented by outside forces from
reaching it. Or they know what the goal is but are ignorant
of the way that leads to it and can find no one to guide and
help them. So they develop that guilt, anxiety, alienation,
degradation that is the spiritual pathology of twentieth-century man.

As an artist Kafka broke radically with the psychological
vogue that has dominated fiction for two centuries, and returned to a preoccupation with myth, parable, allegory and
symbol. In this again he anticipated the wide popular interest

in these subjects which has developed in the last thirty years. But on the question as to just what these myths and parables say, the critics are split apart. Kafka has been interpreted theologically, metaphysically, sociologically, ethnically, from the point of view of psychoanalysis. Which of these is right? As a British scholar put it: "Every man may apply Kafka's general pattern to his own immediate problem. If you are interested in original sin, then the stories are about original sin. If you are the eternal modern exile trying to find a place in a settled land, whether of the body or the spirit, then the story is about that. If you hate the law and think, like Dickens, that life is a trial in a Circumlocution Court, then the book is about that. If your problem is the search for God, the book is about the search for God."

The fascination which Kafka's work has over his readers derives from two sources. The myths, parables and allegories which he creates are tantalizing puzzles which tease the reader's ingenuity; what do the country doctor, the maid, the groom, the sick boy and, above all, the horses in our story "stand for"? And second, Kafka's love of elaborate realistic detail give the reader an illusion that he is in the world of everyday reality when he knows that he is working with fantastic symbols.

To give the reader a pat interpretation of Kafka's allegory would be as tasteless as to reveal the end of a mystery story in advance. But he does need a few hints to work out the details of the allegory for himself. It is clear that the story deals with the existentialist theme of man's search for a meaningful or authentic existence. The country doctor is contemporary man, man since the Renaissance, who is ruled by two opposing forces within him: animal wildness and undirected spirit. Since there is no binding and controlling universal order, even man's espousal of spirituality causes desolation and disorder; it unleashes sensuality and leads to boredom, emptiness and nausea.

# EIN LANDARZT

## von Franz Kafka

ICH WAR in großer Verlegenheit: eine dringende Reise stand
mir bevor; ein Schwerkranker wartete auf mich in einem zehn
Meilen entfernten Dorfe; starkes Schneegestöber füllte den
weiten Raum zwischen mir und ihm; einen Wagen hatte ich,
leicht, großräderig, ganz wie er für unsere Landstraßen taugt;
in den Pelz gepackt, die Instrumententasche in der Hand,
stand ich reisefertig schon auf dem Hofe; aber das Pferd
fehlte, das Pferd. Mein eigenes Pferd war in der letzten Nacht
infolge der Überanstrengung in diesem eisigen Winter verendet; mein Dienstmädchen lief jetzt im Dorf umher um ein
Pferd geliehen zu bekommen; aber es war aussichtslos, ich
wußte es, und immer mehr vom Schnee überhäuft, immer
unbeweglicher werdend, stand ich zwecklos da.

Am Tor erschien das Mädchen, allein, schwenkte die Laterne; natürlich, wer leiht jetzt sein Pferd her zu solcher Fahrt?
Ich durchmaß noch einmal den Hof; ich fand keine Möglichkeit; zerstreut, gequält stieß ich mit dem Fuß an die brüchige
Tür des schon seit Jahren unbenützten Schweinestalles. Sie
öffnete sich und klappte in den Angeln auf und zu. Wärme
und Geruch wie von Pferden kam hervor. Eine trübe Stalla-
terne schwankte drin an einem Seil. Ein Mann, zusammengekauert in dem niedrigen Verschlag, zeigte sein offenes blau-
äugiges Gesicht.

„Soll ich anspannen?" fragte er, auf allen vieren hervor-
kriechend. Ich wußte nichts zu sagen und beugte mich nur,
um zu sehen, was es noch in dem Stalle gab. Das Dienst-

From *Ersaehlungen*, published by Schocken Books, Inc., N. Y.

# A COUNTRY DOCTOR
## by Franz Kafka

I WAS IN great embarrassment. I was faced with an urgent journey; a patient, seriously ill, was waiting for me in a village ten miles away. A heavy snowstorm filled the large space between him and me. I had a carriage, light, with large wheels, entirely suited for our highways. Wrapped in my fur coat, my instrument case in my hand, I stood in the court-yard ready for the journey. But there was no horse, no horse. My own horse had perished last night as a result of over-exertion in this icy winter. My servant girl was now running about in the village to get a loan of a horse. But it was hope-less, I knew it, and I stood there aimlessly, buried deeper and deeper by the snow, becoming more and more immobile.

The girl appeared at the gate alone, swinging her lantern. Naturally; who will now lend his horse for such a journey? I strode through the courtyard again; I found no possibility. Absently, tortured, I kicked my foot against the decaying door of the pigsty which had not been used for years. It opened and banged open and shut on its hinges. Warmth and a smell as of horses came out. A dimly lit stable lantern was swinging from a rope inside the sty. A man, crouching in the low shed, showed his frank, blue-eyed face.

"Shall I hitch up?" he asked, crawling out on all fours. I could say nothing and only bent down to see what else there was in the stable. The servant girl was standing beside

From *The Penal Colony*, published by Schocken Books, Inc., N. Y.

mädchen stand neben mir. „Man weiß nicht, was für Dinge man im eigenen Hause vorrätig hat", sagte es, und wir beide lachten. „Holla, Bruder, holla, Schwester!" rief der Pferdeknecht, und zwei Pferde, mächtige flankenstarke Tiere, schoben sich hintereinander, die Beine eng am Leib, die wohlgeformten Köpfe wie Kamele senkend, nur durch die Kraft der Wendungen ihres Rumpfes aus dem Türloch, das sie restlos ausfüllten. Aber gleich standen sie aufrecht, hochbeinig, mit dicht ausdampfendem Körper.

„Hilf ihm", sagte ich, und das willige Mädchen eilte, dem Knecht das Geschirr des Wagens zu reichen. Doch kaum war es bei ihm, umfaßt es der Knecht und schlägt sein Gesicht an ihres. Es schreit auf und flüchtet sich zu mir; rot eingedrückt sind zwei Zahnreihen in des Mädchens Wange. „Du Vieh", schreie ich wütend, „willst du die Peitsche?", besinne mich aber gleich, daß es ein Fremder ist; daß ich nicht weiß, woher er kommt, und daß er mir freiwillig aushilft, wo alle andern versagen.

Als wisse er von meinen Gedanken, nimmt er meine Drohung nicht übel, sondern wendet sich nur einmal, immer mit den Pferden beschäftigt, nach mir um. „Steig ein", sagt er dann, und tatsächlich: alles ist bereit. Mit so schönem Gespann, das merke ich, bin ich noch nie gefahren, und ich steige fröhlich ein. „Kutschieren werde aber ich, du kennst nicht den Weg", sage ich. „Gewiß", sagt er, „ich fahre gar nicht mit, ich bleibe bei Rosa." „Nein", schreit Rosa und läuft im richtigen Vorgefühl der Unabwendbarkeit ihres Schicksals ins Haus; ich höre die Türkette klirren, die sie vorlegt; ich höre das Schloß einspringen; ich sehe, wie sie überdies im Flur und weiterjagend durch die Zimmer alle Lichter verlöscht, um sich unauffindbar zu machen.

„Du fährst mit", sage ich zu dem Knecht, „oder ich verzichte auf die Fahrt, so dringend sie auch ist. Es fällt mir nicht ein, dir für die Fahrt das Mädchen als Kaufpreis hinzugeben."

„Munter!" sagt er; klatscht in die Hände; [1] der Wagen wird fortgerissen, wie Holz in der Strömung; noch höre ich, wie die Tür meines Hauses unter dem Ansturm des Knechtes birst und splittert, dann sind mir Augen und Ohren von einem zu allen Sinnen gleichmäßig dringenden Sausen erfüllt. Aber

me. "You don't know what sort of things you have on hand in your own house," she said, and we both laughed. "Hello brother, hello sister!" cried the groom. Two horses, mighty animals with powerful flanks, wriggled through the door opening one behind the other, their legs close to their bodies, their well-shaped heads lowered like those of camels; they got through only by twisting their bodies out of the door opening, which they completely filled. They at once stood erect, long-legged, their bodies steaming densely.

"Help him," I said, and the willing girl hastened to hand the groom the harness for the carriage. But she had hardly reached him, when the groom embraces her and puts his face up to hers. She cries out and takes refuge with me. Two rows of teeth have left a red mark in the girl's cheek. "You beast," I cry in fury, "do you want the whip?" But I remember at once that he is a stranger, that I don't know where he comes from and that he is helping me voluntarily when all others have failed me.

As though he read my thoughts, he does not take my threat amiss but only turns to me once, still busy with the horses. "Get in," he then says, and really, everything is ready. This I notice: I've never yet driven such a handsome team, and I climb in cheerfully. "But I'm going to drive, you don't know the way," I say. "Of course," he says, "I'm not even going along, I'll stay with Rosa." "No," Rosa screams and runs into the house with a sound premonition of the inevitable fate that awaits her. I hear the door chain rattle as she thrusts it forward; I hear the lock snap shut; I see her putting out all the lights in the hall and then running through all the other rooms doing the same, so that she cannot be found.

"You're coming along," I say to the groom, "or I'll give up the journey, urgent though it is. I wouldn't dream of giving you the girl as purchase price for the journey."

"Briskly!" he says; claps his hands; the carriage is carried away like logs by the current. I can still hear the door of my house bursting and splintering under the groom's assault; then my eyes and ears are filled by a roaring that penetrates evenly to all my senses. But that, too, lasts only a moment; for, as if

auch das nur einen Augenblick, denn, als [2] öffne sich unmittelbar vor meinem Hoftor der Hof meines Kranken, bin ich schon dort; ruhig stehen die Pferde; der Schneefall hat aufgehört; Mondlicht ringsum; die Eltern des Kranken eilen aus dem Haus; seine Schwester hinter ihnen; man hebt mich fast aus dem Wagen; den verwirrten Reden entnehme ich nichts; im Krankenzimmer ist die Luft kaum atembar; der vernachlässigte Herdofen raucht; ich werde das Fenster aufstoßen; zuerst aber will ich den Kranken sehen.

Mager, ohne Fieber, nicht kalt, nicht warm, mit leeren Augen, ohne Hemd hebt sich der Junge unter dem Federbett, [3] hängt sich an meinen Hals, flüstert mir ins Ohr: „Doktor, laß mich sterben."

Ich sehe mich um; niemand hat es gehört; die Eltern stehen stumm vorgebeugt und erwarten mein Urteil; die Schwester hat einen Stuhl für meine Handtasche gebracht. Ich öffne die Tasche und suche unter meinen Instrumenten; der Junge tastet immerfort aus dem Bett nach mir hin, um mich an seine Bitte zu erinnern; ich fasse eine Pinzette, prüfe sie im Kerzenlicht und lege sie wieder hin. ‚Ja', denke ich lästernd, ‚in solchen Fällen helfen die Götter, schicken das fehlende Pferd, fügen der Eile wegen noch ein zweites hinzu, spenden zum Übermaß noch den Pferdeknecht—.'

Jetzt erst fällt mir wieder Rosa ein; was tue ich, wie rette ich sie, wie ziehe ich sie unter diesem Pferdeknecht hervor, zehn Meilen von ihr entfernt, unbeherrschbare Pferde vor meinem Wagen? Diese Pferde, die jetzt die Riemen irgendwie gelockert haben; die Fenster, ich weiß nicht wie, von außen aufstoßen; jedes durch ein Fenster den Kopf stecken und, unbeirrt durch den Aufschrei der Familie, den Kranken betrachten.

‚Ich fahre gleich wieder zurück', denke ich, als forderten mich die Pferde zur Reise auf, aber ich dulde es, daß die Schwester, die mich durch die Hitze betäubt glaubt, den Pelz mir abnimmt. Ein Glas Rum wird mir bereitgestellt, der Alte klopft mir auf die Schulter, die Hingabe seines Schatzes rechtfertigt diese Vertraulichkeit. Ich schüttle den Kopf; in dem engen Denkkreis des Alten würde mir übel; nur aus diesem Grunde lehne ich es ab zu trinken. Die Mutter steht am Bett und lockt mich hin; ich folge und lege, während mein Pferd laut

my patient's yard opened directly in front of my yard, I am
already there. The horses stand quiet; the snow has stopped
falling; there is moonlight round about me. The patient's
parents hurry out of the house; his sister behind them. They
almost lift me out of the carriage; I can get nothing out of
their confused words. The air in the sick room is scarcely
breathable. The neglected fireplace is smoking. I shall push
the window open; but first I want to see the patient.

Skinny, without fever, not cold, not warm, with vacant
eyes, without a shirt, the boy raises himself under the feather
bed, clings to my neck and whispers into my ear, "Doctor,
let me die."

I look about me; no one has heard it. The parents are
standing silently, bending forward, awaiting my judgment.
The sister has brought a chair for my bag. I open the bag
and hunt among my instruments. The boy keeps groping for
me from his bed, to remind me of his plea. I take hold of a
forceps, test it by the candle light and lay it down again.
"Yes," I think blasphemously, "in such cases the gods help,
send the missing horse, even add a second one because of the
urgency, and as a luxury even grant you a groom——"

Only now I think of Rosa again; what can I do, how can
I rescue her, how can I pull her from under this groom, ten
miles away from here, with unmanageable horses hitched to
my carriage? These horses which have now in some way
loosened the harness straps, open the windows from outside—
I don't know how; each one pokes his head through a
window and, unconcerned by the alarm of the family, is
studying the patient!

"I'm driving right back again," I think, as if the horses
challenged me to take the trip. But I permit the sister, who
thinks I am stunned by the heat, to take my fur coat off me.
A glass of rum is put beside me; the old man slaps me on
the shoulder—the giving up of his treasure justifies this
familiarity. I shake my head; I would feel ill in the old man's
narrow intellectual orbit; for this reason only I refuse to drink.
The mother is standing at the bed, enticing me there. I follow
and, while my horse whinnies loudly toward the ceiling of

zur Zimmerdecke wiehert, den Kopf an die Brust des Jungen,
der unter meinem nassen Bart erschauert. Es bestätigt sich,
was ich weiß: der Junge ist gesund, ein wenig schlecht durchblutet,[4] von der sorgenden Mutter mit Kaffee durchtränkt,
aber gesund und am besten mit einem Stoß aus dem Bett zu
treiben. Ich bin kein Weltverbesserer und lasse ihn liegen.
Ich bin vom Bezirk angestellt und tue meine Pflicht bis zum
Rand, bis dorthin, wo es fast zu viel wird. Schlecht bezahlt,
bin ich doch freigebig und hilfsbereit gegenüber den Armen.
Noch für Rosa muß ich sorgen, dann mag der Junge recht
haben [5] und auch ich will sterben. Was tue ich hier in diesem
endlosen Winter! Mein Pferd ist verendet, und da ist niemand
im Dorf, der mir seines leiht. Aus dem Schweinestall muß
ich mein Gespann ziehen; wären es nicht zufällig Pferde,
müßte ich mit Säuen fahren.

So ist es. Und ich nicke der Familie zu. Sie wissen nichts
davon, und wenn sie es wüßten, würden sie es nicht glauben.
Rezepte schreiben ist leicht, aber im übrigen sich mit den
Leuten verständigen, ist schwer.

Nun, hier wäre [6] also mein Besuch zu Ende, man hat mich
wieder einmal unnötig bemüht, daran bin ich gewöhnt, mit
Hilfe meiner Nachtglocke martert mich der ganze Bezirk, aber
daß ich diesmal auch noch Rosa hingeben mußte, dieses
schöne Mädchen, das jahrelang, von mir kaum beachtet, in
meinem Hause lebte—dieses Opfer ist zu groß, und ich muß
es mir mit Spitzfindigkeiten aushilfsweise in meinem Kopf
irgendwie zurechtlegen, um nicht auf diese Familie loszufah-
ren, die mir ja beim besten Willen Rosa nicht zurückgeben
kann.

Als ich aber meine Handtasche schließe und nach meinem
Pelz winke, die Familie beisammensteht, der Vater schnup-
pernd über dem Rumglas in seiner Hand, die Mutter, von
mir wahrscheinlich enttäuscht—ja, was erwartet denn das
Volk?—, tränenvoll in die Lippen beißend und die Schwester
ein schwer blutiges Handtuch schwenkend, bin ich irgendwie
bereit, unter Umständen zuzugeben, daß der Junge doch
vielleicht krank ist. Ich gehe zu ihm, er lächelt mir entgegen,
als brächte ich ihm etwa die allerstärkste Suppe—ach, jetzt
wiehern beide Pferde; der Lärm soll wohl, höhern Orts ange-
ordnet, die Untersuchung erleichtern—, und nun finde ich:

the room, I place my head on the boy's chest; he shudders under my wet beard. What I already know is confirmed: the boy is healthy, with rather poor circulation, saturated with coffee by his solicitous mother, but healthy; and the best thing to do is to drive him out of bed with a kick. But I'm no world reformer and I let him lie. I'm employed by the district and do my duty to the limit, to the point where it almost gets to be too much. Badly paid, I am nevertheless generous and ready to help the poor. I must still look after Rosa; then the boy may have his way and I too want to die. What am I doing here in this endless winter? My horse has perished and there is no one in the village who will lend me his. I must get my team out of the pigsty; if they didn't happen to be horses I would have to ride with sows.

So it is. And I nod to the family. They know nothing about it, and if they knew they wouldn't believe it. It's easy to write prescriptions, but to come to an understanding with people in other matters is hard.

Well, my visit here is probably over. They've bothered me unnecessarily once again, but I'm used to it; with the help of my night bell the whole district tortures me. But this time I had to sacrifice Rosa too, that beautiful girl who lived in my house for years, scarcely noticed by me—this sacrifice is too great; I must somehow, with the help of subtleties, set it right in my head, if I'm not to fly out at this family— which after all, with the best intentions, can't give Rosa back to me.

As I close my bag and motion for my fur coat, and the family stand together, the father sniffing the rum glass in his hand, the mother, probably disappointed in me—well, what do the people expect?—tearfully biting her lips, and the sister waving a towel heavily soaked in blood, I am somehow ready to admit, under the circumstances, that the boy is perhaps sick after all. I go to him, he smiles at me as if I were perhaps bringing him the very strongest broth. Ah, now both horses are whinnying; I suppose the noise, ordered by a higher authority, is intended to facilitate the examination. And now I find: yes! the boy is sick. In his right side, the region of

ja, der Junge ist krank. In seiner rechten Seite, in der Hüften-
gegend hat sich eine handtellergroße Wunde aufgetan. Rosa,
in vielen Schattierungen, dunkel in der Tiefe, hellwerdend
zu den Rändern, zartkörnig, mit ungleichmäßig sich aufsam-
melndem Blut, offen wie ein Bergwerk obertags. So aus der
Entfernung. In der Nähe zeigt sich noch eine Erschwerung.
Wer kann das ansehen ohne leise zu pfeifen? Würmer, an
Stärke und Länge meinem kleinen Finger gleich, rosig aus
eigenem [7] und außerdem blutbespritzt, winden sich, im
Innern der Wunde festgehalten, mit weißen Köpfchen, mit
vielen Beinchen ans Licht.
Armer Junge, dir ist nicht zu helfen. Ich habe deine große
Wunde aufgefunden; an dieser Blume in deiner Seite gehst
du zugrunde. Die Familie ist glücklich, sie sieht mich in
Tätigkeit; die Schwester sagt's der Mutter, die Mutter dem
Vater, der Vater einigen Gästen, die auf den Fußspitzen, mit
ausgestreckten Armen balancierend, durch den Mondschein
der offenen Tür hereinkommen.
„Wirst du mich retten?" flüstert schluchzend der Junge,
ganz geblendet durch das Leben in seiner Wunde. So sind
die Leute in meiner Gegend. Immer das Unmögliche vom
Arzt verlangen.[8] Den alten Glauben haben sie verloren; der
Pfarrer sitzt zu Hause und zerzupft die Meßgewänder, eines
nach dem andern; aber der Arzt soll alles leisten mit seiner
zarten chirurgischen Hand. Nun, wie es beliebt: ich habe
mich nicht angeboten; verbraucht ihr mich zu heiligen
Zwecken, lasse ich auch das mit mir geschehen; was will ich
Besseres, alter Landarzt, meines Dienstmädchens beraubt!
Und sie kommen, die Familie und die Dorfältesten, und
entkleiden mich; ein Schulchor mit dem Lehrer an der Spitze
steht vor dem Haus und singt eine äußerst einfache Melodie
auf den Text:

> Entkleidet ihn, dann wird er heilen,
> Und heilt er nicht, so tötet ihn!
> 's ist nur ein Arzt, 's ist nur ein Arzt.

Dann bin ich entkleidet und sehe, die Finger im Barte, mit
geneigtem Kopfe die Leute ruhig an. Ich bin durchaus gefaßt
und allen überlegen und bleibe es auch, trotzdem es mir nichts
hilft, denn jetzt nehmen sie mich beim Kopf und und bei den

the hip, a wound the size of my palm has opened. Pink, in many shades, dark at the bottom, getting lighter towards the edges, of a delicate grain, with the blood congealing unevenly, open like a surface mine. So it is from a distance. From close up another difficulty reveals itself.

Who can look at that without whistling softly? Worms, the size of my little finger in thickness and length, pink themselves and spattered with blood besides, with small white heads and many tiny legs, held fast in the interior of the wound, writhe their way to the light.

Poor boy, there is no help for you. I have discovered your great wound; you are being destroyed by this flower in your side. The family is happy, seeing me active. The sister tells her mother about it, the mother tells the father, the father tells some guests, who enter on tiptoe through the moonlight of the open door, balancing themselves with outstretched arms.

"Will you save me?" the boy whispers, sobbing, wholly dazzled by the life in his wound. That's the way the people in my region are; they always expect the impossible from the doctor. They have lost the old faith; the minister sits at home pulling his vestments to shreds, one after another; but the doctor is supposed to do everything for them with his delicate surgeon's hand. Well, as you wish: I didn't offer myself. If you use me up for sacred purposes, I'll submit to that too; what more do I want, old country doctor, deprived of my maid! And they come, the family and the village elders, and undress me. A school choir with the teacher at the head stands in front of the house singing an extremely simple melody to the text:

> Undress him, then he'll cure you,
> And if he does not cure, then kill him.
> He's but a doctor, he's but a doctor.

Then I'm undressed and, with bowed head and my fingers in my beard, calmly look at the people. I am completely composed and superior to them all, and I'll stay this way, though it is no use to me, for now they are taking me by the head

Füßen und tragen mich ins Bett. Zur Mauer, an die Seite der
Wunde legen sie mich. Dann gehen alle aus der Stube; die
Tür wird zugemacht; der Gesang verstummt; Wolken treten
vor den Mond; warm liegt das Bettzeug um mich; schatten-
haft schwanken die Pferdeköpfe in den Fensterlöchern.

„Weißt du", höre ich, mir ins Ohr gesagt, „mein Vertrauen
zu dir ist sehr gering. Du bist ja auch nur irgendwo abge-
schüttelt, kommst nicht auf eigenen Füßen. Statt zu helfen,
engst du mir mein Sterbebett ein. Am liebsten kratzte ich dir
die Augen aus." „Richtig", sage ich, „es ist eine Schmach.
Nun bin ich aber Arzt. Was soll ich tun? Glaube mir, es wird
auch mir nicht leicht." „Mit dieser Entschuldigung soll ich
mich begnügen? Ach, ich muß wohl. Immer muß ich mich
begnügen. Mit einer schönen Wunde kam ich auf die Welt;
das war meine ganze Ausstattung."

„Junger Freund," sage ich, „dein Fehler ist: du hast
keinen Überblick. Ich, der ich schon in allen Krankenstuben,
weit und breit, gewesen bin, sage dir: deine Wunde ist so
übel nicht. Im spitzen Winkel mit zwei Hieben der Hacke
geschaffen. Viele bieten ihre Seite an und hören kaum die
Hacke im Forst, geschweige denn, daß sie ihnen näher
kommt." „Ist es wirklich so oder täuschest du mich im
Fieber?" „Es ist wirklich so, nimm das Ehrenwort eines
Amtsarztes mit hinüber."

Und er nahm's und wurde still. Aber jetzt war es Zeit, an
meine Rettung zu denken. Noch standen treu die Pferde an
ihren Plätzen. Kleider, Pelz und Tasche waren schnell zusam-
mengerafft; mit dem Ankleiden wollte ich mich nicht aufhalten; beeilten sich die Pferde wie auf der Herfahrt, sprang ich
ja gewissermaßen aus diesem Bett in meines. Gehorsam zog
sich ein Pferd vom Fenster zurück; ich warf den Ballen in den
Wagen; der Pelz flog zu weit, nur mit einem Ärmel hielt er
sich an einem Haken fest. Gut genug. Ich schwang mich aufs
Pferd. Die Riemen lose schleifend, ein Pferd kaum mit dem
andern verbunden, der Wagen irrend hinterher, der Pelz als
letzter im Schnee.

„Munter!" sagte ich, aber munter ging's nicht; langsam
wie alte Männer zogen wir durch die Schneewüste; lange
klang hinter uns der neue, aber irrtümliche Gesang der Kinder:

and feet and are carrying me to the bed. They put me next to the wall, on the side of the wound. Then they all leave the room; the door is closed; the singing dies out. Clouds obscure the moon; the bed covers lie warmly about me; the horses' heads sway shadow-like in the window openings.

"Do you know," I hear someone say into my ear, "my confidence in you is very slight. Really, you've only been shaken off somewhere; you don't come on your own feet. Instead of helping, you take up space in my deathbed. I'd like most of all to scratch out your eyes." "Right," I say, "it is a shame. But I'm a doctor. What am I to do? Believe me, it isn't easy for me either." "Am I to be satisfied with this excuse? Oh, I suppose I must. I always have to be satisfied. I came into the world with a beautiful wound; that was my total equipment."

"Young friend," I say, "your weakness is that you have no overall picture. I, who have been in every sickroom far and wide, say to you: your wound is not so bad—merely made with two blows of the axe at an acute angle. Many offer their sides and scarcely hear the axe in the forest, to say nothing of its coming closer to them." "Is it really so, or are you deceiving me in my fever?" "It is really so, take the word of honor of an official doctor with you."

And he took it and became quiet. But now it was time to think of saving myself. The horses were still standing faithfully in their places. Clothes, fur coat and bag were soon snatched together; I did not want to waste time by dressing. If the horses hurried as much as they did on the journey here, I would in a sense jump from this bed into my own. Obediently one horse withdrew from the window; I threw the bundle into the carriage; the fur coat went too far, it clung to a hook only by one sleeve. Good enough. I mounted the horse. The harness dragged loosely, one horse was scarcely linked with the other, the carriage strayed along behind, the fur coat brought up the rear in the snow.

"Briskly!" I said, but it did not go briskly; slowly, like old men, we moved through the snow desert. For a long time we heard behind us the new but erroneous song of the children:

Freuet euch, ihr Patienten,
Der Arzt ist euch ins Bett gelegt!

Niemals komme ich so nach Hause; meine blühende Praxis ist verloren; ein Nachfolger bestiehlt mich, aber ohne Nutzen, denn er kann mich nicht ersetzen; in meinem Hause wütet der ekle Pferdeknecht; Rosa ist sein Opfer; ich will es nicht ausdenken. Nackt, dem Froste dieses unglückseligen Zeitalters ausgesetzt, mit irdischem Wagen, unirdischen Pferden, treibe ich alter Mann mich umher. Mein Pelz hängt hinten am Wagen, ich kann ihn aber nicht erreichen, und keiner aus dem beweglichen Gesindel der Patienten rührt den Finger. Betrogen! Betrogen! Einmal dem Fehlläuten der Nachtglocke gefolgt—es ist niemals gutzumachen.

Rejoice, you patients,
The doctor has been put to bed with you!

I'll never get home this way. My flourishing practice is ruined. A successor is defrauding me, but in vain, for he can't replace me. In my house the disgusting groom rages; Rosa is his victim; I won't think the matter through. Naked, exposed to the frost of this unhappy age, with an earthly carriage and unearthly horses, I roam about, an old man. My fur coat hangs at the rear of the carriage, but I can't reach it, and not one of the mob of limber patients stirs a finger. Deceived! Deceived! Once the deceptive sound of the night bell has been followed—it can never be made good.

difference

# Ilse Aichinger

## (1921–     )

ILSE AICHINGER was born and raised in Vienna. She finished
high school just before the Second World War began. Because of her Jewish ancestry she was not permitted to continue
her education but spent the war years working in a factory.
When the Nazi regime collapsed, she became a medical student, but gave up her studies and turned to literature as a
profession. For a time she was a reader for the publishing firm
of S. Fischer. She was also the co-founder of the adult education institute which the Resistance heroine Inge Scholl established in Ulm. She is the wife of the poet Günther Eich.

Various literary honors have come her way—the literary
prizes of different German and Austrian cities, election to the
PEN Club, election to the "Gruppe 47," an association of
young writers which represents the best among the new post-
war talents.

Ilse Aichinger's output is as yet small, but her work is
distinguished. The influence of Kafka is obvious; she too
depicts the absurdities and anxieties of modern life, fusing
dream and reality, the normal and the grotesque, social reality
and myth. She has the true poet's gift of depicting the universal in the particular.

The short story reprinted here, from the volume *Der Gefesselte* (The Man in Chains) which appeared in 1953, reveals
Ilse Aichinger's special talent for satire. It is a satire on three
abnormal types one meets everywhere and who, through some
special foible, reveal themselves and arouse our pity or our

irritation. All three seem trivial: the man who is too timid to admit defeat or even a mistake; the woman who calls attention to herself through some act or gesture of self-effacement; the paranoid who feels that everyone is laughing at him and is finally driven to self-destruction by his insecurity. All three types have this in common: that they cannot live an inner-directed life but are over-dependent on outside sanctions. However, one must not look for metaphysical profundities in this sketch. It is a delightful piece whose strength lies in the detail of its execution; above all, it is a story that improves on longer acquaintance.

# SEEGEISTER

## von Ilse Aichinger

DEN SOMMER über [1] beachtet man sie wenig oder hält sie
für seinesgleichen, und wer den See mit dem Sommer verläßt,
wird sie nie erkennen. Erst gegen den Herbst zu [2] beginnen
sie, sich deutlicher abzuheben. Wer später kommt oder
länger bleibt, wer zuletzt selbst nicht mehr weiß, ob er noch
zu den Gästen oder schon zu den Geistern gehört, wird sie
unterscheiden. Denn es gibt gerade im frühen Herbst Tage, an
denen die Grenzen im Hinüberwechseln noch einmal sehr
scharf werden.

---

Da ist der Mann, der den Motor seines Bootes, kurz bevor
er landen wollte, nicht mehr abstellen konnte. Er dachte
zunächst, das sei weiter kein Unglück und zum Glück sei der
See groß, machte kehrt und fuhr vom Ostufer gegen das
Westufer zurück, wo die Berge steil aufsteigen und die großen
Hotels stehen. Es war ein schöner Abend, und seine Kinder
winkten ihm vom Landungssteg, aber er konnte den Motor
noch immer nicht abstellen, tat auch, als [3] wollte er nicht
landen, und fuhr wieder gegen das flache Ufer zurück. Hier—
zwischen entfernten Segelbooten und Schwänen, die sich
weit vorgewagt hatten—brach ihm angesichts der Röte, die
die untergehende Sonne auf das östliche Ufer warf, zum
erstenmal der Schweiß aus den Poren, denn er konnte seinen
Motor noch immer nicht abstellen. Er rief seinen Freunden,
die auf der Terrasse des Gasthofes beim Kaffee saßen, fröhlich zu, er wolle noch ein wenig weiterfahren, und sie riefen
fröhlich zurück, das solle er nur. Als er zum drittenmal kam,
rief er, er wolle nur seine Kinder holen, und seinen Kindern

294

# LAKE GHOSTS

## by Ilse Aichinger

THROUGHOUT THE summer you pay little attention to them or take them to be like yourself; and if you leave the lake at the end of the summer you'll never recognize them. Only toward fall do they begin to stand out more clearly. If you come later or stay longer, if you finally no longer know yourself whether you still belong among the guests or are already one of the ghosts, you'll distinguish them. For there are actually days in the early fall when the boundaries become sharp once more as they make a transition.

---

There is the man who couldn't shut off the motor of his boat just before he wanted to land. At first he thought it was nothing serious and that fortunately the lake was big; he turned around and rode back from the eastern shore to the western shore, where the mountains rise up steep and the big hotels are located. It was a beautiful evening, and his children waved to him from the wharf; but he still couldn't shut off the motor, pretended that he didn't want to land, and again rode back to the flat shore. Here, amid distant sailboats and swans which had ventured far out, in view of the red glow which the setting sun cast on the eastern shore, the sweat came out of his pores for the first time, for he still couldn't shut off his motor. He cheerfully called out to his friends who were sitting at coffee on the terrace of the hotel, that he wanted to ride around just a little longer and they cheerfully called back, why didn't he do just that. When he came by for the third time he called that he only wanted to get his children, and to his children he called that he only wanted

rief er zu, er wolle nur seine Freunde holen. Bald darauf
waren Freunde und Kinder von beiden Ufern verschwunden,
und als er zum viertenmal kam, rief er nichts mehr.

Er hatte entdeckt, daß sein Benzintank leck war, das Benzin
war längst ausgelaufen, aber das Seewasser trieb seinen Motor
weiter. Er dachte jetzt nicht mehr, das sei weiter kein Unglück
und zum Glück sei der See groß. Der letzte Dampfer kam vorbei, und die Leute riefen ihm übermütig zu, aber er antwortete
nicht, er dachte jetzt: „Wenn nur kein Boot mehr käme!"
Und dann kam auch keins mehr. Die Jachten lagen mit einge-
zogenen Segeln in den Buchten, und der See spiegelte die
Lichter des Hotels. Dichter Nebel begann aufzusteigen, der
Mann fuhr kreuz and quer [4] und dann die Ufer entlang, irgendwo schwamm noch ein Mädchen und warf sich den
Wellen nach, die sein Boot warf, und ging auch an Land.

Aber er konnte, während er fuhr, den lecken Tank nicht
abdichten und fuhr immer weiter. Jetzt erleichterte ihn nur
mehr [5] der Gedanke, daß sein Tank doch eines Tages den See
ausgeschöpft haben müsse, und er dachte, es sei eine merkwürdige Art des Sinkens, den See aufzusaugen und zuletzt
mit seinem Boot auf dem Trockenen zu sitzen. Kurz darauf
begann es zu regnen, und er dachte auch das nicht mehr. Als
er wieder an dem Haus vorbeikam, vor dem das Mädchen
gebadet hatte, sah er, daß hinter einem Fenster noch Licht war,
aber uferaufwärts, in den Fenstern, hinter denen seine Kinder
schliefen, war es schon dunkel, und als er kurz danach wieder
zurückfuhr, hatte auch das Mädchen sein Licht gelöscht. Der
Regen ließ nach, aber das tröstete ihn nun nicht mehr.

Am nächsten Morgen wunderten sich seine Freunde, die
beim Frühstück auf der Terrasse saßen, daß er schon so früh
auf dem Wasser sei. Er rief ihnen fröhlich zu, der Sommer
ginge zu Ende, man müsse ihn nützen, und seinen Kindern,
die schon am frühen Morgen auf dem Landungssteg standen,
sagte er dasselbe. Und als sie am nächsten Morgen eine Ret-
tungsexpedition nach ihm ausschicken wollten, winkte er ab,
denn er konnte doch jetzt, nachdem er sich zwei Tage lang
auf die Fröhlichkeit hinausgeredet hatte, [6] eine Rettungsexpe-
dition nicht mehr zulassen; vor allem nicht angesichts des
Mädchens, das täglich gegen Abend die Wellen erwartete,
die sein Boot warf. Am vierten Tag begann er zu fürchten,

to get his friends. Soon after that both friends and children had vanished from both shores, and when he came by for the fourth time he no longer called anything.

He had discovered that his gas tank was leaking and his gas had long since run out, but the lake water was driving his motor. Now he no longer thought that it was nothing serious and that fortunately the lake was big. The last steamer passed and the passengers called to him in high spirits, but he did not reply; he now thought: "If only no more boats came!" And then none came. The yachts lay in the bays with furled sails and the lake mirrored the lights of the hotels. A thick mist began to rise, the man rode criss-cross and then along the shores. Somewhere a girl was still swimming; she threw herself into the waves which his boat churned up and then went in to land.

But he could not mend the leaking tank while he was driving and so he kept going on. Now his only relief was the thought that some day his tank must exhaust the lake; and he thought it was a strange sort of sinking—to suck up the lake, and finally to be sitting in his boat on the dry bed. Shortly after that it began to rain and he gave up this idea too. When he again passed the house where the girl had been bathing he saw that there was still light behind a window; but upshore, in the windows behind which his children were sleeping, it was already dark; and when he rode by again shortly after that, the girl, too, had put out her light. The rain stopped but this did not comfort him any longer.

Next morning his friends, who were sitting on the terrace at breakfast, were surprised that he was out on the water so early. He called to them cheerfully that the summer was nearing its end; you had to make use of it! And he said the same thing to his children who were on the wharf even this early in the morning. And next morning, when they wanted to send out a rescue expedition after him, he waved them off; for after all, now that he had talked himself into cheerfulness for two whole days, he couldn't permit a rescue expedition any more, especially in the face of the girl, who, every day toward evening, waited for the waves that were thrown up by his boat. On the fourth day he began to fear that people

daß man sich über ihn lustig machen könne, tröstete sich
aber bei dem Gedanken, daß auch dies vorüberginge. Und es
ging vorüber.

Seine Freunde verließen, als es kühler wurde, den See, und
auch die Kinder kehrten zur Stadt zurück, die Schule begann.
Das Motorengeräusch von der Uferstraße ließ nach, jetzt
lärmte nur noch sein Boot auf dem See. Der Nebel zwischen
Wald und Gebirge wurde täglich dichter, und der Rauch aus
den Kaminen blieb in den Wipfeln hängen.

Als letztes verließ das Mädchen den See. Vom Wasser her
sah er sie ihre Koffer auf den Wagen laden. Sie warf ihm eine
Kußhand zu und dachte: „Wäre er ein Verwunschener, ich
wäre länger geblieben, aber er ist mir zu genußsüchtig!"

Bald darauf fuhr er an dieser Stelle mit seinem Boot aus
Verzweiflung auf den Schotter. Das Boot wurde längsseits
aufgerissen und tankt von nun an Luft. In den Herbstnächten
hören es die Einheimischen über ihre Köpfe dahinbrausen.

———————

Oder die Frau, die vergeht, sobald sie ihre Sonnenbrille
abnimmt.

Das war nicht immer so. Es gab Zeiten, zu denen sie mitten
in der hellen Sonne im Sand spielte, und damals trug sie keine
sonnenbrille. Und es gab Zeiten, zu denen sie die Sonnenbrille trug, sobald ihr die Sonne ins Gesicht schien, und sie
abnahm, sobald sie verging—und doch selbst nicht verging.[7]
Aber das ist lange vorbei, sie würde, wenn man sie fragte,
selbst nicht sagen können, wie lange, und sie würde sich eine
solche Frage auch verbitten.

Wahrscheinlich rührt all das Unglück von dem Tag her, an
dem sie begann, die Sonnenbrille auch im Schatten nicht
abzunehmen, von dieser Autofahrt im Frühsommer, als es
plötzlich trüb wurde und jedermann die dunklen Gläser von
den Augen nahm, nur sie nicht. Aber man sollte Sonnenbrillen niemals im Schatten tragen, sie rächen sich.

Als sie wenig später während einer Segelfahrt auf der Jacht
eines Freundes die Sonnenbrille für einen Augenblick abnahm,
fühlte sie sich plötzlich zu nichts werden, Arme und Beine
lösten sich im Ostwind auf. Und dieser Ostwind, der die
weißen Schaumkämme über den See trieb, hätte sie sicher

might begin to make fun of him, but he comforted himself with the thought that this too would pass. And it did pass.

When it got cooler his friends left the lake and his children, too, returned to the city—school was beginning. The roar of motors from the shore road abated; now the only noise was that of his boat on the lake. The mist between the forest and the mountains became denser every day and the smoke from the chimneys remained in the tree tops.

The girl was the last to leave the lake. From the water he saw her loading her suitcases into the car. She threw him a kiss and thought: "If he were a man under a curse, I would have stayed longer, but he's too much of a pleasure-seeker for me."

Soon after, in despair, he ran his boat onto the gravel at this spot. The boat was torn open lengthwise and since then the tank has been using air. In the autumn nights the natives hear it roaring over their heads.

---

Or the woman who vanishes as soon as she takes off her sunglasses.

It wasn't always so. There were times when she played in the sand in the bright sun, and then she wore no sunglasses. And there were times when she wore the sunglasses as soon as the sun shone into her face, and took them off as soon as it disappeared—and yet she did not vanish herself. But that is long past; if you asked her she would not be able to say herself how long, and she would also forbid such a question being asked.

Probably the whole misfortune stems from that day when she began not taking off her sunglasses even in the shade; from that car ride in early summer when it suddenly grew dim and every one except she took the dark glasses from their eyes. But one should never wear sunglasses in the shade; they avenge themselves.

When, a little later, she took off her sunglasses for a moment during a sailing trip on a friend's yacht, she felt herself suddenly becoming nothing. Her arms and legs dissolved in the east wind. And this east wind, which drove the white crests of foam over the lake, would certainly have blown her

wie nichts über Bord geweht, wäre sie nicht geistesgegen-
wärtig genug gewesen, ihre Sonnenbrille sofort wieder auf-
zusetzen. Derselbe Ostwind brachte aber zum Glück gutes
Wetter, Sonne und große Hitze, und so fiel sie während der
nächsten Wochen weiter nicht auf. Wenn sie abends tanzte,
erklärte sie jedem, der es wissen wollte, sie trüge die Sonnenbrille gegen das starke Licht der Bogenlampen, und bald begannen viele sie nachzuahmen. Freilich wußte niemand, daß
sie die Sonnenbrille auch nachts trug, denn sie schlief bei
offenem Fenster und hatte keine Lust, hinausgeweht zu werden
oder am nächsten Morgen aufzuwachen und einfach nicht
mehr da zu sein.

Als für kurze Zeit trübes Wetter und Regen einsetzte,
versuchte sie noch einmal, ihre Sonnenbrille abzunehmen,
geriet aber sofort in denselben Zustand der Auflösung, wie das
erste Mal, und bemerkte, daß auch der Westwind bereit war,
sie davonzutragen. Sie versuchte es daraufhin nie wieder, sondern hielt sich solange abseits und wartete, bis die Sonne
wiederkam. Und die Sonne kam wieder. Sie kam den ganzen
Sommer über immer wieder. Dann segelte sie auf den Jachten
ihrer Freunde, spielte Tennis oder schwamm auch, mit der
Sonnenbrille im Gesicht, ein Stück weit in den See hinaus.
Und sie küßte auch den einen oder den anderen und nahm
die Sonnenbrille dazu nicht ab. Sie entdeckte, daß sich das
meiste auf der Welt auch mit Sonnenbrillen vor den Augen
tun ließ. Solange es Sommer war.

Aber nun wird es langsam Herbst. Die meisten ihrer
Freunde sind in die Stadt zurückgekehrt, nur einige wenige
sind noch geblieben. Und sie selbst—was sollte [8] sie jetzt mit
Sonnenbrillen in der Stadt? Hier legt man ihre Not noch als
persönliche Note aus, und solange es sonnige Tage gibt und
die letzten ihrer Freunde um sie sind, wird sich nichts ändern.
Aber der Wind bläst mit jedem Tag stärker, Freunde und
sonnige Tage werden mit jedem Tag weniger. Und es ist keine
Rede davon, daß sie die Sonnenbrille jemals wieder abneh-
men könnte.

Was soll geschehen, wenn es Winter wird?

---

Da waren auch noch drei Mädchen, die am Heck des
Dampfers standen und sich über den einzigen Matrosen lustig

overboard as if she were nothing, if she hadn't had enough presence of mind to put on her sunglasses at once. But fortunately the same east wind brought good weather, sun and great heat, and so she caused no surprise during the next weeks. When she danced in the evening she told everyone who wanted to know, that she wore the sunglasses to protect her eyes against the strong light of the arc lamps; and soon many people began to imitate her. Of course no one knew that she wore the sunglasses at night too; for she slept with an open window and had no desire to be swept out, nor to wake up next morning and simply not be there any more.

When dull weather and rain set in for a short time, she tried to take off her sunglasses once more, but promptly got back into the same state of dissolution as the first time; and she noticed that the west wind too was ready to carry her off. Thereafter she never tried it again, but kept herself to one side and waited till the sun came out again. And the sun came out again. It came out again and again throughout the whole summer. Then she sailed on her friends' yachts, played tennis or even swam, with the sunglasses on her face, for a distance far out into the lake. And she also kissed this man or that and did not take off her sunglasses for the purpose. She discovered that most things in the world could be done with sunglasses before one's eyes. As long as it was summer.

But now it is slowly becoming autumn. Most of her friends have returned to the city, only very few have remained behind. And she herself—what should she do in the city with sunglasses now? Here her distress is still being interpreted as a personal note; and as long as there are sunny days and the last of her friends are about her, nothing will change. But the wind is blowing stronger every day; friends and sunny days are getting fewer every day. And there is no question of her being able to take off her sunglasses ever again.

What will happen when winter comes?

---

Then there are also three girls who stood at the stern of the steamer and made fun of the only sailor the steamer

machten, den es auf dem Dampfer gab. Sie stiegen am flachen Ufer ein, fuhren an das bergige Ufer hinüber, um dort Kaffee zu trinken, und dann wieder an das flache zurück.

Der Matrose beobachtete vom ersten Augenblick an, wie sie lachten und sich hinter der vorgehaltenen Hand Dinge zuriefen, die er wegen des großen Lärms, den der kleine Dampfer verursachte, nicht verstehen konnte. Aber er hatte den bestimmten Argwohn, daß es ihn und den Dampfer betraf; und als er von seinem Sitz neben dem Kapitän herunterkletterte, um die Fahrkarten zu markieren, und dabei in die Nähe der Mädchen kam, wuchs ihre Heiterkeit, so daß er seinen Argwohn bestätigt fand. Er fuhr sie an und fragte sie nach ihren Karten, aber sie hatten sie leider schon genommen, und so blieb ihm nichts anderes übrig, als die Karten zu markieren. Dabei fragte ihn eines der Mädchen, ob er auch den Winter über keine andere Beschäftigung hätte, und er antwortete: „Nein." Gleich darauf begannen sie wieder zu lachen.

Aber von da ab hatte er die Empfindung, seine Mütze hätte das Schild verloren, und es fiel ihm schwer,[9] den Rest der Karten zu markieren. Er kletterte zum Kapitän zurück, nahm aber diesmal nicht die Kinder der Ausflügler vom Verdeck mit hinauf, wie er es sonst tat. Und er sah den See von oben grün und ruhig unten liegen, und er sah den scharfen Einschnitt des Bugs—schärfer konnte auch ein Ozeanriese nicht die See durchschneiden—, aber das beruhigte ihn heute nicht. Vielmehr erbitterte ihn die Tafel mit der Aufschrift „Achtung auf den Kopf!", die über dem Eingang zu den Kabinen angebracht war, und der schwarze Rauch, der aus dem Kamin bis zum Heck wehte und die flatternde Fahne schwärzte, als hätte er die Schuld daran.

Nein, er tat auch im Winter nichts anderes. Weshalb denn der Dampfer auch im Winter verkehre, fragten sie ihn, als er wieder in ihre Nähe kam. „Wegen der Post!" sagte er. In einem lichten Augenblick sah er sie dann ruhig miteinander sprechen, und das tröstete ihn für eine Weile; aber als der Dampfer anlegte und er die Seilschlinge über den Pflock auf dem kleinen Steg warf, begannen sie, obwohl er den Pflock haargenau getroffen hatte, wieder zu lachen, und konnten sich, solange er sie sah, nicht mehr beruhigen.

had. They boarded at the flat shore, rode over to the mountainous shore to drink coffee and then back again to the flat shore.

The sailor noticed from the first moment how they laughed and said things to each other behind their hands held before their mouths, things which he could not understand because of the great noise the little steamer made. But he had the definite suspicion that it concerned him and the steamer; and when he climbed down from his seat beside the captain to mark the tickets, and in doing so came close to the girls, their merriment increased, so that he found his suspicion confirmed. He barked at them as he asked for their tickets, but they had already bought some, so there was nothing left for him to do but to mark their tickets. As he did so, one of the girls asked him whether he had no other job throughout the winter, and he replied: "No." At once they began to laugh again.

But from then on he had the feeling that his cap had lost its visor and he found it hard to mark the rest of the tickets. He climbed back to the captain, but this time he didn't take the children of the excursionists up with him from the deck, as he usually did. And he saw the lake from above lying green and calm below, and he saw the sharp slicing of the bow—even an ocean giant could not cut the sea more sharply—but this did not calm him today. Rather, he was embittered by the sign with the inscription "Watch Your Head!" that was posted over the entrance to the cabins, and by the black smoke which blew out of the smokestack toward the stern and blackened the fluttering flag, as if he were to blame.

No, he did nothing else in the winter. But why did the steamer run in the winter too, they asked him when he came near them again. "Because of the mail," he said. In a bright moment he saw them talking calmly with each other and that comforted him for a while; but when the steamer docked and he threw the rope over the peg on the little landing dock, they began to laugh again, although he had hit the peg most accurately; and as long as he saw them, they could not regain their calm.

Eine Stunde später stiegen sie wieder ein, aber der Himmel hatte sich inzwischen verdüstert, und als sie in der Mitte des Sees waren, brach das Gewitter los. Das Boot begann zu schaukeln, und der Matrose ergriff die Gelegenheit beim Schopf,[10] um den Mädchen zu zeigen, was er wert war. Er kletterte in seiner Ölhaut öfter als nötig über das Geländer und außen herum und wieder zurück. Dabei glitt er, da es inzwischen immer stärker regnete, auf dem nassen Holz aus und fiel in den See. Und weil er mit den Matrosen der Ozeanriesen gemeinsam hatte, daß er nicht schwimmen konnte, und der See mit der See, daß es sich darin ertrinken ließ, ertrank er auch.

Er ruht in Frieden, wie es auf seinem Grabstein steht, denn man zog ihn heraus. Aber die drei Mädchen fahren noch auf dem Dampfer und stehen am Heck und lachen hinter der vorgehaltenen Hand. Wer sie sieht, sollte sich von ihnen nicht beirren lassen. Es sind immer dieselben.

An hour later they got in again, but the sky had meanwhile grown gloomy; and when they were in the middle of the lake, the storm broke loose. The boat began to sway, and the sailor seized the opportunity to show the girls what he was worth. He climbed over the railing in his oilskins more often than was necessary, and around the outside and back again. In doing so he slipped on the wet wood, since the rain had meanwhile increased in force, and fell into the lake. And because he had this in common with the sailors on ocean giants: that he could not swim; and the lake had this in common with the sea: that one could drown in it; he drowned too.

He rests in peace, as is written on his tombstone, for he was pulled out. But the three girls still ride on the steamer and stand at the stern and laugh behind their hands. Whoever sees them should not let himself be misled by them. They are still the same girls.

# Wolfgang Borchert

## (1922–1947)

WOLFGANG BORCHERT died at the age of twenty-six, from hunger and privation suffered during the Second World War; his complete works comprise one sole volume. He was born and raised in Hamburg, trained as a bookseller and began a career as an actor. He fought on the Russian front, where he was severely wounded. Twice he was arrested for "defeatist" remarks he had made about the Führer and the Nazi regime; for one of these offences he was sentenced to death, but pardoned after spending six weeks in the death cell, then sent back to the eastern front to "prove" himself. But he was so ill that he was discharged and sent home. During and after the war he worked in a Hamburg theater and cabaret, acting, directing and reading from his own writings. In 1947 a few of his friends sent him off to Switzerland in the hope of bringing him back to health; but it was too late. He died in November of that year, the night before his drama *Draußen vor der Tür* (Outside in Front of the Door) was given its premiere in his native Hamburg.

Borchert's published work, which is the product of the last two years of his life, stands completely in the shadow of the war experience and the catastrophe resulting from it, the total destruction of men's bodies and minds and of their physical surroundings. Borchert's righteous indignation at times interferes with his art; his tone becomes strident and accusing. But he is a writer of great power; and our story shows that he can be tender and profoundly poetical. His general cry of

despair at the human condition allows for occasional flashes of human dignity and kindness to cast a soft glow over his work.

In this tender vignette Borchert has taken one of the basic religious motifs of Western civilization—the legend of the adoration of the Magi—and given it a new setting amidst the ruins of devastated Europe, a devastation resulting from man's rapacity and brutality. He shows that the values which underlie the Biblical story are applicable at all times and under all social conditions. The Holy Family can be ignorant, insignificant nonentities; the magi can be three anonymous hoboes. A touch of love transforms misery and brutishness into beauty and happiness.

# DIE DREI DUNKLEN KÖNIGE

## von Wolfgang Borchert

ER TAPPTE durch die dunkle Vorstadt.[1] Die Häuser standen abgebrochen gegen den Himmel. Der Mond fehlte und das Pflaster war erschrocken über den späten Schritt. Dann fand er eine alte Planke. Da trat er mit dem Fuß gegen,[2] bis eine Latte morsch aufseufzte und losbrach. Das Holz roch mürbe und süß. Durch die dunkle Vorstadt tappte er zurück. Sterne waren nicht da.

Als er die Tür aufmachte (sie weinte dabei, die Tür), sahen ihm die blaßblauen Augen seiner Frau entgegen. Sie kamen aus einem müden Gesicht. Ihr Atem hing weiß im Zimmer, so kalt war es. Er beugte sein knochiges Knie und brach das Holz. Das Holz seufzte. Dann roch es mürbe und süß ringsum. Er hielt sich ein Stück davon unter die Nase. „Riecht beinahe wie Kuchen," lachte er leise. „Nicht," sagten die Augen der Frau, „nicht lachen. Er schläft."

Der Mann legte das süße mürbe Holz in den kleinen Blechofen. Da glomm es auf und warf eine Handvoll warmes Licht durch das Zimmer. Die fiel hell auf ein winziges rundes Gesicht und blieb einen Augenblick. Das Gesicht war erst eine Stunde alt, aber es hatte schon alles, was dazugehört: Ohren, Nase, Mund und Augen. Die Augen mußten groß sein, das konnte man sehen, obgleich sie zu waren. Aber der Mund war offen und es pustete leise daraus. Nase und Ohren waren rot. Er lebt, dachte die Mutter. Und das kleine Gesicht schlief.

„Da sind noch Haferflocken," sagte der Mann. „Ja," ant-

# THE THREE DARK KINGS

## by Wolfgang Borchert

HE GROPED his way through the dark suburb. The houses
stood in a broken line against the sky. The moon was absent
and the pavement was frightened by the late step. Then he
found an old plank. He kicked against it with his foot until
a lath gave a rotten sigh and broke loose. The wood smelled
rotted and sweet. Through the dark suburb he groped his way
back. There were no stars.

When he opened the door (it wept as he did so, the door),
the pale blue eyes of his wife looked towards him. They came
from a tired face. Her breath clung white in the room, it was
so cold. He bent his bony knee and broke the wood. The
wood sighed. Then there was a rotting and sweet smell about
them. He held a piece of it under his nose. "Almost smells
like cake," he laughed softly. "No," said his wife's eyes,
"don't laugh. He's asleep."

The man placed the sweet, rotting wood into the small
tin stove. There it flamed up and cast a handful of warm
light through the room. This fell brightly on a tiny round
face and stayed for a moment. The face was only an hour old
but it already had everything that belongs to a face: ears, nose,
mouth and eyes. The eyes must be big, one could see that,
although they were closed. But the mouth was open and a
gentle puffing came from it. The nose and ears were red. He
lives, the mother thought. And the little face slept.

"There's some rolled oats left," said the man. "Yes," his

wortete die Frau, „das ist gut. Es ist kalt." Der Mann nahm noch von dem süßen weichen Holz. Nun hat sie ihr Kind gekriegt und muß frieren, dachte er. Aber er hatte keinen, dem er dafür die Fäuste ins Gesicht schlagen konnte. Als er die Ofentür aufmachte, fiel wieder eine Handvoll Licht über das schlafende Gesicht. Die Frau sagte leise: „Kuck, wie ein Heiligenschein, siehst du?" Heiligenschein! dachte er und er hatte keinen, dem er die Fäuste ins Gesicht schlagen konnte.

Dann waren welche [3] an der Tür. „Wir sahen das Licht," sagten sie, „vom Fenster. Wir wollen uns zehn Minuten hinsetzen." „Aber wir haben ein Kind," sagte der Mann zu ihnen. Da sagten sie nichts weiter, aber sie kamen doch ins Zimmer, stießen Nebel aus den Nasen und hoben die Füße hoch. „Wir sind ganz leise," flüsterten sie und hoben die Füße hoch. Dann fiel das Licht auf sie.

Drei waren es. In drei alten Uniformen. Einer hatte einen Pappkarton, einer einen Sack. Und der dritte hatte keine Hände. „Erfroren," sagte er, und hielt die Stümpfe hoch. Dann drehte er dem Mann die Manteltasche hin. Tabak war darin und dünnes Papier. Sie drehten Zigaretten. Aber die Frau sagte: „Nicht, das Kind."

Da gingen die vier vor die Tür und ihre Zigaretten waren vier Punkte in der Nacht. Der eine hatte dicke umwickelte Füße. Er nahm ein Stück Holz aus seinem Sack. „Ein Esel," sagte er, „ich habe sieben Monate daran geschnitzt. Für das Kind." Das sagte er und gab es dem Mann. „Was ist mit den Füßen?" fragte der Mann. „Wasser," [4] sagte der Eselschnitzer, „vom Hunger." „Und der andere, der dritte?" fragte der Mann und befühlte im Dunkeln den Esel. Der dritte zitterte in seiner Uniform: „Oh, nichts," wisperte er, „das sind nur die Nerven. Man [5] hat eben zuviel Angst gehabt." Dann traten sie die Zigaretten aus und gingen wieder hinein.

Sie hoben die Füße hoch und sahen auf das kleine schlafende Gesicht. Der Zitternde nahm aus seinem Pappkarton zwei gelbe Bonbons und sagte dazu: „Für die Frau sind die."

Die Frau machte die blassen blauen Augen weit auf, als sie die drei Dunklen über das Kind gebeugt sah. Sie fürchtete sich. Aber da stemmte das Kind seine Beine gegen ihre Brust und schrie so kräftig, daß die drei Dunklen die Füße aufhoben und

wife replied, "that's good. It's cold." The man took some more of the sweet, soft wood. Now she's had her child and must be freezing, he thought. But he had no one whose face he could bash in with his fist for that. When he opened the door of the stove another handful of light fell over the sleeping face. The woman said softly: "Look, like a halo, do you see?" Halo! he thought, and he had no one whose face he could bash in with his fist.

Then there were some people at the door. "We saw the light," they said, "from the window. We want to sit down for ten minutes." "But we have a child," the man said to them. They said nothing more, but they came into the room all the same, breathed mist out of their noses and lifted their feet high. "We'll be very quiet," they whispered and lifted up their feet. Then the light fell on them.

There were three of them. In three old uniforms. One had a cardboard box, one a sack. And the third one had no hands. "Frozen off," he said holding up his stumps. Then he turned the pocket of his overcoat to the man. There was tobacco in it and thin paper. They rolled cigarettes. But the woman said: "No, the child."

So the four of them went outside the door and their cigarettes were four points in the night. One of them had his feet in thick wrappings. He took a piece of wood out of his sack. "A donkey," he said, "I carved at it for seven months. For the child." He said that and gave it to the man. "What's with your feet?" the man asked. "Water," said the donkey-carver, "from hunger." "And the other, the third one?" the man asked and felt the donkey in the dark. The third man was trembling in his uniform. "Oh, nothing," he whispered, "it's only my nerves. I've simply had too much anxiety." Then they put out their cigarettes and went in again.

They lifted their feet high and looked at the small sleeping face. The trembling man took two yellow candies out of his cardboard box and said: "These are for your wife."

The woman opened her pale eyes wide when she saw the three dark men bending over the child. She was afraid. But at that moment the child dug its legs into her chest and cried so vigorously that the three dark men lifted up their feet and

zur Tür schlichen. Hier nickten sie nochmal, dann stiegen sie in die Nacht hinein.

Der Mann sah ihnen nach. „Sonderbare Heilige," sagte er zu seiner Frau. Dann machte er die Tür zu. „Schöne Heilige sind das," brummte er und sah nach den Haferflocken. Aber er hatte kein Gesicht für seine Fäuste.

„Aber das Kind hat geschrien," flüsterte die Frau, „ganz stark hat es geschrien. Da sind sie gegangen. Kuck mal, wie lebendig es ist," sagte sie stolz. Das Gesicht machte den Mund auf und schrie.

„Weint er?" fragte der Mann.

„Nein, ich glaube, er lacht," antwortete die Frau.

„Beinahe wie Kuchen," sagte der Mann und roch an dem Holz, „wie Kuchen. Ganz süß."

„Heute ist ja auch Weihnachten," sagte die Frau.

„Ja, Weihnachten," brummte er und vom Ofen her fiel eine Handvoll Licht hell auf das kleine schlafende Gesicht.

crept to the door. Here they nodded once more, then they went out into the night.

The man looked after them. "Queer saints," he said to his wife. Then he shut the door. "Fine saints they are," he grumbled and looked after the rolled oats. But he had no face for his fists.

"But the child cried," the woman whispered, "it cried quite hard. Then they went. Just look how alive it is," she said proudly. The face opened its mouth and cried.

"Is he crying?" the man asked.

"No, I think he's laughing," the woman replied.

"Almost like cake," said the man and smelled the wood, "like cake. Quite sweet."

"Why it's Christmas today," said the woman.

"Yes, Christmas," he grumbled and from the stove a handful of light fell brightly on the little sleeping face.

# NOTES

1. *indem . . . pflegte,* equivalent to the gerund: *by being accustomed to.*
2. *Alexandria* (more commonly Alexandrien): in Egypt.
3. *wußte,* i.e., was able.
4. *um so mehr,* all the more.
5. *beladen.* Grammar requires *beladenes.* (The omission of the adjective ending is older usage.)
6. *der Kinder wegen,* because of the children.
7. *bald . . . bald,* now . . . again.
8. *gleich = obgleich.*
9. *der Deinigen,* of your kin.
10. *aller Tage Abend,* i.e., the end of your life.
11. *siehst du.* A conditional clause.
12. *ward = wurde.*
13. *Frauenzimmer,* the older word for *woman,* now used only in a comical or derogatory sense.
14. *keinen . . . ,* literally: form no other resolve.
15. *Langenweile,* usual form: *Langeweile.*
16. The force of *erst* is: more than ever.
17. *ging . . . Rate:* literally: he went inside himself for counsel.
18. *du . . . werden,* you take such great pains.
19. *davon = wovon.*
20. *ein für allemal,* once and for all.
21. German often uses *Brust* where we would say *heart.*
22. *andern,* following.
23. *ließ . . . gefallen,* allowed [it] to please her; i.e., accepted.
24. *Halbläden,* shutters covering only the lower half of the windows.
25. *um sich gegriffen hatte,* literally: had reached all about her.
26. *Bologna,* city in Italy; seat of a famous university.

27. *Verhältnisse*, literally: relationships, conditions; i.e., reality as opposed to wish.

28. *der Sofa*, usually *das*.

29. *ging . . . hin*, passed.

30. *dem ersten besten*, i.e., the first is as good as any other.

31. *ins Freie*, into the open.

32. *lang*, i.e., tedious.

33. *wagte*, imperfect subjunctive expressing deference: would venture.

34. *dagegen*, i.e., in return for the miracle.

35. *glücklich*, i.e., successful.

36. *Seele*, mind.

37. *fiel*, was.


HOFFMANN

1. *Ew* = *Eure*.

2. *Wirtstafel*, table d'hôte; here: dining room of the inn.

3. *Taler*, three marks; *Groschen*, about a dime.

4. *stellen . . .* , add to the bill.

5. *regno all pianto*, reign of lamentation; Hoffmann's own words to describe the character of this section of the overture.

6. *Notte . . .* , Night and day I slave; the first words of the opera, spoken by Leporello.

7. *Ah che piacere*, Ah, what a delight; Hoffmann's own phrase.

8. *Non sperar . . .* , There's no hope, unless you kill me; Donna Anna's first words.

9. The proscenium is the front part of the stage that is still visible when the curtain is lowered.

10. *Mephistopheles*: the devil in Goethe's *Faust*.

11. *rot . . .* , of red and white stripes.

12. *Ma qual . . .* , But what fateful spectacle presents itself to my eyes; sung by Donna Anna as she discovers her father's corpse.

13. *Brust*, often used in German where we would say *heart*.

14. *Tu nido d'inganni*, you nest of deception; spoken by Donna Elvira to Don Juan.

15. *parla . . .* , she speaks like a printed book; spoken by Leporello after Donna Elvira's tirade against Don Juan.

16. *Fin . . .* , Now that the wine has heated their heads; Don Juan's aria toward the end of Act I.

17. *Terzett*, tercet; a song for three voices.

18. Roland and Cymork are characters in the medieval French epic *Chanson de Roland*.

19. *Frauenzimmer*, the older word for *lady* or *woman*, now used in a comical or derogatory sense.
20. *Toskanisch*, the Italian dialect spoken in Tuscany.
21. *Theodor*, a fictitious character to whom Hoffmann addresses some of his stories.
22. *Phrase*, empty, pompous talk; here used in our sense of *phrase* or *sentence*.
23. *Roulade*, a rapid succession of notes sung to one syllable.
24. *aufgegangen*, supply *ist*: has opened up.
25. *Già . . . ,* the table is already prepared; the opening aria of the finale, sung by Don Juan.
26. *brausende Geister*, effervescent spirits; i.e., alcohol.
27. *Marmorkoloß*, marble colossus; the statue of Donna Anna's dead father, the Commandatore.
28. *pygmäisch*, as small as a pygmy.
29. *konsterniert*, the French word gives the gentleman's speech an air of affectation and snobbery and is used with satirical effect.
30. *es war mir*, I felt.
31. *Stündlein*. The diminutive indicates the small span of time still left him.
32. *ihrer . . . ,* the dearest of her bosom children.
33. *Sündenfall*, the fall of man (Genesis II).
34. *aus*, i.e., to leave it.
35. Orcus is the underworld in Greek mythology.
36. *lascia . . . ,* allow, o dear one, another year for the relief of my heart.
37. *Crudele*, cruel one.
38. *forse . . . ,* perhaps some day Heaven may yet have pity on me.
39. *non mi dir . . . ,* do not tell me, my handsome lover.
40. Jinnestan is the ideal region in which the jinn and peris reside (Oriental mythology).
41. *erkoren*, archaic past participle of *kiesen* = *wählen* choose.

STIFTER

1. *mag . . . ,* they may feel.
2. *als* = *als ob*.
3. *länglicher Kreis*, i.e., ellipse.
4. *bergen in ihrem Schoße*, conceal in their lap; i.e., harbor.
5. *von dem Tale aus*, from the valley.
6. *es . . . ,* they never change anything.
7. *Mittag*, south.
8. *inneren*, i.e., underground.
9. *daraus* = *woraus*.

10. *heißen* = *nennen*.
11. *Geschiebe,* sérac; a pointed mass or pinnacle of ice left among the crevasses of a glacier.
12. *was . . . betrifft,* as far as . . . is concerned.
13. *lauter,* nothing but.
14. *auch,* really or does indeed.
15. *frei,* open.
16. *nicht einmal,* not even.
17. *die* = *diejenigen, die.*
18. *Mitternacht . . . ,* north, east and west.
19. *Wegstunden.* Germans often indicate distance by the time it takes to cover it.
20. *großen Verkehr,* communication with the outside world.
21. *ersten,* second; the ground floor does not count as a story.
22. *nach rückwärts,* at the rear (lit.: backwards).
23. *nur mehr,* now only.
24. *sich . . . läßt,* hasn't the remotest intention.
25. *auf Wanderung,* i.e., the journeymen years—the years following the period of apprenticeship—spent on the road working for various masters.
26. *Lodenrock,* coat made of loden cloth; i.e., rough, unshorn wool.
27. *künstlich.* Usually: artificially; here: artistically.
28. *weit und breit,* far and wide.
29. *hieß es,* it was said.
30. *bei . . . ,* had him do their work.
31. *der . . . ,* who had a mind of his own.
32. *seiner Ehre willen,* for the sake of his honor.
33. *daß es ihm zu tun gewesen,* that he had been interested.
34. *nicht . . . ,* did not permit that intimacy and equality to develop.
35. *in kurzem,* in a short time.
36. *sich verkühlen,* South German and Austrian for *sich erkälten.*
37. *hatte . . . ,* had been able to finish with the girl (lit.: come into the clear).
38. *Kreuze,* i.e., by making the sign of the Cross over them.
39. *in das Freie,* into the open.
40. *was . . . ,* how mother was.
41. *etwa . . . ,* should a wind come toward evening.
42. *dem Heiligen Grabe,* the Holy Sepulchre, the grave in which Jesus lies buried.
43. *es macht nichts,* it doesn't matter.
44. *es tut nichts,* it doesn't matter.
45. *staken* = *steckten.*
46. *weitere,* fairly distant (absolute comparative).

47. *machte sich geltend,* made itself felt.
48. *erst,* especially.
49. *ist.* South German and Austrian usage.
50. *zog,* i.e., needed.
51. *Fest,* Holy Mass.
52. *schießende Schnuppe,* shooting star.
53. *zu erkennen,* perceptible.
54. *größerer,* fairly great (absolute comparative).
55. *alle Male = immer.*
56. *waren gleich nicht,* though these were not.
57. *so,* however.
58. *war es,* it seemed.
59. *das . . . ,* What a Christmas this is!
60. *Wandlung,* the change of the wine and wafer into the blood and flesh of Christ. This is the central mystery of the Mass and is known as *transubstantiation.*
61. *Wandlungsglöcklein.* The celebrating priest rings a handbell to indicate the moment at which the change occurs.
62. *auf alle Fälle,* in case of emergency.
63. *tat,* put.

## KELLER

1. Later in the story Keller mentions two Gregories: St. Gregory of Nazianzus (c.329–c.390), the rhetorician, and St. Gregory, Bishop of Nyssa (c.331–c.396), the theologian and neo-platonic thinker. Both were eminent fathers of the Eastern Church.
2. *jegliche = jede.*
3. *die Beine übereinanderschlagen,* cross one's legs.
4. [*es*] *warm hatte,* felt warm.
5. *gab sich zu erkennen,* identified himself.
6. *geistlich,* properly: ecclesiastical; here: spiritual.
7. *stutzig machen,* disconcert.
8. *ansonst = sonst.*
9. *ehe . . . , versah,* before she suspected it.
10. *es hieß,* it was said.
11. *Aushilfe leisten,* help out.
12. *nach . . . Sache,* when their job was finished.
13. Martha the sister of Lazarus and Mary of Bethany, in whose house Jesus was a frequent visitor. Martha served Him and is therefore the patron of housewives (Luke 10:38ff.).
14. St. Cecilia (†230 A.D.), Roman martyr, patron saint of music.
15. *Pierians,* the inhabitants of Pieria in Thessaly, the home of the Muses.

16. *Terpsichore,* the Muse of dancing; *Polyhymnia,* of sacred song; *Euterpe,* of flute playing.
17. *Erato,* Muse of the lyre.
18. *es hoch herging,* things were going merrily.
19. *Stündchen,* (little hour) a short while.
20. *Urania,* Muse of astronomy.
21. *geriet außer Fassung,* lost control of himself.


## Schnitzler

1. *war,* South German for *hatte.*
2. *Stilfser Joch,* Stelvio Pass.
3. *war ihm als,* it seemed to him as if.
4. *ward = wurde.*
5. *dichtere,* unusually dense (absolute comparative).
6. *habt's = habt ihr* (colloquial Austrian).
7. *gnädiger Herr,* sir.
8. German often uses a singular verb with a plural subject.
9. *wird . . . ,* the future perfect, used to express high probability in the past = must have.
10. *war,* South German for *hatte.*
11. *Frauenzimmer,* the older word for *woman;* now used in a comical or derogatory sense.
12. *schlechter Laune* (genitive), in a bad mood.
13. *daneben,* i.e., outside the hat.
14. *Lügen strafen,* make a liar of.
15. *Sparkassa,* Austrian for *Sparkasse.*
16. *wandert sich,* equivalent to the gerund: *wandering.*
17. *der, he* (emphatic).
18. *heuer,* this year (Austrian).
19. *nun ja,* is that so?; irrelevant words spoken in perplexity.
20. *sei,* South German for *hätte.*
21. *einer,* someone.
22. *es . . . ,* that's just the way it is.
23. *was tut's,* what does it matter.
24. *wie,* what.
25. *eins,* i.e., a punch.


## Mann

1. Schiller was at this time professor of history at the University of Jena in Thuringia.
2. *auszutrinken.* Supply *war* (the last word in the sentence).
3. *alles,* everyone.

4. *nach* . . . , i.e., knock-kneed.
5. *ließ frei*, exposed.
6. Christian Gottfried Körner was a wealthy man, an admirer and patron of Schiller. There is an extensive published correspondence between the two men.
7. Schiller's early drama *Don Carlos*.
8. *sich stellen*, take a position.
9. *sich begegnen*, i.e., treat himself.
10. Schiller, a rhetorician by instinct, imagines he is delivering a speech.
11. *ohne weiteres*, simply (lit. without further [ado]).
12. The original title of Schiller's *Philosophische Briefe* was *Briefe Julius' an Raphael*.
13. In a letter to Goethe (March 18, 1796), Schiller wrote that his creative works originated in a certain musical mental mood without a clear object.
14. Orphic; allusion to the Greek mysteries associated with the name of Orpheus.
15. An allusion to Schiller's ode *Das Lied von der Glocke*.
16. An allusion to the line *Männerstolz vor Königsthronen* in Schiller's ode *An die Freude*.

## Hesse

1. *irgend*, in any way.
2. *Braut*, fiancée and bride.
3. *so* . . . *verlangte*, however much he wanted.
4. *fein*, sensitive.
5. *der du*, who.
6. *will*, claims or can.
7. *Wesen*, essence; i.e., mind or soul.
8. *es* . . . *gelegen*, it matters little.
9. *damit*, thereby.
10. *war ihm als*, he felt as if.
11. *war*. German often uses a singular verb with several subjects.
12. *diesem*: i.e., *Lampenfest*.

## Kafka

Kafka wrote this story as one single paragraph. It has been broken into a number of paragraphs to balance the German and English texts.

1. *klatscht* . . . , claps his hands.
2. *als = als ob*.

3. *Federbett,* a comforter filled with feathers or down; used in Europe instead of blankets.
4. *schlecht durchblutet,* with poor circulation.
5. *recht haben,* i.e., in his wish to die.
6. *wäre,* the subjunctive indicates a slight uncertainty.
7. *aus eigenem,* literally: on their own.
8. *verlangen:* the infinitive.

## Aichinger

1. *über,* throughout.
2. *gegen . . . zu,* toward.
3. *tat . . . als,* moreover, acted as if.
4. *kreuz und quer,* crisscross.
5. *nur mehr,* only.
6. *sich . . . hatte,* had talked himself into cheerfulness.
7. There is an ambiguity here on *verging.* The sun (*sie*) disappeared, but the woman (*doch selbst*) did not.
8. *sollte.* Supply *machen.*
9. *fiel schwer,* was difficult.
10. *ergriff . . . Schopf,* seized the opportunity by the forelock. (*Schopf,* tuft of hair at the front, forelock.)

## Borchert

1. *Vorstadt.* In European cities the suburbs are inhabited by the poor people.
2. *gegen = dagegen.*
3. *welche,* some (people).
4. *Wasser,* i.e., an edema or swelling caused by an abnormal accumulation of fluid in some part of the body.
5. *man.* The use of this impersonal pronoun indicates that this condition could happen to anyone. Translate: a fellow.

# QUESTIONNAIRE

### GOETHE

1. In welchem Lande spielt diese Geschichte?
2. Warum kann der Kaufmann seinen Reichtum nicht genießen?
3. Was für eine Frau heiratet er?
4. Welchen Rat gibt er seiner Frau, ehe er abreist?
5. Wie empfängt die Frau diesen Rat?
6. Warum ruft sie den Prokurator zu sich?
7. Mit welcher List besiegt der Prokurator die Frau?
8. Welche Wirkung übt das Fasten auf die Frau aus?
9. Was sieht die Frau endlich ein?
10. Zu welcher Gattung der Novelle gehört diese Erzählung?

### HOFFMANN

1. Was hört der Reisende in seinem Zimmer?
2. Wohin führt ihn der Kellner?
3. Welche Oper wird im Theater aufgeführt?
4. Wer erscheint dem Reisenden in der Fremdenloge?
5. Was für ein Gespräch findet an der Wirtstafel statt?
6. Wohin geht der Reisende um die Mitternacht?
7. Was geschieht um zwei Uhr?
8. Was erfährt der Reisende am folgenden Tag?
9. Woraus besteht der größte Teil dieser Novelle?

### STIFTER

1. Welches Fest wird am Anfang dieser Novelle geschildert?
2. Wen besuchen die Kinder am Heiligen Abend?
3. Welche Wandlung hatte im Charakter des Schusters nach seiner Heirat stattgefunden?

4. Was gab die Großmutter den Kindern mit?
5. Was war die Unglücksäule?
6. Wo brachten die Kinder Weihnachten zu?
7. Warum wurde das Heilige Amt verschoben?
8. Durch welche Zeichen wurde verkündet, daß man die Kinder gefunden hatte?
9. Was für ein Licht sahen die Kinder in der Nacht am Himmel?

## KELLER

1. Welches Thema behandelt diese Legende?
2. Welche zwei Religionen werden hier gegeneinandergestellt?
3. Warum erscheint gerade König David der Musa?
4. Ist der Schluß der Legende versöhnlich oder nicht?

## SCHNITZLER

1. Wo spielt diese Geschichte?
2. Warum hat Carlo ein böses Gewissen seinem Bruder gegenüber?
3. Wovon leben die zwei Brüder?
4. Welchen Argwohn hegt der Blinde gegen den Bruder?
5. Wer hat diesen Argwohn in ihm erregt?
6. Wie will Carlo das Vertrauen des Bruders wiedergewinnen?
7. Warum verlassen die Brüder das Wirtshaus?
8. Was sieht der Blinde am Ende der Novelle endlich ein?

## MANN

1. Wer sind die zwei Hauptpersonen dieser Novelle?
2. Zu welcher Zeit des Tages spielt sie?
3. In welchem physischen Zustand lebt Schiller?
4. Warum ist er geistig bedrückt?
5. Wie alt ist er jetzt?
6. Wie denkt Schiller über das Talent?
7. Was ist der Grundunterschied zwischen Schiller und Goethe?
8. Was ist Schillers Verhältnis zu seiner Gattin?

## HESSE

1. Welchen Drang spürte der junge Dichter in sich?
2. Warum verließ er seine Heimat?
3. Wer war der alte Mann, dem er folgte?
4. Wie lange blieb er von Zuhause weg?
5. Was ist der Sinn dieser Parabel?

## KAFKA

1. Wohin mußte der Landarzt gehen?
2. Was hält ihn von der Reise ab?
3. Wer erscheint aus dem Schweinestall?
4. Wer begleitet ihn auf die Reise?
5. Wer ist der Kranke?
6. Wie findet der Arzt den Kranken?
7. Was ist das spätere Urteil des Arztes über den Kranken?
8. Wie legt der Arzt den Rückweg zurück?
9. Wodurch wurde er verraten?

## AICHINGER

1. Welche drei Episoden schildert die Dichterin?
2. Was trug die Dame immer?
3. Warum wollte der Mann keine Hilfe annehmen?
4. Was stellen die Mädchen im Schiff vor?
5. Was hat den Matrosen ums Leben gebracht?

## BORCHERT

1. Wer sind die drei Könige dieser Erzählung?
2. Welches biblische Motiv behandelt sie?
3. Wer ist die heilige Familie?
4. Wozu kommen die drei Besucher in die Hütte?
5. Was für Geschenke bringen sie?
6. Welche bittere Erfahrung ist ihnen zuteil geworden?
7. Welche Nacht ist es, an der die Geschichte spielt?

# VOCABULARY

This vocabulary omits words which should be familiar to students who have had one year of college or two years of high school German. Where a verb is given, the noun which is easily derived from it is omitted and vice versa. The same is true of adjectives easily derived from nouns.

Past participles of weak (or modern) verbs are not given unless they have a special meaning.

Strong verbs are listed exactly as they occur in the text: gab aus, vorgeschoben, tritt zusammen.

The plural of weak feminine nouns is omitted, as it is always formed by adding -n or -en to the singular.

## A

*ab-biegen* o o turn aside
*ab-dichten* seal off, mend
*ab-dienen* serve
*die Abenddämmerung* evening twilight
*das Abenteuer* — adventure
*abenteuerlich* adventurous, daring, strange, grotesque
*abermals* again
*ab-geben* form, deliver
*ab-gehen* go down, be missing
*abgelegen* remote
*der Abgesandte –n* emissary
*abgeschieden* (*scheiden*) separated
*abgewogen* weighed off
*der Abglanz* reflection
*abglitt* (*gleiten*) glided off
*ab-grenzen* delimit

*der Abgrund ∸e* abyss
*ab-halten* keep, celebrate
*der Abhang ∸e* slope
*ab-hängen* depend
*sich ab-härmen* pine away
*sich ab-heben* stand out
*ab-holen* fetch
*die Abkürzung* abbreviation
*ab-lauschen* overhear
*ab-lehnen* decline
*ab-leiten* lead astray
*ab-lenken* turn off, divert
*ab-lösen* replace
*ab-nehmen* remove, purchase
*ab-nötigen* force from
*ab-räumen* clear away
*ab-reden* agree upon
*ab-rieseln* trickle away
*der Absatz ∸e* ledge
*der Abschnitt –e* chapter, section

*sich abschnitten* stood out
*abschüssig* precipitous
*ab-schütteln* shake off
*ab-schwenken* turn aside
*abseits* aside, away
*ab-setzen* sell
*die Absicht* intention
*die Absingung* singing
*absonderlich* strange
*sich ab-spiegeln* be reflected
*ab-statten* pay
*ab-stäuben* dust off
*ab-stechen* contrast
*ab-stellen* stop, shut off
*abstritt (streiten)* disputed
*der Absturz* ⁼e drop
*die Abteilung* group
*ab-wägen* weigh
*abwechselnd* alternating
*die Abwechslung* change, variation
*ab-weichen i i* deviate
*ab-weisen ie ie* refuse, reject
*sich ab-wenden* turn away
*ab-winken* decline (with a nod or gesture)
*ab-ziehen* depart
*die Acht* attention; *außer — lassen* disregard; *— haben* take care
*acht-geben* look out
*achtlos* unsuspecting
*die Achtung* respect, attention
*der Adler* — eagle
*ahnen* suspect, have a premonition
*der Ahnherr* ancestor
*die Akazie* locust tree
*der Akkord* –e chord
*albern* silly
*die Allee* avenue
*die Alleinherrlichkeit* monopoly
*allemal* always
*allenfalls* possibly
*allenthalben* everywhere
*allerart* all kinds of
*allerdings* to be sure
*allerhand* all kinds of
*allerorten* everywhere

*allgemach* gradual
*das Almosen* — alms
*alsbald* soon
*alsdann* then
*alsobald* immediately
*alsogleich* at once
*das Alter* old age
*die Ampel* lamp
*der Amtsarzt* ⁼e official doctor
*der Amtsrat* ⁼e district councillor
*an-belangen* concern
*an-bieten o o* offer
*der Anblick* –e sight, look, appearance
*an-brechen* break
*die Andacht* devotion
*das Andenken* — memory
*ander* next
*an-deuten* indicate, suggest
*aneinander-schmettern* smash against each other
*das Anerbieten* — offer
*an-fallen* attack
*an-fertigen* make
*der Anflug* ⁼e touch
*die Anforderung* demand
*an-fühlen* feel, touch
*angab* indicated
*angeboren* innate
*angeboten (ie o o)* offered
*angebracht* attached, affixed
*angeflogen* delicately laid on
*an-gehen* go, be done, begin
*der Angehörige* –n staff member
*die Angel* hinge
*die Angelegenheit* affair, concern
*angelegentlich* solicitously, earnestly
*angelehnt* ajar
*angesehen* prominent, regarded
*das Angesicht* –er countenance
*angesichts* in the face of, in view of
*angestrichen* painted
*angetan* dressed
*das Angreifende* the emotionally gripping
*der Angriff* –e attack; *in — nehmen* attack

*mich angriff* made efforts
*ängstlich* anxious, causing anxiety
*angstvoll* anxious, fearful
*der Anhalt –e* stop
*anhaltend* sustained, steady
*anhing* clung to
*die Anhöhe* height, hill
*an-klagen* accuse
*sich an-klammern* cling to
*der Anklang ⁼e* harmony
*sich an-kündigen* announce oneself
*die Ankunft* arrival
*die Anlage* setting
*an-langen* reach, arrive
*der Anlaß ⁼e* occasion, cause, beginning
*an-legen* build, dock
*die Anleitung* direction
*an-locken* attract
*die Anmerkung* note, footnote
*die Anmut* grace, charm
*sich an-schicken* prepare oneself
*an-ordnen* order, command, direct
*an-raten ie a* counsel
*die Anregung* stimulus
*an-reihen* co-ordinate
*an-reizen* stimulate
*an-rühren* touch
*an-sagen* announce
*der Anschein* appearance
*an-schlagen* estimate
*sich an-schließen* join
*an-schneiden* cut into
*das Ansehen* sight, appearance, dignity, prominence, respect
*ansehnlich* considerable, substantial, prominent
*die Ansicht* view, aspect
*sich an-siedeln* settle
*an-spannen* hitch, harness
*die Anspielung* allusion
*der Anspruch ⁼e* claim; *in — nehmen* claim, consider
*der Anstand* dignity, decorum, bearing, hesitation
*anständig* respectable
*an-starren* stare at

*an-stellen* employ
*an-strengen* strain, exert
*der Ansturm ⁼e* assault
*antat* did
*der Anteil –e* share
*der Antrag ⁼e* offer
*an-treiben* urge on, whip up
*an-treten* take over
*die Anweisung* direction
*an-wenden* apply, use
*das Anwesen* property
*anwesend* present
*die Anzahl* number
*die Anzeige* notice, advice
*an-zeigen* indicate, announce
*an-ziehen* attract, pull at
*an-zünden* light
*der Arbeitslohn –e* wage
*arg* bad, severe
*ärgerlich* annoyed, vexed
*der Argwohn –e* suspicion
*die Armut* poverty
*artig* pretty, nice, kindly
*die Artigkeit* attention, pleasing behavior
*die Arznei* medicine
*aschenhaft* ashen
*der Ast ⁼e* branch
*atembar* breathable
*das Attentat –e* attack
*auf und zu* open and shut
*auf-atmen* give a sigh of relief; *hoch —* breathe deeply
*auf-bewahren* keep, save
*auf-brechen* set out, depart
*auf-bürden* impose on
*auf-decken* serve
*auf-drücken* press open
*der Aufenthalt –e* stay
*auf-erlegen* impose
*auf-fallen* be noticeable, be striking, surprise
*auf-fangen* catch
*auf-fassen* grasp
*auf-fordern* challenge, incite
*auf-führen* perform
*das Aufgebot –e* bann, publication
*aufgedrungen* forced on [one]

*aufgefunden* discovered
*auf-gehen* be opened, become loose
*aufgelegt* inclined
*aufgeregt* excited
*aufgetragen* served up
*aufgetürmt* piled up
*aufgewölbt* arched up
*aufgezogen* raised
*aufgriff* snatched up
*sich auf-halten* stay, stop, detain, delay
*auf-häufen* pile up
*auf-heitern* cheer up
*sich aufhielten* stopped
*auf-horchen* listen
*sich auf-klären* be cleared up
*auf-kreischen* squeak, shriek
*auf-lachen* laugh aloud
*auf-lauern* lie in wait for
*sich auf-lehnen* rebel
*auf-lodern* flame up
*auf-lösen* loosen; *sich —* dissolve
*aufmerksam* attentive
*auf-muntern* encourage
*die Aufnahme* reception
*auf-nötigen* compel, press
*auf-opfern* sacrifice
*auf-passen* pay attention, watch out
*sich auf-raffen* pull oneself together
*auf-ragen* tower up
*auf-rechnen* charge
*sich auf-recken* stretch upward
*auf-regen* stir, excite
*auf-richten* erect; *sich —* stand up[right]
*sich auf-sammeln* gather
*auf-saugen* suck up
*auf-schlagen* open, raise, set up
*der Aufschrei* outcry
*die Aufschrift* sign, inscription
*der Aufschub* delay
*auf-setzen* put on; *sich —* sit up
*auf-seufzen* give a deep sigh
*auf-stacheln* stimulate
*auf-stoßen ie o* push open
*auf-tauchen* arise, appear

*auf-tauen* thaw out
*auf-tragen* serve
*auf-treten* step out, appear
*sich auf-tun* open
*auf-warten* wait on, call on
*die Aufzeichnung* notation
*auf-zwingen a u* force on
*aus-bilden* instruct, train, apprentice
*der Ausblick —e* outlook, view
*der Ausbruch ⸗e* eruption
*aus-bügeln* iron
*aus-dampfen* steam out
*die Ausdauer* perseverance
*der Ausdruck ⸗e* expression
*auseinander-setzen* explain
*der Ausflügler —* excursionist
*ausgebreitet* extensive
*ausgeglichen* balanced
*ausgenommen* excepted
*ausgeschlagen* faced, lined
*ausgesucht* choice
*aus-halten* hold out, endure
*aushilfsweise* by way of help
*das Auskommen* livelihood
*auskömmlich* adequate
*aus-kratzen* scratch out
*aus-laufen* depart
*aus-legen* interpret
*aus-machen* amount to, matter
*die Ausnahme* exception
*das Ausnahmstübchen* old folks' home
*aus-nützen* make the most of, exploit
*aus-putzen* clean out
*aus-recken* stretch out
*die Ausrede* excuse, explanation
*aus-richten* carry out, convey
*die Aussage* statement
*aus-schalten* exclude
*aus-schlagen* refuse
*aus-schließen* exclude
*aus-schöpfen* exhaust
*die Ausschweifung* excess
*das Äußere —n* external appearance
*äußern* express, utter
*äußerst* exceedingly, extremely;

*aufs* –*e* to an extreme, to the utmost
*aus-setzen* set, expose, offer
*die Aussicht* view, prospect
*aus-spannen* unharness
*der Ausspruch* ⹀*e* assertion
*aus-statten* provide, outfit, equip, settle, bestow on
*die Ausstattung* trousseau
*aus-stecken* hoist
*der Austrag* ⹀*e* conclusion
*die Ausübung* exercise
*der Auswärtige* –*n* outsider
*auswärtssüchtig* eager to be away
*aus-weichen i i* avoid, yield
*die Auszackung* serration
*aus-zeichnen* distinguish
*der Auszug* ⹀*e* extract

## B

*der Bach* ⹀*e* brook
*die Backe* cheek
*der Backenbart* side whiskers
*bahnen* lay out
*sich bahnen* make [one's] way
*der Balken* — beam
*der Balkon* –*e* balcony
*der Ballen* — ball, bundle
*ballen* clench
*bankerott* bankrupt
*bannen* hold fast
*barhäuptig* bare headed
*die Bartstoppel* beard stubble
*der Baß* ⹀*e* bass voice
*die Bauart* architecture
*der Bauernhof* ⹀*e* farm
*baumeln* dangle
*beachten* notice, heed
*beängstet* anguished, full of anxiety
*beanstehen* object
*der Becher* — [wine] cup
*das Becken* — basin
*der Bedacht* thought, reflection
*bedächtig* measured, cautious
*der Bedarf* need
*das Bedenken* consideration, doubt, reserve
*bedeuten* signal

*die Bedingung* condition
*bedürfen* need
*beeist* ice covered
*beengend* constricting
*befangen* held, caught, involved
*die Beförderung* advancing
*befrachten* load
*sich befremden lassen* be alarmed
*befremdet* astonished, puzzled
*befriedigen* satisfy
*sich begeben* go, happen
*begehen* celebrate
*begehren* desire
*die Begeisterung* enthusiasm, inspiration
*die Begierde* desire, eagerness
*beging* went around, committed, celebrated
*die Beglückung* bliss
*sich begnügen* be contented
*begossen* (*begießen*) watered
*das Begräbnis* –*se* burial
*der Begriff* –*e* concept
*begriffen* occupied
*begründen* establish
*begünstigen* favor
*begütigen* soothe
*behagen* suit
*die Behandlung* treatment
*beharren* persist, persevere
*behaupten* assert
*die Behendigkeit* nimbleness
*behüten* guard
*behutsam* cautious
*bei-behalten* keep
*der Beichtvater* father confessor
*beifällig* approving
*bei-fügen* add
*beirren* fool
*beisammen* together
*bei-schrieb* added, recorded
*der Beistand* help
*bei-stehen* help
*bekennen* confess; *sich* — identify oneself
*sich beklagen* complain
*beklatschen* applaud
*beklommen* uneasy, embarrassed
*bekümmert* worried, sorrowful

*beladen* laden
*belagern* besiege
*belauschen* spy on
*beleben* animate
*das Belegstück –e* covering document
*beleidigen* insult, offend
*belieben* please
*die Belohnung* reward
*sich belustigen* make merry
*bemühen* bother; *sich —* strive, busy oneself, pay attention
*das Benehmen* conduct
*die Benennung* naming
*der Benzintank –s* gas tank
*beobachten* observe
*die Beratung* deliberation
*berauben* rob of
*berauschen* intoxicate
*die Berechtigung* justification
*beredt* eloquent
*bereift* covered with hoar frost, rimed
*bereits* already
*bergen a o* hide
*der Berghang =e* mountain slope
*der Bergrücken —* mountain ridge
*berichten* report
*besäen* sow
*besagt* said
*besäße (besitzen)* possessed
*beschaffen* constituted
*die Beschäftigung* occupation
*beschatten* cast a shadow over
*bescheiden* modest
*beschenken* reward
*beschieden* allotted to, in store
*beschleunigen* hasten
*beschrieb* described
*beschritt* walked about, bestrode
*der Beschützer* protector
*die Beschwerde* difficulty
*beschwert* weighted
*beseelen* animate, inspire
*besehen* inspect
*besessen* possessed
*besetzen* occupy, fill, set, trim
*besiegen* conquer

*sich besinnen a o* reflect on, remember
*die Besonnenheit* reflection
*besonnt* sunny
*besorgen* look after, attend to, provide, procure
*die Besorgnis –se* anxiety
*beständig* constant
*bestätigen* confirm
*bestäuben* cover with dust
*bestehen* exist
*bestehlen a o* steal from
*bestimmen* determine, intend, destine
*das Bestreben* effort
*bestreiten itt itt* dispute
*die Bestürzung* amazement, consternation, dismay
*betäubt* stunned, stupefied
*beteuern* assert, emphasize
*betrachten* regard, contemplate, consider, observe, study
*betraf* concerned
*betreiben* carry on
*betreten* enter, visit
*betreten* surprised, startled
*betreuen* wait on, take care of
*betroffen* dismayed
*betrogen (betrügen)* deceived, cheated
*sich betrüben* be saddened, grieve
*betrügen o o* deceive, cheat
*betteln* beg
*das Bettzeug* bedclothes
*die Beurlaubung* furlough
*das Beutelchen* little pouch
*bevorstehend* impending
*bewahren* preserve, protect
*sich bewältigen* control oneself
*die Bewegung* emotion, commotion
*beweisen ie ie* prove, demonstrate
*bewirken* achieve
*bewirten* entertain
*bewölkt* clouded, troubled
*bewundern* admire
*das Bewußtsein* consciousness
*bezeichnen* measure
*sich beziehen* refer, be concerned

*die Beziehung* connection
*der Bezirk –e* district
*bezogen* imported, gotten
*die Biederkeit* honesty
*die Bienenzucht* beekeeping
*beten* pray
*bilden* form, educate
*die Bildung* personality
*billig* fair, proper, right
*die Binde* necktie
*die Birke* birch
*birst (bersten)* bursts
*bisherig* until now
*bitten lassen* request
*blank* shining
*das Blasrohr –e* blowpipe
*die Blässe* pallor
*die Bläue* blueness
*der Blechofen ⸗* tin stove
*bleich* pale
*bleiern* leaden
*blenden* dazzle
*blinzeln* blink, flash
*blöde* dull-witted, timid, shy
*blühen* bloom, flourish
*blutbespritzt* spattered with
    blood
*der Bock ⸗e* driver's seat, box
*der Bodenraum ⸗e* attic
*der Bogen ⸗* arch[way]
*die Bogenlampe* arc lamp
*der Bolzen —* arrow, dart
*die Bonne* maid
*der Bonvivant* playboy
*die Börse* purse
*boshaft* malicious, evil
*der Bote –n* messenger
*die Braut ⸗e* fiancée, bride
*der Bräutigam –e* fiancé, bride-
    groom
*brav* good, nice
*breit* elaborate
*brennen* roast
*der Brennpunkt –e* focal point
*das Brett –er* shelf
*die Brettersäge* sawmill
*bringen um* deprive, rob
*der Brocken —* scrap
*brüchig* damaged, decayed

*das Brückengeländer —* bridge
    railing
*brüllen* roar
*brummen* grumble, rumble
*der Brustaufschlag ⸗e* lapel
*die Brüstung* railing
*die Bucht* bay
*das Büchschen* little box
*der Büchsenstein* flint
*sich bücken* bend down
*der Bug –e* bow
*der Bühel —* hill
*das Bündel —* bundle
*der Bundschuh –e* peasant boot
*bunt* gay, bright
*die Burg* castle
*der Bursch(e) –n* lad, boy, fellow
*der Busen —* bosom
*die Buße* atonement, penitence

# C

*der Champagnerkelch –e* cham-
    pagne glass
*der Chirurg –en* surgeon
*der Chor ⸗e* choir
*das Chorgeländer* choir railing
*der Christabend* Christmas Eve

# D

*da* since, when
*dabei* present, at the same time,
    meanwhile, in doing so
*die Dachlehne* slanting roof
*dafür* in its place, on the other
    hand, in return
*dahin-brausen* roar away
*dahin-bringen* accomplish, man-
    age
*dahin-reißen i i* carry away
*dahin-schreiten itt itt* stride
    along
*der Damm ⸗e* roadway
*das Dämmern* haze
*die Dämmerung* twilight, dawn
*der Dampfer —* steamship
*dann und wann* now and again
*von dannen* from there
*darauf* after that; *–hin* after that

*darben* starve
*sich darbieten o o* offer itself
*dar-legen* display
*dar-stellen* represent, perform;
  *sich* — reveal itself
*das Dasein* being, existence
*daselbst* there
*die Dauer* permanence
*davon* away
*dazu-gehören* belong to [it]
*dazumal* then
*decken* cover, provide, conceal,
  supply
*dehnen* extend, stretch
*die Deichsel* shaft
*das Demiprofil –e* semi-profile
*demnach* accordingly
*die Demut* humility
*der Denkkreis –e* mental sphere
*dereliquieren* abandon
*dergestalt* to such an extent, thus
*dergleichen* the like of which
*dermaßen* to such an extent
*desohngeachtet* or *desungeachtet*
  nevertheless
*um dessentwillen* for the sake of
  that
*dicht* thick, dense, close
*der Diebstahl ≠e* theft
*die Diele* floor
*der Dienstbote –n* servant
*dienstfertig* officious, obsequious
*die Doppelbüchse* double bar-
  reled rifle
*der Doppelgänger* — double
*der Dörfler* — villager
*dortig* of that place
*die Dose* [snuff] box
*der Drache –n* dragon
*der Draht ≠e* wire
*der Drang ≠e* urge, impulse
*drang (dringen)* urged
*drängen* urge, squeeze, press; *sich*
  — press, crowd
*dringen a u* penetrate, urge
*drohen* threaten
*dröhnen* sound, echo, hum, roar
*drüben* over there
*der Druck –e* pressure

*drücken* oppress
*sich ducken* duck
*der Duft ≠e* fragrance, aroma
*dulden* endure
*dummklug* stupidly sly
*dumpf* dull, heavy, muffled, muddled, damp
*die Dunkelheit* obscurity
*dünkelvoll* conceited
*dünken* seem
*durchaus* absolutely
*durchbohrend* piercing
*durcheinander* in confusion, all
  together
*der Durchlaß* opening
*durchmessen a e* muster
*durchsichtig* transparent
*durchtränken* saturate
*durchtrieben* sly
*durchwacht* sleepless
*durchwoben (weben)* interlaced
*durchzucken* dart through
*dürftig* needy, scanty, poor,
  meager
*dürr* dry, withered, lean
*die Dürrbodenpflanze* heath
  plant
*düster* gloomy

# E

*das Ebenbild –er* image
*die Ebene* plain
*echt* genuine
*der Edelsteinsplitter* — fragment
  of jewel
*der Efeu* ivy
*egal,* equal, indifferent
*die Ehe* marriage
*ehemals* formerly
*ehrenfest* honorable
*ehrenwert* respectable
*das Ehrenwort* word of honor
*die Ehrerbietung* respect
*die Ehrfurcht* reverence
*der Ehrgeiz* ambition
*ehrwürdig* dignified, respectable,
  reverent
*der Eifer* zeal, eagerness
*die Eifersucht* jealousy

*eigen* characteristic
*die Eigenschaft* quality
*eigensinnig* stubborn
*das Eigentum* ⸗er property, possession
*eigentümlich* peculiar
*der Eimer* — pail
*ein-bescheren* present
*die Einbildung* imagination
*eindringlich* urgently
*der Eindruck* ⸗e impression
*ein-engen* constrict
*ein-ernten* harvest
*der Einfahrtsschwibbogen* ⸗ arch over the driveway
*der Einfall* ⸗e idea
*ein-fallen* occur
*einfältig* simple
*ein-fressen* eat through
*die Einfuhr* hauling in
*der Eingang* ⸗e entrance
*der Eingeborene* –n native
*sich eingefunden* appeared
*eingegossen* poured down
*eingelegt* inlaid
*das Eingemachte* –n preserves
*eingenommen* taken, captivated
*eingeschlagen* taken
*eingeschüchtert* intimidated, overawed
*eingesogen (saugen)* sucked in
*eingetreten* appeared, attendant
*eingezogen* withdrawn, secluded, furled, retiring
*ein-greifen iff iff* interfere
*das Eingreifende* –n incisive nature
*der Einheimische* –n native
*einher-schreiten itt itt* stride forward
*das Einhorn* ⸗er unicorn
*ein-hüllen* wrap up
*ein-kassieren* cash
*ein-kehren* stop off, go in
*ein-leiten* introduce
*einlief* arrived
*einmal: auf* — suddenly
*sich ein-mischen* interfere
*ein-mummen* bundle up

*ein-nehmen* occupy, take up, include, savor
*ein-reden* persuade
*ein-richten* arrange, do, fix up
*einsam* lonely, solitary
*der Einsatz* ⸗e stake
*ein-schärfen* impress
*ein-schenken* pour out
*sich ein-schiffen* embark
*ein-schlagen* take, strike up
*ein-schließen* lock up, include
*ein-schlingen a u* swallow up
*ein-schlügen* struck
*ein-schlummern* fall asleep
*ein-schneien* snow in
*der Einschnitt* –e incision
*ein-schränken* curb, limit
*ein-schüchtern* intimidate
*ein-sehen* understand, realize
*ein-setzen* stake
*die Einsicht* judgment, understanding
*die Einsiedelei* hermitage
*ein-spannen* harness
*der Einspänner* — one horse vehicle
*ein-sperren* lock up
*die Einsprache* objection
*ein-springen* click shut
*einst* once
*ein-stecken* pocket
*das Einstehen* stepping into the breach
*sich ein-stellen* appear
*einstmals* formerly
*ein-stimmen* tune up
*einstweilen* for the present
*ein-tauschen* exchange
*die Eintracht* harmony
*ein-treffen* appear, be realized
*ein-treten* appear, enter
*eintrug* entered, brought in
*ein-üben* practice
*ein-wickeln* wrap up, muffle
*der Einzug* ⸗e entry
*der Eisenschimmel* — iron gray horse
*die Eisenstange* iron pole
*der Eissaum* ⸗e ice edge

die Eisspalte crevasse
das Eistäfelchen little sheet of ice
die Eitelkeit vanity
ekel disgusting
das Elend misery
empfand felt
empfangen receive
die Empfängnis –se conception
empfehlen a o recommend
empfinden a u feel
die Empfindungsfaser sensory fiber
empfunden felt
empor-ragen jut out, stand up
empor-schnellen spring up
emsig eager, zealous
entbehren do without, renounce
entblößen bare, expose
entbunden released
entfärben drain the color from
sich entfernen remove oneself, leave
entfischen fish from
entflammen inflame
die Entführung abduction
entgegengesetzt opposite
sich entgegen-setzen oppose
entgegen-stellen oppose
entgegen-treten confront
sich enthalten control oneself, abstain, refrain from
enthüllen reveal
entkleiden undress
sich entledigen rid oneself
entleeren empty
entnehmen gather
entrann escaped, left
entreißen i i tear from
entrichten pay
entrinnen a o escape
entrissen (reißen) snatched from
entronnen (entrinnen) escaped
entsagen refuse, forfeit, renounce
die Entscheidung decision
entschieden decided
sich entschlagen give up
entschlief fell asleep
entschlummern fall asleep

der Entschluß ⸗e decision, resolve; einen — fassen form a resolve
entsetzlich horrible
entsprechen correspond
entstehen arise, ensue, originate
enttäuschen disappoint
entwaffnen disarm
entwickeln develop, untangle
sich entwölken clear
entziehen withdraw, remove
entzücken delight, enrapture
entzünden light, kindle
entzwei apart, asunder
erbaulich edifying
das Erbe inheritance
erbeben quiver
erben inherit
der Erbfeind –e hereditary foe
erblassen turn pale
erbleicht blanched, pale
erblühen burst into bloom
das Erdgeschoß ground floor
erdolchen stab [to death]
erdulden endure
das Ereignis ⸗se event
die Erfahrung experience
erfassen seize, grasp
erfochten (fechten) won
der Erfolg –e success
erfordern demand
sich erfreuen enjoy
erfrieren o o freeze [to death]
erfroren frozen [to death]
sich ergab yielded, turned out
ergänzend complementary
ergeben devoted
sich erging took a walk
erglänzen shine
das Ergötzen delight
der Erguß ⸗e eruption, outflow
erhaben elevated, prominent, sublime
erhalten maintain, preserve
erhärten harden
erheitern cheer
sich erhellen be lit
sich erhitzen get overheated

*erhoben* elevated

*erhöhen* heighten, increase, raise, elevate

*sich erholen* recover

*erinnerlich sein* remember

*das Erkennen* consciousness, reason

*die Erkenntnis* —se knowledge

*erklecklich* substantial

*erklimmen o o* climb

*erklingen a u* ring

*sich erkundigen* inquire

*erlauern* watch for

*erleben* experience

*erleichtern* facilitate, relieve

*erleichtert* relieved, easier

*erlernen* learn successfully

*erleuchten* illuminate

*das Erliegen* defeat

*erlitten (leiden)* suffered

*erloschen* extinct, extinguished

*ermahnen* exhort, admonish

*die Ermangelung* default, lack

*sich ermannen* encourage oneself, pluck up courage

*die Ermattung* fatigue

*ermessen a e* judge

*ermitteln* ascertain

*ermorden* murder

*ernähren* support

*die Erniedrigung* humiliation

*ernten* harvest

*eröffnen* reveal

*erraten ie a* guess, surmise

*erregen* rouse, stir, excite

*erringen a u* achieve

*erröten* blush

*erschauern* shudder

*die Erscheinung* apparition, phenomenon

*erschlaffen* grow slack

*erschlagen* kill

*erschlichen (schleichen)* obtained by fraud

*erschöpfen* exhaust

*erschrecken* frighten

*die Erschwerung* difficulty

*ersetzen* replace

*ersichtlich* visible

*erspähen* spy out, see, look out for

*ersparen* save, spare

*erstarrt* numbed, rigid

*das Erstaunen* astonishment

*erstieg* climbed

*erstochen (stechen)* stabbed [to death]

*sich erstrecken* stretch, extend

*erteilen* grant

*ertönen* resound

*ertragen* bear, endure

*ertrinken* drown

*erübrigen* save

*die Erwähnung* mention

*sich erwehren* refrain

*erweisen ie ie* show

*der Erwerb* acquisition

*erwidern* return, reply

*erworben (werben)* acquired

*erwünscht* desirable

*erzeugen* engender, produce

*erzielen* achieve

*erzogen* brought up

*erzucken* quiver

*der Erzvater* patriarch

*die Esche* ash tree

*etwa* possibly, perhaps, about

*das Evangelium* Gospel

# F

*die Fackel* torch

*der Faden* ⸗ thread

*fadenscheinig* threadbare

*fahl* pale

*das Fähnchen* — tatter

*die Fahne* flag, head

*das Fahrzeug* —e vehicle, vessel

*fallrecht* perpendicular

*der Fallstrick* -e snare

*die Falte* fold, pleat

*die Familienverfolgung* family persecution

*fand sich ein* appeared

*das Farbenwesen* spectrum

*der Färber* — dyer

*das Faß* ⸗er barrel, keg

*fassen* hold in, grasp, understand, collect; *einen Entschluß* —

form a resolve; *Mut* — pluck up courage; *gefaßt* composed

*fassungslos* disconcerted, distracted

*die Fastnacht* carnival

*die Fastnachtslüge* carnival lie

*fatal* unpleasant

*fauchen* sputter

*die Faust* ≈e fist

*das Federmesser* — pen knife

*feenhaft* fairy like

*das Fehlläuten* misringing

*feierlich* solemn

*feiern* celebrate, be idle

*feindselig* hostile

*feingezackt* finely serrated

*das Felderzeugnis* –se field produce

*der Feldrand* ≈er edge of the field

*die Feldwirtschaft* farm

*das Fenstergesims* –e window ledge

*der Fensterladen* ≈ shutter

*das Fenstersims* –e window sill

*das Fernrohr* –e telescope

*die Fessel* bond

*fest-setzen* fix, establish

*feucht* moist, damp

*fiel über ihn her* threw herself on him

*finster* dark, sinister

*der Firn* –e last year's snow

*der Firnis* –se varnish

*der Firnschrund* ≈e glacial cleft

*der Fittich* –e wing, pinion

*die Fläche* surface

*flackern* flicker

*flankenstark* powerful in their flanks

*flattern* flutter

*der Flaum* down, fluff

*die Flechte* plait [of hair]

*der Fleck* –e spot

*flehen* implore

*flicken* patch

*fliegend* fleeting

*flimmern* glimmer

*das Flittergold* gold tinsel

*das Floß* ≈e raft

*flöße heran (fließen)* flowed towards

*der Flötenbläser* — flute player

*flüchten* rescue, flee; *sich* — take refuge

*der Flüchtling* –e refugee

*der Flügel* — wing, [grand] piano, nostril

*der Flur* –e hall

*die Flur* field

*flüstern* whisper

*folgendermaßen* as follows

*folglich* consequently

*folgsam* obedient

*foltern* torment, torture

*fordern* demand

*die Forelle* trout

*forschen* search

*sich fort-beschäftigen* continue to occupy oneself

*fort-dauern* continue, last

*fortgerissen (reißen)* carried off

*fortlaufend* serial

*fort-schaffen* send away

*der Fortschritt* –e progress

*fortwährend* constant, continuous

*fort-wirken* last

*fransenartig* fringe-like

*die Frechheit* insolence

*frei* open

*das Freibeutertum* piracy

*im Freien* in the open

*freien um* court

*freilich* to be sure

*die Fremdenloge* visitors' box

*der Fremdling* –e stranger

*sich freuen auf* look forward to

*der Frevel* — crime

*der Friedensrichter* — justice of the peace

*fugiert* written in fugue form

*frisch* brisk

*frisiert* arranged, styled (of headdress)

*der Frohsinn* joy

*fromm* pious, religious

*fruchtbar* fertile

*die Frühe: in aller* — very early

das Frühjahr –e spring
fügen add; sich — happen
die Fügung dispensation
fuhr an lashed out
der Fuhrmann, Fuhrleute driver
das Fuhrwerk –e vehicle, baby
carriage
die Fülle fullness
der Funkens –n spark
die Fürbitte intercession
die Furche furrow, rut
der Furchenaufwurf ≈e mound
of earth thrown up by a rut
fürchterlich fearful
furchtsam timid
die Fußstapfe footprint
der Fußtritt –e footstep
füttern feed, line

**G**

gab sich in yielded
die Gabe gift
gäbe ein inspired
gähnen yawn
der Galanteriedegen — dress
sword
das Galion –s –en figurehead
es galt the idea was, it was meant
for; was — what value had
der Gang ≈e passage, walk, corridor, hall, course, sequel,
dance step
ganz und gar wholly
die Garbe sheaf
gären ferment
das Garn –e yarn
der Gastfreund –e host
die Gastfreundschaft hospitality
der Gasthof ≈e inn
das Gastmahl ≈er banquet
die Gattin spouse, wife
die Gaukelei jugglery
das Gazegewand ≈er gauze gown
geädert veined
geängstet frightened
die Gebärde gesture
sich gebärden gesture, bustle
about
das Gebaren behavior

gebenedeit blessed
das Gebet –e prayer
das Gebilde — structure
der Gebirgsbundschuh –e mountain boot
die Gebirgsfußbekleidung mountain footwear
der Gebirgszug ≈e mountain
range
geblümt flowered
geborsten (bersten) burst open
gebräuchlich customary
gebrechlich fragile
gebührend proper, due
das Gebüsch –e bushes
das Gedächtnis –se memory
gedenken plan, think of
das Gedränge — thronging, press
die Geduld patience
gedunsen puffed up, swollen
das Gefährt –e vehicle
der Gefährte –n companion
gefällig pleasant, pleasing, kind
die Gefangenschaft captivity
gefaßt composed, prepared
das Gefilde — field
geflochten (flechten) plaited
gegen . . . hin toward
das Gehänge — slope
geheim secret, mysterious
das Geheul –e howling
sich gehören be proper, be due
der Gehorsam obedience
die Geige violin, fiddle
die Geißel scourge
die Geistesgegenwart presence of
mind
geistlich ecclesiastical
geistreich witty, clever
das Gelächter laughter
das Gelage — banquet
gelagert laid flat
das Gelände — country
das Geländer — railing, balus-
trade
es gelänge (gelingen) it would
succeed
gelangen arrive, attain
das Gelaß –e room

*gelegentlich* occasionally

*geliehen* (*leihen*) loaned

*gellend* shrill

*geloben* vow

*gelten a o* be worth, pass for

*das Gelübde* — vow

*das Gemach* ⸗er chamber

*gemacht* feigned, affected

*der Gemahl* ⸗e spouse, husband

*gemahnen* remind

*gemäß* in accordance with

*das Gemeindehaus* town hall

*der Gemeindemitbruder* fellow parishioner

*das Gemenge* — crowd

*gemessen* (*messen*) measured

*der Gemsewildschütze* –n chamois poacher

*das Gemüt* –er mind, heart, disposition, soul

*genesen a e* recover

*genialisch* of genius, brilliant

*genießen o o* enjoy

*der Genosse* –n associate

*genugsam* sufficient, adequate

*die Genugtuung* satisfaction

*der Genuß* ⸗e enjoyment

*genußsüchtig* greedy for pleasure

*das Gepäck* –e baggage

*gepflogen* (*pflegen*) carried on

*gequollen* (*quellen*) swollen

*geradezu* straight out

*geraten ie a* fall into, get into

*geraten* (*raten*) advised

*geraum* spacious, considerable

*geräumig* spacious

*das Geräusch* –e noise

*der Gerber* — tanner

*gerecht* just

*gereichen* prove to be

*das Gericht* –e court of law

*geriet* (*geraten*) fell into, came

*gering* slight, meager

*gering-achten* slight, disparage

*das Gerippe* — skeleton

*gerissen* (*reißen*) slashed

*gerochen* (*riechen*) smelled

*das Geröll* –e gravel

*der Geröllstrom* ⸗e rock slide

*der Geruch* ⸗e smell

*das Gerücht* –e rumor

*das Gerüst*(*e*) –e scaffolding

*gesandt* (*senden*) sent

*die Gesandtschaft* embassy

*die Geschäftigkeit* business, activity, officiousness

*gescheit* smart

*das Geschenk* –e gift

*die Geschicklichkeit* capacity, skill

*geschickt* apt, alert

*geschieden* separate

*das Geschirr* –e dishes, china, harness

*geschlängelt* serpentine

*das Geschlecht* –er race, sex, family

*geschliffen* (*schleifen*) polished

*der Geschmack* ⸗e taste

*geschmeidig* supple

*geschoben* (*schieben*) pushed, thrust

*gescholten* (*schelten*) scolded

*das Geschöpf* –e creature

*der Geschützdonner* thunder of cannon

*das Geschwader* — squadron

*geschweige denn* let alone, to say nothing of

*geschwind* swift

*sich gesellen* join

*die Gesellenstube* journeyman's room

*gesellig* social

*gesetzt* sedate

*der Gesichtszug* ⸗e feature

*das Gesinde* servants

*das Gesindel* — mob, servants

*gesinnt* minded

*die Gesinnung* sentiment

*gesonnen* (*sinnen*) planned

*das Gespann* –e team

*gespentisch* ghostlike, spectral

*die Gespielin* –nen playmate

*gesprenkelt* speckled

*gestehen* confess

*gestirnt* starry

*gestrig* of yesterday

*das Gesuch* –e request
*gesucht* choice
*der Gesundheitsumstand* =e state of health
*getan* put
*das Getränk* –e drink
*sich getrauen* dare
*das Getreide* — wheat
*getreu* faithful
*das Getriebe* — bustle
*getrost* confidently
*gewahren* observe, perceive
*gewähren* offer, grant, afford
*das Gewand* =er gown
*gewandt* dexterous, adroit
*gewärtigen* wait
*das Gewäsch* –e rubbish
*das Gewerbe* — trade
*der Gewerbsmann* –leute handworker
*die Gewissensqual* torment of conscience
*gewissermaßen* so to speak
*das Gewitter* — storm
*der Gewitterstoff* –e electricity
*gewoben (weben)* woven
*das Gewölb* –e arch, vault, store
*das Gewühl* –e throng
*gewürfelt* checked
*der Giebel* — gable
*die Gier* greed
*giftig* poisonous
*das Gitterfenster* latticed window
*der Glanz* glitter, splendor, radiance, prosperity
*das Gläserkästchen* — china cabinet
*die Glastafel* glass panel
*glatt* smooth, polished
*gläubig* credulous
*gleich wie wenn* as if
*gleichen i i* resemble
*das Gleichgewicht* balance
*gleichgültig* indifferent
*gleichmäßig* even, uniform
*der Gleichmut* equanimity
*das Gleichnis* –se symbol
*gleichsam* as if, as it were, somewhat

*das Gleis* –e track
*der Gletscher* — glacier
*glomm auf (glimmen)* flamed up
*glorreich* glorious
*glückselig* happy, blissful
*glückverheißend* lucky
*die Glut* fire
*die Gnade* grace, favor
*gönnen* grant
*goß (gießen)* poured
*gotisch* Gothic
*der Graben* = ditch
*gradaus* outright
*der Graf* –en Count
*der Gram* grief
*die Granate* pomegranate
*gräßlich* horrible
*der Grat* –e or =e ridge
*das Grauen* horror
*das Grausen* horror
*greis* aged, hoary
*der Griff* –e grasp, stroke, grip
*griff (greifen)* put [his hand]
*griff herum* reached around
*grimmig* furious
*das Grinsen* grin
*grob* coarse
*großartig* magnificent
*großmütig* generous
*großrädrig* with large wheels
*die Grube* pit
*grübeln* brood
*der Grund* =e low place
*grundsätzlich* on principle
*der Grundstock* basis
*das Grundstück* –e property
*gucken* peep, look
*günstig* favorable
*der Günstling* –e favorite
*die Gurke* cucumber
*das Gut* =er estate, good(s), property
*die Güte* goodness, quality
*gutmütig* goodnatured
*der Gutsherr* estate owner

# H

*die Habseligkeit* possession
*die Hacke* axe

*der Hafen* = harbor
*die Haferflocke* rolled oat
*haften* cling to
*der Hagel* hail
*hager* lean, haggard
*der Haken* – hook
*halber* on account of
*der Halm* –e blade
*halsstarrig* stiffnecked
*das Halstuch* =er kerchief
*halten* behave; *sich* — stick to;
— *für* take for
*der Händedruck* handshake
*der Handel* = matter, affair, deal,
quarrel
*der Handelsmann* –leute merchant
*handfest* solid
*handhaben* handle
*die Handlung* ceremony
*der Handstreich* –e trick
*der Handteller* – palm
*der Handwerksbursche* –n journeyman
*der Harm* grief
*der Harnisch* –e armor
*harren* wait
*die Härte* hardness
*das Haselnußgehege* –e grove of
hazelnut bushes
*haspeln* spin
*häßlich* ugly
*die Hast* haste
*der Haufen* – mob
*häufen* pile up
*häufig* often, frequent
*das Haupt* =er head, chief; *zu
Häupten* at the head
*der Hauptbestandteil* –e chief ingredient
*haushälterisch* economical
*der Hausgenosse* –n housemate
*häuslich* domestic
*der Hauswirt* –e landlord
*das Heck* –e stern
*die Heerschar* host
*heften* fix, fasten
*heftig* violent, vehement, impetuous

*hegen* support, nurse
*hehr* sublime
*der Heideboden* = heath soil
*das Heidekraut* =er heather
*heidnisch* heathen
*das Heil* salvation
*der Heiland* –e savior
*der Heilige* –n saint
*das Heiligenbild* –er icon
*der Heiligenschein* –e halo
*heillos* hopeless
*heimlich* secret, mysterious
*heim-suchen* visit
*heißen* be said
*heiter* serene, bright, clear, merry,
happy
*der Held* –en hero
*das Hemmnis* –se block, hindrance
*herabgriff (greifen)* reached
down
*herab-klatschen* splash down
*herab-starren* stare down
*heran-kommen* come up, approach
*herauf-tönen* sound upwards
*heraus-gucken* peep out
*heraus-ragen* jut out
*sich heraus-stellen* turn out,
come to light
*sich heraus-wagen* venture out
*herbei-eilen* hurry up
*herbei-locken* lure, entice
*herbei-schaffen* procure
*die Herberge* inn
*der Herdofen* = stove
*herein-brechen* a o break in, arrive
*herein-gucken* peep in
*herein-schimmern* shine in
*die Herfahrt* journey here
*her-geben* give up, donate
*her-gehen* proceed
*die Herkömmlichkeit* tradition
*sich hernieder-lassen* come down
*heroben* up here
*her-richten* arrange
*die Herrschaften* ladies and gentlemen

*herrschen* reign, command, prevail

*her-rühren* come from

*her-schauen* look toward

*her-schenken* give, donate

*her-setzen* record

*herum-lagern* lie about

*herum-stolzieren* strut about

*herum-streifen* roam about

*herum-trillen* drill, train

*herum-ziehen* wander about

*herunter-klettern* climb down

*hervor-heben* emphasize

*hervor-kriechen o o* crawl forth

*hervor-ragen* stand out, jut out, project

*hervor-stoßen ie o* ejaculate

*hervor-strahlen* radiate

*hervor-tauchen* loom up

*hervor-wandeln* emerge

*herzig* beloved

*der Herzog –e* duke

*hetzen* hunt, chase, pursue

*das Heu* hay

*heuer* this year

*der Hieb –e* blow

*hieb (hauen)* lunged

*hielt an* stopped

*hielt inne* stopped

*hielt sich auf* stayed

*hierauf* then

*ums Himmelswillen* for Heaven's sake

*das Himmelszelt –e* canopy of heaven

*hin* away; — *und her* up and down; — *und wieder* now and again

*hinab-rücken* move down

*hinab-senken* descend

*hinab-stürzen* rush down

*hinan-gleiten* lead on

*hinan-klimmen o o* climb up

*hinauf-fühlen* grope one's way upwards

*hinauf-reichen* extend up

*hinauf-schleppen* drag up

*hinauf-steigern* elevate

*hinauf-tasten* grope one's way up

*hinauf-wallen* rise

*hinaus-kehren* sweep out

*hinaus-schleichen i i* steal out

*hin-bringen* spend

*das Hindernis –se* hindrance

*hin-drehen* turn to

*hinein-geraten ie a* fall into

*hinein-rieseln* trickle in

*hinein-schlüpfen* slip in

*hin-fahren* pass, go on

*hin-fallen* fall down, collapse

*hin-fühlen* feel along

*die Hingabe* surrender, sacrifice, yielding

*hin-geleiten* guide

*hingeworfen (werfen)* casually thrown in

*hin-laufen* run along

*hin-locken* lure there

*hin-reichen* be adequate

*hinreißend* deeply moving

*hin-schreiben* write down

*hinschob (schieben)* pushed over

*hin-sinken* sink down, fall

*sich hin-stellen* take up a position, place oneself

*hin-streichen* stretch out

*hin-stürzen* dash toward, rush

*hintan-setzen* neglect, put behind

*hin-tasten* feel one's way along

*hinterbringen* bring

*hinterher* behind

*das Hinterpförtchen* — little back gate

*hinüber-wechseln* change over

*hinunter-sausen* roar down

*hin-wandeln* walk along

*hinweg-räumen* clear away

*hinzu* up to, in addition

*hinzu-fügen* add

*hitzig* inflamed

*die Hoboe* oboe

*das Hochamt* High Mass

*die Hochebene* high place

*der Hochwald ⸗er* timber forest

*hochzeitlustig* desirous for marriage

*der Hof ⸗e* court, farm

*der Höhepunkt –e* climax

*die Höhle* hollow, cave
*der Hohn* scorn, mockery
*hold* gracious, lovely
*holdselig* gracious, lovely
*die Hölle* hell
*die Holunderstaude* elderberry bush
*das Holz* forest
*der Holzapfel* = crab apple
*hölzern* wooden
*der Holzhauer* — woodcutter
*die Holzhütte* wooden hut
*der Holzknecht* —e lumberman
*die Holztreppe* wooden staircase
*der Holzweg* —e lumber road
*hörbar* audible
*horchen* listen
*die Hüfte* hip
*huldreich* gracious
*hülfe (helfen)* helped, would help
*die Hülle* wrap, envelope
*hüpfen* skip, leap
*huschen* flit by
*husten* cough
*hüten* guard; *sich* — beware
*die Hütte* hut

I

*die Ichsucht* egotism
*ihrerseits* for their part
*ihretwegen* on her account
*immerfort* constantly
*immerhin* still
*immerwährend* constant
*immerzu* always
*imstande* in a position
*die Inbrunst* fervor
*indes[sen]* meanwhile
*infolge* as a result
*der Inhalt* —e content
*inne-haben* possess, hold
*inne-halten* stop, pause
*inne-werden* become aware
*nach innen* inwardly
*das Innere* —n interior, mind, soul
*innewohnend* innate
*innig* fervent, intimate

*innigst* innermost
*insbesondere* especially
*die Inschrift* inscription
*inständig* urgent
*irdisch* earthly
*irr* wild, confused
*irren* stray; *sich* — get lost
*der Irrgänger* — wanderer, venial sinner
*der Irrsal* =e labyrinth, [wandering in a] maze

J

*die Jacht* yacht
*die Jagdbüchse* shotgun
*der Jagdwagen* — dog cart
*der Jäger* — hunter
*die Jahresgeschichte* seasonal story
*der Jahrmarkt* =e annual fair
*das Jammerbild* —er picture of misery
*jammern* lament, cry
*jauchzend* exulting
*je . . . je* the . . . the
*jeglich* each
*jenseitig* far, opposite
*jenseits* beyond
*das Joch* —e yoke, mountain pass
*jubeln* exult, be jubilant
*der Jugendmut* youthful spirit
*der Jünger* — disciple
*die Jungfrau* virgin, maiden
*der Junker* — squire

K

*das Kabinettstück* —e rare piece
*die Kachel* tile
*der Kaffeeabsud* —e coffee concentrate
*der Kaffeeaufguß* =e liquid coffee
*kahl* bare, bleak, bald
*das Kalbfell* —e calfskin
*kam sich vor* seemed to himself
*der Kamin* —e chimney
*die Kammer* bedroom
*der Kanarienkäfig* —e canary cage
*kariert* squared, with squares
*die Karwoche* Holy week

der Kasten = wardrobe
der Kattun -e calico
käuflich purchasable
der Kegel — cone
die Kegelbahn bowling alley
kehren [re]turn; *in sich gekehrt* turned in upon oneself
kehrt machen turn around
keimen germinate
der Kelch -e chalice, cup
das Kellergewölbe — cellar vault
die Kellnerin waitress
keltern press grapes
der Kerl -e fellow
der Kern -e kernel, seed
die Kerze candle
keuchen pant
der Kiesel — pebble
das Kindermädchen — nursemaid
die Kirchweih church fair
die Kiste chest
die Klafter fathom
die Klage lament, complaint
kläglich wretched
die Klammer clamp
klappen bang
die Klapperschlange rattlesnake
klatschen clap, slap, splash
die Klause cell
kleben stick, cling
der Kleiderzipfel — corner of dress
die Kleinigkeit trifle
das Kleinod -ien jewel
klettern climb
die Klingelschnur bell rope
klingend resonant
klirren rattle
klopfen slap, beat
das Klößchen — dumpling
die Kluft =e cleft, fissure
knarren crack, creak
der Knecht -e servant, groom
knicken break
der Knicks -e curtsey
der Knirps -e urchin
knistern crackle
der Knöchel — ankle
die Knolle clump

das Kolleg -s lecture
die Kommode chest of drawers, cupboard
das Können ability
konsternieren cause consternation
der Korb =e basket
das Körperstück -e object
kosen chat
die Kost fare
kostbar precious
kosten taste
köstlich precious
kostspielig expensive
kotig muddy
das Krachen crack
die Krähe crow
die Kralle claw
der Krampf =e cramp
kränkelnd ailing
kränken offend
krankhaft morbid
der Kranz =e wreath
das Kräuterbüschel — cluster of herbs
die Kresse cress
das Kreuz -e cross
kriechen o o crawl, creep
kriegen get
das Krügelchen little jug
sich krümmen writhe
die Krümmung curve, bend, turn
die Küchenschürze kitchen apron
kuck look
kühn bold
der Kummer sorrow, grief, worry
der Kunde -n customer
die Kunde information, news
kundgeworden revealed
der Kundige -n knowing one
künftig future
kunsterfahren aesthetically experienced
das Kunsterzeugnis -se manufactured product
kunstgerecht artistic, professional
das Kunststück -e trick, stunt
die Kuppe knob
vor kurzem a short time ago

*die Kußhand* hand kiss
*der Kutscher* — coachman

## L

*lackieren* lacquer
*die Lade* drawer
*das Lager* — couch, bed, pallet
*lagern* lie, settle; *gelagert* laid flat
*lähmen* paralyze
*lallen* mumble
*der Landbebauer* — farmer
*das Landeswohl* national prosperity
*landläufig* current
*der Landregen* — steady rain
*der Landsmann* –*leute* fellow countryman
*die Landstraße* highway
*der Landstreicher* — tramp
*der Landungssteg* –*e* wharf
*die Landwirtschaft* agriculture, farm
*die Länge* length; *der* — *nach* lengthwise, flat
*langhingestreckt* prostrate
*längs* along
*längsseits* lengthwise
*längst* long ago, for a long time
*die Larve* mask
*die Last* burden, load
*lästern* blaspheme
*die Laterne* lantern
*die Latte* lath
*laublos* leafless
*laulicht* lukewarm
*die Laune* whim, humor
*die Laute* lute
*läuten* ring, sound, peal
*lauter* pure, nothing but
*lautlos* noiseless
*die Lawine* avalanche
*lebensfroh* jovial
*die Lebenslust* high spirits, joie de vivre
*der Lebensunterhalt* means of livelihood
*lebhaft* lively, acute, vigorous, vivid, vivacious

*bei Lebzeiten* during the life
*leck* leaking
*lecken* lick
*lecker* tasty
*der Lederfleck* –*e* scrap of leather
*lediglich* mere, sole
*das Legegeld* –*er* entrance fee
*sich legen* subside
*lehnen* lean
*leichtbeschwingt* light-winged
*leichtfertig* superficial, frivolous
*leichtlich* easily
*der Leichtsinn* frivolity
*die Leidenschaft* passion
*leidig* nasty
*leisten* achieve, perform
*das Leitseil* –*e* reins
*lenken* guide
*die Leuchte* fireplace
*leugnen* deny
*der Leumund* repute
*liebenswürdig* charming, amiable, kind, courteous
*der Liebhaber* — lover
*lieblich* charming, lovely, delightful
*der Liebling* –*e* favorite
*die Liebschaft* amour
*liefern* supply
*lieh (leihen)* borrowed
*ließ nach* let up, abated
*ließ zu* allowed
*die Linde* linden tree
*die List* cunning, stratagem
*der Literat* –*en* literary man
*lobenswürdig* praiseworthy
*der Lobgesang* hymn
*locken* entice
*locker* loose
*die Lockerheit* loose place
*die Lohe* glow, fire
*der Lohn* –*e* reward
*der Lohstampf* –*e* bark crusher
*los-fahren* fly out
*löschen* extinguish
*lösen* loosen, solve
*los-sprechen* release
*das Lüftchen* breeze
*lüften* lift, loosen; *sich* — take

off overthings
*der Luftraum* =e atmosphere
*der Luftzug* =e draught
*lugen* look, peer
*der Lügner* liar
*die Lustbarkeit* entertainment
*lüstern* covetous, lascivious, sensual
*sich lustig machen über* make fun of

# M

*mager* skinny
*die Mahlmühle* grist mill
*mahnen* urge, exhort
*die Mandel* almond
*der Mangel* = lack
*die Mannschaft* company of men
*die Mappe* portfolio
*markieren* mark
*der Marktfleck* -e market spot
*die Marter* torture
*das Maß: über die* –en excessively
*mäßig* moderate
*der Matrose* –n sailor
*matt* faint, dull, weary
*die Matte* mat, meadow
*mattlich* insipid
*das Mauerkästchen* — wall cupboard
*das Meerwunder* — sea monster
*meinen* say
*meinetwegen* on my account
*melden* announce, report
*die Menge* throng
*mengen* mix
*das Menschenalter* — generation
*das Menschengedenken* human memory
*merkwürdig* noticeable, strange, peculiar, remarkable
*die Messe* fair
*das Meßgewand* =er Church vestment
*die Miene* countenance
*mieten* rent
*sich mildern* abate
*mißdeuten* misinterpret
*mißlang (mißlingen)* failed

*das Mißtrauen* distrust
*die Mitgift* dowry
*mithin* therefore
*das Mitleiden* sympathy
*die Mittagsrichtung* southern direction
*mittelmäßig* medium sized
*mittlerweile* meanwhile
*das Moos* –e moss
*morsch* rotten
*das Motorengeräusch* –e noise of the motor
*die Mühe* effort, labor
*die Mühseligkeit* hardship
*die Mulde* hollow
*das Mundbärtchen* — mustache
*munter* gay, lively
*die Münze* coin
*mürbe* soft
*die Muschel* shell
*das Musikbübchen* music boy
*müßig* idle
*der Müßiggang* idleness
*der Mut* spirit, courage
*mutwillig* high-spirited, mischievous
*die Myrte* myrtle

# N

*nach und nach* gradually
*nach-ahmen* imitate
*nach-denken* consider, reflect
*nach-geben* yield
*nach-halten* last
*nach-hängen* cling to, pursue, entertain
*nach-holen* catch up
*nach-kommen* meet, keep up
*nach-lassen* diminish, abate
*die Nachlässigkeit* neglect
*nach-legen* add
*nachsichtig* indulgent
*der Nachtrag* =e epilogue
*nach-winken* make gestures after [someone]
*der Nadelbaum* =e conifer
*nahm sich aus* looked
*nahm sich vor* planned
*nahm um* gathered about him

*die Nahrung* nourishment, profession
*namentlich* especially
*namhaft* considerable
*nämlich* for, in fact, same
*närrisch* silly
*nebenan* nearby
*der Nebenbuhler* — rival
*nebst* beside, together with
*necken* tease
*neidisch* envious
*neigen* bow, incline
*die Neigung* affection
*der Nervenzufall* ⸗e nervous attack
*der Neubau* –ten new building
*neuerdings* again, anew
*die Neugier*[de] curiosity
*nichtsdestoweniger* nevertheless
*nichtig* worthless
*nicken* nod
*niedergeschlagen* downcast
*die Niederlage* defeat
*sich niederließ* sank down
*nieder-schlagen* settle
*niederstach (stechen)* stabbed [to death]
*niedlich* nice, pretty
*noch* nor
*nüchtern* sober, plain, colorless
*nunmehr* now
*die Nuß* ⸗e nut
*der Nutzen* use

## O

*obbenannt* above-named
*das Obdach* shelter
*obendrein* moreover
*oberflächlich* superficial
*oberhalb* above
*oberst* topmost
*die Oberstube* upstairs room
*obertags* on the surface
*der Obstgarten* ⸗ fruit garden
*öde* desolate
*das Ofenrohr* –e stove pipe
*offenbar* obvious
*öffentlich* public
*ohnedem* in any case

*die Ohnmacht* swoon, loss of consciousness
*opfern* sacrifice, give up
*ordentlich* proper, decent, real
*ordinär* common, vulgar
*die Ordnung* order, arrangement; *in der* — right
*die Orgel* organ
*die Ortschaft* place, locality
*das Ostern* Easter
*das Ostufer* — eastern shore

## P

*packen* seize
*der Papagei* –en parrot
*die Pappel* poplar tree
*der Pappkarton* –s cardboard box
*das Parterre* orchestra
*der Passagier* –e passenger
*passieren* pass, happen
*pathetisch* lofty in feeling, emotional
*das Pathos* emotional transport
*der Patron* –e employer, boss
*der Paukenschlag* ⸗e bass drumbeat
*pausbäckig* chubby-cheeked
*die Pein* pain, anguish
*die Peitsche* whip
*der Peitschenknall* –e cracking of a whip
*der Pelz* –e fur
*der Pfad* –e path, way
*das Pfännchen* — little pan
*der Pfarrer* – pastor, clergyman, priest
*der Pfarrhof* ⸗e parsonage
*die Pfauenfeder* peacock's feather
*der Pferdeknecht* –e groom
*das Pfingsten* Whitsuntide, Pentecost
*das Pflaster* — pavement
*pflegen* be accustomed to, care for
*pflichtgemäß* dutiful
*pflichtmäßig* dutiful
*der Pflock* ⸗e peg
*der Pfosten* — post
*der Pilgerstab* ⸗e pilgrim's staff

die *Pinzette* pincette
der or das *Plaid* –s wrap, rug
die *Planke* board fence
die *Platte* slab
*plaudern* chat
*pochen* pound
der *Pöller* — small mortar
*polstern* upholster
*poltern* bluster
*possierlich* comical
die *Post* stagecoach, mail coach
der *Posten* — post, station
das *Posthorn* ≠er stagecoach horn
der *Postwagen* – mail coach
die *Pracht* splendor
*prahlen* brag
*prangend* splendid
*prasseln* rattle
*preisen* ie ie praise, esteem
die *Presse* ironing room
*prickeln* patter
der *Priestertalar* –e priest's robe
die *Prise* pinch of snuff
*probieren* try, test
der *Prokurator* –s –en attorney
*prüfen* test, examine, investigate
die *Prunkstube* best room
*purzeln* tumble
*pusten* puff
der *Putz* decoration, jewelry
*putzen* adorn, deck out; *geputzt* overdressed

## Q

*quaken* quack
die *Qual* torment, torture
der *Qualm* smoke
*quer* straight across

## R

die *Rache* vengeance
*rädern* break on the wheel
*raffen* gather
*ragen* tower, project
*rahmen* frame
der *Rand* ≠er edge, border
das *Ränzchen* — little satchel, paunch

*rasch* swift
*rascheln* rustle
der *Rasen* — turf, grass, lawn
die *Rast* rest, pause; *ohne* — relentlessly
*ratlos* helpless
*ratschlagen* take counsel
*rätselhaft* enigmatic
der *Ratsherr* alderman, councilman
das *Rauchfeuer* smoke signal
die *Rauchsäule* column of smoke
das *Rauchzeug* smokes
*rauh* raw
*räumlich* spatial
der *Rausch* ≠e drunkenness, intoxication
*rauschen* rustle, roar, march noisily
das *Rauschmittel* — stimulant
das *Rebengelände* vineyard country
*recht* real, proper, decent; — *behalten* be right
*rechtfertigen* justify
*rechtlich* righteous, honest, legal
*rechtmäßig* justified
der *Rechtsgelehrte* –n attorney
die *Redensart* phrase
die *Redlichkeit* honesty
*rege* alive, stirring
*regelmäßig* regular
*regieren* control, govern, drive
*reglos* motionless
*regsam* active, stirring
die *Regung* stirring
*reiben* ie ie rub
*reichen* reach, pass
*reichlich* plentiful
der *Reichtum* ≠er wealth
der *Reif* hoarfrost
der *Reifen* — hoop
der *Reigen* — round dance
die *Reihe* turn
der *Reiher* — heron
das *Reiserchen* — twig
*reizbar* susceptible
*reizen* stimulate, irritate, charm, attract

restlos wholly
retten save, rescue
die Reue remorse, regret
das Rezept –e prescription
der Riemen — strap
der Riese –n giant
riesenmäßig gigantic
ringen a u struggle
die Rinne trough, hollow
die Rippe rib
der Ritter — knight
roch (riechen) smelled
das Rohr –e pipe, boot-top
rosa pink
die Röte redness
der Rücken — ridge
der Rückfall ⸗e relapse
der Rückhalt restraint
die Rückkunft ⸗e return
die Rücksicht consideration, deference, respect
der Ruhm fame
ruhmvoll meritorious
die Rundsicht panorama
der Rußfleck –e soot stain
rüsten prepare
rüstig brisk
das Rütchen little rod
rütteln shake

## S

sacht(e) gently
der Sachwalter — attorney
die Sackuhr pocket watch
sägen saw
sah ab realized, saw
sah ein understood
die Saite string, chord
der Sammet or Samt velvet
samt together with
sämtlich all
die Sanftmut gentleness
sann nach (sinnen) reflected
satt satiated: sich — essen eat one's fill; sich — sehen tire of looking; — bekommen get tired
sattsam sufficient
der Satz ⸗e leap

die Säule pillar, column
der Saum ⸗e hem
säumen delay
säuseln rustle
sausen roar
schadenfroh malicious
schadhaft damaged
schädlich harmful
der Schafspelz –e sheep's pelt
die Schale shell, pod
schalkhaft roguish, jesting, jocular
der Schall –e or ⸗e sound
schalt (schelten) scolded
die Scham shame
die Schande shame
die Schar flock, band, troop
die Schattierung shade
schätzen esteem, value, treasure
die Schaubühne stage
der Schauer — horror, shudder, fright
schaukeln sway
der Schaum foam
der Schaumkamm ⸗e crest of foam
der Schauplatz ⸗e spectacle
die Schaustellung exhibit
scheckig spotted
das Scheibengewehr –e target rifle
der Scheideweg –e crossroad
der Schein –e halo
scheinbar apparently
schellen ring
die Schelmerei roguishness
schelten a o scold, condemn
die Schenke bar, taproom
scherzen joke, jest, sport
die Scheu fear, shyness
sich scheuen hesitate
sich scheuern rub clean
die Scheune barn
schicklich proper
das Schicksal –e destiny
schicksallenkend guiding [man's] destiny
der Schieber — clasp
schied (scheiden) parted
schief slanting, low

*schier* almost
*schiffen* sail, navigate
*der Schild* –e shield
*das Schild* –er peak (of a cap)
*schildern* describe
*das Schillern* iridescence
*schimmergrün* with a green shimmer
*schimpfen* scold, complain
*die Schindel* shingle
*schlachten* slaughter
*schlaff* loose, limp, weak
*der Schlafrock* ⸗e dressing gown
*der Schlafwandel* somnambulism
*der Schlag* ⸗e door
*der Schlamm* –e mud
*sich schlängeln* coil, wind
*schlank* slim
*schlechthin* simply, casually
*der Schlegel* — drumstick
*schleichen* i i creep, steal, sneak
*der Schleier* veil
*schleifen* drag, glide
*schleppen* drag
*schleudern* hurl
*schleunig* swift
*schlicht* simple
*schlichten* solve, settle
*schließen* o o conclude
*die Schlinge* snare
*die Schlittenbahn* sledding track
*schluchzen* sob
*der Schluck* –e swallow
*das Schlückchen* — little sip or swallow
*sich schlug* dragged oneself
*schlug auf* opened
*schlug aus* refused
*schlug ein* took (a road)
*schlug um* put about [him], turned
*schlüpfrig* slippery
*schlürfen* sip
*der Schlüsselbund* ⸗e bunch of keys
*die Schmach* shame
*schmecken* taste
*schmeicheln* flatter
*schmuck* trim

*der Schmuck* –e jewelry, adornment
*das Schmuckkästchen* — jewel box
*schnappen* snap
*der Schneeabhang* ⸗e snowy slope
*das Schneegestöber* —snow storm
*die Schneehaube* snow hood
*die Schneelehne* snow-covered slope
*schneuzen* trim; *sich* — blow one's nose
*schnippen* tap
*schnitzen* carve
*schnob* (*schnauben*) snorted, puffed
*schnöde* base, low
*schnupfen* sniff, take snuff
*der Schnupfen* catarrh, head cold
*das Schnupftuch* ⸗er handkerchief
*schnuppern* sniff
*die Schnur* ⸗e rope, cord
*schnüren* lace
*das Schnurrbärtchen* — little mustache
*die Scholle* clod
*schonen* care, spare
*der Schöpfer* — creator
*der Schoß* ⸗e skirt
*der Schotter* gravel
*schräg* oblique
*der Schrecken* fear, fright
*die Schreibkommode* secretary
*das Schreibzeug* writing tools
*der Schritt* –e trot
*der Schrund* ⸗e crevasse
*schüchtern* shy
*der Schulgegenstand* ⸗e school matter
*schützen* protect
*schwanken* totter, swing
*schwärmend* enthusiastic
*schwatzen* prattle
*schweben* hover, float, balance, roar
*schweifen* roam
*der Schweiß* sweat
*die Schwelle* threshold

*schwenken* swing, wave, brandish
*schwerlich* hardly
*schwermütig* melancholy
das *Schwert* —*er* sword
*schwirren* whir, vibrate
*schwören* o o swear
*schwül* sultry, close
die *Schwungfeder* wing
*schwunglos* prosaic
der *Schwur* =*e* oath
*sechseckig* hexagonal
*seelenvoll* soulful
*segeln* sail
*sehnlich* yearning, ardent
die *Sehnsucht* longing, yearning
*seiden* silken
die *Seifenblase* soap bubble
das *Seil* —*e* rope
die *Seilschlinge* rope sling
die *Seinen* his relatives
*seinesgleichen* one's equals
die *Seinigen* his relatives
*selbig* same
die *Selbstüberwindung* self-control
*selbstverständlich* as a matter of course
*selig* blessed, blissful, late [deceased]
die *Semmel* roll
die *Sendung* mission
*senken* lower, let fall
*senkrecht* perpendicular
*seufzen* sigh
die *Sicherheit* security
*sichtlich* obvious
*sieden sott gesotten* boil
die *Sideralpe* Sider meadow
der *Sieg* —*e* victory
*siehe* behold
der *Sinn* —*e* sense, mind, meaning, heart
das *Sinnbild* —*er* symbol
das *Sinnen* thinking, perceiving, feeling
die *Sinnesart* frame of mind
*sinnlich* sensuous, sensual
die *Sitte* custom
die *Sittlichkeit* morality

*sittsam* modest, virtuous
*so . . . auch* however
*sodann* then
*sogenannt* so-called
der *Sohlenabschnitt* —*e* remnant of sole
das *Sommergewand* =*er* summer clothing
*sommersprossig* freckled
*sonderbar* strange
*sonderlich* special
*sonnbeglänzt* sun-flooded
die *Sorgfalt* care
*sowieso* in any case
der *Spalt* —*e* crack, split
die *Spalte* crack, opening
der *Span* =*e* chip of wood
*spannen* stretch, charge, make tense
die *Sparkasse* savings bank
der *Spaß* =*e* fun, joke; *Späße treiben* make fun
*spenden* grant, bestow, give
*sperren* block
der *Spielgeselle* —*n* playmate
*spitz* pointed, acute
die *Spitze* point, head
die *Spitzfindigkeit* subtlety
das *Spitzenjabot* —*s* lace jabot
der *Spor* —*en* spur
der *Spötter* — mocker
der *Sprachgebrauch* [linguistic] usage
der *Sprenkel* — speckle
*sprudeln* gush
*sprühen* spew, spray
der *Sprung* =*e* leap, caper
die *Spur* trace, track
*spüren* feel
der *Stabsoffizier* —*e* staff officer
der *Stachel* — sting, goad
die *Stadtneuigkeit* city news
*stahl* (*stehlen*) stole
der *Stallknecht* —*e* stable boy
das *Stammschloß* =*er* family castle
der *Stand* =*e* position, calling
*standhaft* steadfast
der *Standort* —*e* location

die Stange pole
stark vigorous
die Stärke strength
der Starkmut courage
starr rigid, staring
die Stätte place
statt-finden take place
stattlich stately, elegant, splendid
das Staunen astonishment
stechend stinging, sharp
stecken lie, be latent
der Steg -e [foot]path, way, wharf
das Steigeisen — climbing iron
steigern increase, stimulate
steil steep
steilrecht perpendicular
der Steinbruch ²e quarry
sich stellen behave
stemmen press
der Stengel — stick
stet continual, constant
stetig steady
der Stich -e sting, prick
die Stickerei embroidery
der Stiefel — boot
die Stiege staircase
stieren stare
stieß auf ran into
die Stiftsdame canoness
stimmen tune
die Stimmung mood
der Stirnmuskel — muscle of the forehead
stocken stop, be blocked
das Stockwerk -e story, floor
stöhnen groan
der Stoß ²e push, kick
strafen lügen give the lie, contradict
die Strapaze hardship
der Straßengraben ² ditch
der Straßenrand ²er ditch
der Strauch ²er shrub
streben strive
der Streich -e stroke, act
streicheln stroke, pat
streichen stir, pass, stroke
der Streif -e strip, line

der Streit -e conflict, quarrel, strife
streuen strew
der Strick -e rope
der Strohsack ²e straw bag, pallet
der Strolch -e tramp, vagabond
die Strömung current
der Stümper — bungler
stumpf dull
stünde (stehen) would stand
das Stündlein short while
stürzen fall, hurl, rush
stutzen stop short, start
stützen support
stutzerhaft foppish
summen hum, buzz
der Sünder — sinner
sündigen sin

T

das Taburett -e stool
der Tadel censure
die Tafel meal
an den Tag kommen come to light
der Tagesanbruch daybreak
der Takt -e bar, beat, measure
talabwärts down the valley
die Talkrümme winding of the valley
tändeln dally, play
tanken use as gas
die Tapete wall paper
tapezieren paper
tapfer brave
tappen grope
die Taste piano key
tasten grope, feel one's way
die Tätigkeit activity
tatsächlich factual
tatselig happy in doing
tat weg removed
die Tatze paw
der Tau dew
die Taube dove
tauchen dive, bob, dip
der Taufname baptismal name
taugen be suited
taumeln stumble, stagger

*täuschen* deceive, delude
*teilhaftig sein* possess
*die Teilnahme* interest, sympathy, participation
*der Teppich –e* carpet
*der Teufel* — devil
*tilgen* annihilate
*das Toilettenwerkzeug –e* toilet article
*toll* mad
*tollen* lead a wild life
*der Tölpel* — dolt, dope
*tönen* ring, sound
*der Tor –en* fool
*der Torbogen =* arch, city gate
*die Torheit* folly
*töricht* foolish
*torkeln* stumble, stagger
*der Trab* trot
*die Tracht* dress
*trachten* plan
*tränenvoll* tearful
*das Tränenvergießen* shedding of tears
*der Trank =e* drink
*tränken* water
*trat aus* stamped out
*trat ein* set in
*trauern* mourn
*traulich* cosy
*trefflich* excellent
*treiben ie ie* drive, act, carry on;
*Späße* — make fun
*der Trieb –e* impulse, instinct
*trieb an* whipped up, impelled
*das Trinkgeld –er* tip
*trippeln* trip, skip
*tritt ein* occurs
*die Troddel* tassel
*der Trompetenstoß =e* blare of the trumpet
*der Tropfen* — drop
*der Troß –e* crowd
*der Trost* comfort
*trostlos* sad, forlorn
*trotzen* defy
*trüb(e)* dull, gloomy, dim, muddy
*trübselig* sad, poor

*der Trüffel* truffle
*trug auf* charged
*die Truggestalt* deceptive figure
*die Trümmer* debris
*trunken* intoxicated
*das Tuch =er* cloth, shawl
*tüchtig* real, capable, able, vigorous, efficient, considerable, respectable
*die Tugend* virtue
*die Türkette* door chain
*der Turm =e* tower
*der Turmknopf =e* knob of the tower

## U

*übel nehmen* take amiss
*übel werden* feel ill
*überallher* from everywhere
*die Überanstrengung* overexertion
*überaus* exceedingly
*überbauen* bridge over
*der Überblick –e* overall view
*überdies* moreover, besides
*der Überdruß* surfeit
*überein-stimmen* agree
*der Überfall =e* attack
*überflügeln* outdistance
*übergossen* drenched, suffused
*überhaucht* breathed on
*überhäufen* bury
*überhoben* absolved
*überlegen* consider
*überlegen* superior
*übermannen* overcome
*zum Übermaß* with excessive generosity
*übermütig* spiritedly
*die Überraschung* surprise
*überreden* persuade
*der Überrock =e* overcoat
*überschreiten itt itt* pass, cross over
*die Überschrift* sign
*die Übersicht* perspective
*übersiedeln* move, settle
*übersinnlich* supersensuous, supernatural

*überstehen* survive
*übersteigen* surpass
*überstreuen* strew
*übertragen* transfer
*übertreffen* exceed
*übertreiben* exceed
*überwiegen o o* outweigh
*überwinden a u* overcome
*überzeugen* convince
*überzog* covered
*im übrigen* besides
*übrigens* otherwise, for the rest
*um* after
*umarmen* embrace
*um-bilden* transform
*um-bringen* kill, destroy
*der Umfang =e* circumference, size
*umfangen* embrace
*umfassen* embrace
*die Umgangsformen* manners
*umgarnen* ensnare
*umgeben* surround
*umgebunden* tied around
*um-gehen* haunt, handle
*umgekehrt* converse
*umgetan* put on
*umher-hüpfen* hop about
*umher-irren* wander about
*umhertrieb* pushed about
*sich umher-wälzen* whirl about
*um-kehren* reverse
*die Umkehrung* converse
*umklammern* embrace
*umkrallen* claw
*der Umlauf =e* circulation
*der Umriß –e* shape, outline
*um-schlagen* be reversed
*umschlang (schlingen)* ensnared
*umschloß* enclosed
*umschlug* enveloped
*umschlungen (schlingen)* surrounded
*die Umsicht* prudence, alertness
*umsonst* in vain
*der Umstand =e* circumstance
*umstand* surrounded
*umständlich* elaborate
*um-wandeln* transform

*der Umweg –e* detour
*sich umwenden* turn around
*umwickeln* wrap up
*unabänderlich* invariably
*die Unabhängigkeit* independence
*unablässig* incessant, constant
*die Unablässigkeit* perseverance
*die Unabwendbarkeit* inevitability
*unantastbar* irreproachable
*unauffindbar* unfindable
*unaufhörlich* incessant
*unausgesetzt* constant
*unauslöschlich* inextinguishable
*unbarmherzig* merciless
*unbedenklich* instinctively
*unbedingt* absolutely
*die Unbefangenheit* naturalness
*unbeherrschbar* uncontrollable
*unbeholfen* clumsy
*unbeirrt* unconcerned
*unbenützt* unused
*unbeschreiblich* indescribable
*unbestimmt* indefinite
*unbewacht* unguarded
*unbeweglich* motionless
*unbewegt* unmoved
*unbewußt* unconscious
*unbezweifelt* beyond doubt
*unbezwinglich* unconquerable
*der Undank* ingratitude
*undeutlich* indistinct
*undurchdringlich* impenetrable
*undurchsichtig* opaque
*die Unebenheit* uneven ground
*uneigennützig* unselfish
*uneingedenk* heedless
*unentbehrlich* indispensable
*unentgeltlich* gratis
*unentschlossen* indecisively
*unerbittlich* inexorable
*unergründlich* unfathomable
*unermeßlich* boundless
*unersättlich* insatiable
*unerschüttert* unshaken
*unerträglich* unbearable
*unfehlbar* inevitably
*ungeachtet* irrespective

*ungefüge* ungainly
*ungeheuer* enormous, immense, monstrous
*ungelenk* clumsy
*ungelichtet* impenetrable
*die Ungeschicklichkeit* awkwardness
*ungeschlacht* crude
*ungenügsam* inadequate, dissatisfied
*ungeschminkt* without make-up
*ungestört* undisturbed
*ungestüm* impetuous, violent
*ungleichmäßig* uneven
*die Unglücksäule* accident pillar or column
*die Ungnade* displeasure
*das Unheil* misfortune
*unheimlich* uncanny
*unlängst* not long ago
*unmittelbar* direct
*unmutvoll* peevish
*unregelmäßig* irregular
*die Unruhe* disquiet, uneasiness, restlessness
*unsäglich* unspeakable
*unschicklich* improper
*unschlüssig* undecided
*unselig* unhappy
*unsersgleichen* the like of us
*unsichtbar* invisible
*die Unsterblichkeit* immortality
*untadlig* blameless
*untätig* inactive
*unter* common
*unterbrechen* interrupt
*unterdessen* meanwhile
*unterdrücken* suppress
*untereinander* among themselves
*der Untergang* ⸗e destruction
*unterhalb* below
*unterhalten* entertain, converse
*die Unterhandlung* negotiation
*das Unterholz* undergrowth
*unterirdisch* subterranean
*das Unterkommen* shelter, place, employment
*die Unterlage* basis
*der Unterleib* ⸗er abdomen

*unterscheiden ie ie* distinguish
*unterst* lowest
*die Untersuchung* examination
*unterzeichnen* sign
*untröstlich* disconsolate
*unverdorben* (*verderben*) unspoiled
*unverhohlen* unconcealed
*unverkennbar* unmistakable
*unverletzt* unbroken
*unvermeidlich* unavoidable
*unvermerkt* unconsciously
*unvermittelt* directly, abruptly
*unversehens* inadvertently, unexpectedly
*unversehrt* intact
*unverständlich* unintelligible, confused
*unverwandt* fixedly
*unverweilt* at once
*unverwüstlich* imperturbable
*unwillkürlich* involuntary
*unwirsch* roughly
*unwürdig* unworthy
*üppig* luxurious
*das Urbild* ⸗er archetype
*der Urgroßvater* great grandfather
*der Urlaub* furlough
*urplötzlich* very suddenly
*der Ursprung* ⸗e origin
*der Urzustand* ⸗e primitive state

### V

*verabreden* agree upon, [pre] arrange
*sich verabschieden* take leave
*verachten* despise, hold in contempt
*veranstalten* bring about, arrange
*der Verband* ⸗e wrapping
*verbarg* (*bergen*) concealed
*die Verbesserlichkeit* perfection
*verbindlich* courteous, obliging
*die Verbindung* binding, union
*sich verbitten* decline, disallow
*verbleichen* blanch
*verblühen* fade

*verborgen (bergen)* hidden, secret
*verbrämen* edge
*verbrauchen* use up
*das Verbrechen* — crime
*der Verdacht* suspicion
*die Verdammnis* damnation
*verdarb (verderben)* spoiled, corrupted
*das Verdeck –e* deck
*das Verderben* destruction, ruin
*verderbt* corrupt
*verdienen* earn, deserve
*der Verdienst –e* gain, pay
*das Verdienst* merit
*verdrießlich* annoyed, discontented
*der Verdruß* annoyance
*sich verdüstern* turn dark
*verdutzt* puzzled
*verehren* admire, respect, revere
*die Vereinigung* union
*verenden* perish
*verewigen* perpetuate
*das Verfahren* procedure
*verfertigen* finish
*verfiel* fell
*verfolgen* pursue, persecute
*sich verfügen* go
*eine Verfügung treffen* gain control
*verführen* seduce
*vergänglich* transitory
*vergeblich* in vain
*vergebens* in vain
*das Vergehen* misdemeanor
*vergüten* make good
*verhallen* die away
*verhalten* hold back; *sich —* behave
*das Verhältnis* relationship
*verhängen* impose
*das Verhängnis –se* fate
*verhängt* obscured, hanging
*verharren* persevere
*verheißen* promise
*verhext* bewitched
*sich verhielt* kept

*verhöhnen* ridicule, mock
*verhüllen* conceal
*verhungern* starve [to death]
*sich verirren* lose one's way
*die Verirrung* aberration
*der Verkehr* communication
*verkehren* navigate
*verklären* transfigure
*die Verkleidung* costume
*sich verkühlen* catch cold
*verkünden* announce, promulgate
*verkündigen* proclaim
*das Verlangen* desire, yearning
*verlassen* abandon
*der Verlauf ∸e* course
*verleben* spend
*verlegen* embarrassed, confused
*verleiten* lead astray
*verletzen* hurt, wound
*verliebt* enamored, amorous
*verlieh (leihen)* imparted, bestowed
*verloben* engage
*verlöschen* extinguish
*der Verlust –e* loss
*die Vermählung* marriage
*vermeiden ie ie* avoid
*vermöge* because of
*das Vermögen* — fortune, wealth
*vermögen* be able
*vermuten* surmise
*vernachlässigen* neglect
*vernagelt* stupid
*vernehmen* hear, perceive
*die Vernunft* reason
*verödet* desolate
*die Verpflichtung* obligation
*verprassen* squander
*der Verräter* — traitor, betrayer
*verreisen* take a trip
*verrichten* do, accomplish
*die Verrichtung* arrangement, deal
*sich verringern* decrease
*verrückt* insane
*versagen* fail, deny
*versah* provided; *— sich* anticipated, looked ahead

versammeln assemble, gather
versäumen fail, neglect
verschaffen procure
verschenken give away, present
verscheuchen frighten away
verschieben o o postpone
die Verschiebung dislocation
der Verschlag ⸗e shed, locker
verschlucken swallow
verschmähen scorn
verschmerzen heal
verschoben (schieben) postponed, out of place
verschränken fold
verschüchtert intimidated
verschulden incur guilt
verschwiegen discreet, silent, taciturn
verschworen (schwören) sworn, conspiring
versehen provide
versenden send away
versetzen transplant, throw, reply
versiegeln seal up
versöhnen reconcile
verspätet belated
versperren bolt, fasten
versprochen promised
verspüren feel
sich verständigen come to an understanding
verstatten permit
verstecken hide
verstimmt out of humor
verstohlen stealthily
verstört disturbed
der Verstoß ⸗e faux pas
verstoßen ie o cast out, offend
sich versündigen commit blasphemy, sin
versunken sunk
vertauschen change
verteidigen defend
verteilen divide, share
vertieft engrossed
das Vertrauen trust, confidence
vertraulich confidential, intimate
vertraut familiar
verursachen cause

vervollkommnen perfect
verwachsen become overgrown
verwahren guard, preserve, protect
verwahrlost wild, abandoned
verwandeln transform
verwandt applied, related
verwaschen faded
verweilen remain, delay, linger
verweisen expel
verwenden employ
verwickeln involve
verwirren confuse
der Verwunschene –n man under a curse
verwünscht cursed
verzagen despair, be despondent
verzehren consume
der Verzicht –e renunciation
verziehen distort, twist, spoil
verzieren adorn, decorate
verzweifelt in despair
das Vieh cattle
vielmehr rather
das Viereck –e square
der Vierspänner — carriage with four horses
vollbracht completed
vollenden complete, perfect, accomplish
vollkommen perfect, completed
die Vollstreckung execution
vonnöten haben need
vor allem above all, preeminently
vor sich hin to himself; aside
voraus ahead; im — in advance
vorausgefahren preceding
vor-beugen bend forward
vorderhand for the present
vorderst front
die Voreingenommenheit preoccupation
vorerst first, at this point
der Vorfall ⸗e event, incident
sich vorfand was
der Vorgang ⸗e action
vor-geben pretend
das Vorgefallene –n what has occurred

*das* Vorgefühl *–e* premonition
*vor-gehen* occur
*vorgenommen* proposed
*vorgeschlagen* proposed
*vorgeschoben* (*schieben*) protruding
*vor-haben* intend, plan, be engaged in
*vorhanden* extant, at hand, in existence
*der* Vorhang *=e* curtain, drape
*vorher* formerly, before
*vorig* former, last
*vor-kommen* occur, seem
*vorlag* was present
*vorläufig* for the present, preliminary
*vor-legen* serve, push forward
*die* Vorliebe preference
*der* Vorname first name
*vornehm* distinguished, elegant
*der* Vorrat *=e* supply, stock
*die* Vorrichtung equipment
*vor-rücken* advance
*der* Vorsatz *=e* plan
*zum* Vorschein *kommen* appear
*das* Vorschreiten progress
*die* Vorschrift prescription
*der* Vorschlag *=e* proposal
Vorschub *leisten* promote, advance
*sich* vor-sehen prepare
*die* Vorsicht caution
*der* Vorsprung *=e* projection
*vorstehend* projecting
*vor-stellen* represent; *etwas —* be important; *sich —* imagine
*die* Vorstellung conception, representation, image
*der* Vorteil *–e* advantage
*vortrefflich* excellent
*vortrug* presented
*sich* vor-wagen venture forth
*der* Vorwand *=e* pretext
*vorweg-stehlen a o* steal from under one's very nose
*der* Vorwurf *=e* reproach
*vorzeiten* long ago

*der* Vorzug *=e* advantage, excellence

# W

*waagerecht* horizontal
*wacker* good
*die* Waffe weapon
*wagen* dare, risk
*der* Wahnsinn madness, frenzy, insanity
*wähnen* think
*wahren* preserve
*wahrhaftig* true, actual
*wahrheitsgetreu* truthful, exact
*wahr-nehmen* perceive
*der* Waldbestand *=e* stand of trees
*die* Waldblöße clearing
*die* Wälderlast forest mass
*die* Walkmühle fulling mill
*das* Walkwerk *–e* fulling mill
*der* Wall *=e* rampart
*wallen* flow
*walten* prevail
*der* Wandel way of life, course
*wandeln* stroll, change
*die* Wandlung change
*wandte* (*wenden*) turned
*wanken* stagger, waver
*das* Wappen — coat of arms
*ward =* wurde
*das* Warengewölbe — salesroom
*das* Warenlager — assortment of goods
*was auch* whatever
*die* Wäsche linen
*die* Wasserfrau nymph
*der* Wassergraben *=* water ditch
*der* Wasserspiegel surface of the water
*waten* wade
*der* Wechsel — check
*weg-schmelzen o o* melt away
*der* Wegweiser — guide
*das* Wehen wafting, blowing, fluttering
*wehmütig* sad, melancholy
*wehrlos* helpless, defenseless
*das* Weibergut *=er* dowry

*weichen i i* retreat, withdraw, recede, yield
*die Weide* pasture, willow
*der Weidegrund ⸗e* pasture land
*die Weihe* consecration
*weilen* dwell
*die Weise* tune, air
*weisen ie ie* show, point
*die Weissagung* prophecy
*weiten* expand
*jedes weitere* everything else
*weiterhin* further
*weithin* extremely, really, far off
*weitläufig* rambling
*der Wellenringel* — wave ringlet
*die Welteroberung* world conquest
*wenn auch* even if
*wenden* turn
*wenngleich* though
*wennschon* though
*werben a o [um]* court
*der Werg* cotton waste
*das Werk ⸗e* factory
*die Werkstätte* workshop
*wertgeschätzt* esteemed
*das Wesen* being, essence, character, nature, creature, manner, air
*weswegen* on which account
*der Wettstreit* competition
*wich aus (weichen)* avoided
*wich zurück* receded, retreated
*wickeln* wrap
*widerprallend* resilient
*widerraten ie a* dissuade
*sich widersetzen* object
*widerspiegeln* reflect, mirror
*der Widerspruch ⸗e* contradiction
*der Widerstand* resistance
*widerstreben* resist
*widmen* dedicate
*wie* as though
*wieder-erlangen* regain
*wiederum = wieder*
*wiegen* sway
*wiehern* neigh, whinny
*die Wiese* meadow

*wies nach (weisen)* proved
*die Wimper* eyelash
*sich winden a u* writhe
*die Windfahne* weather vane
*die Windung* winding, turn
*der Winkel* — corner, angle
*winken* motion, beckon, wave, make signs
*winzig* tiny
*der Wipfel* — tree top
*wirken* produce, take effect
*wirr* confused
*der Wirrwarr* confusion
*der Wirtssaal –säle* drawing room
*die Wirtsstube* taproom
*wohlbehalten* intact
*wohlgebildet* of fine culture
*das Wohlgefallen* pleasure
*wohlgefüttert* well fed
*wohlgepolstert* well upholstered
*wohlhabend* prosperous
*der Wohllaut* euphony
*die Wohltat* comfort, benefit, benevolence
*das Wohlwollen* benevolence
*wohnlich* comfortable
*der Wolkenstreifen* — cloud strip
*die Wölbung* vaulting
*die Wollust* voluptuousness, sensuality
*wühlen* stir
*wund* sore, smarting
*wunderlich* strange
*die Würde* worth, dignity
*würfeln* throw dice
*die Wurzel* root
*würzen* spice
*wüst* desolate
*die Wut* rage, fury

## Z

*die Zacke* jagged point
*zaghaft* hesitating, timid
*der Zähler* — integer
*das Zäpfchen* — little cone
*sich zanken* quarrel
*zartkörnig* of delicate grain

der Zauber magic
die Zeche bill
die Zehrung food
zeichnen sketch; sich — stand out
sich zeigen show off
zeitlebens all one's life
zeitlich earthly, temporal
der Zeitvertreib –e pastime
die Zelle cell
zerfallen at odds
zerfloß melted
zerrütten shake up
zerstören destroy
zerstreuen scatter, amuse, distract
zerzupfen pull to shreds
das Zeug –e thing, silverware
das Zeugnis –se testimony
ziehen cultivate
das Ziel –e goal, aim
sich ziemen be fitting
der Zierat decoration
zieren adorn, decorate
zierlich pretty, dainty, graceful, elegant
das Zimmergewahrsam keeping to one's room
zimperlich fastidious
die Zipfelhaube peaked bonnet
zog vor preferred
zögern hesitate
der Zoll =e toll, tribute
die Zubereitung preparation
die Zucht discipline
zucken quiver, tremble
zu-denken intend
zudringlich importunate
sich zu-eignen appropriate
der Zufall =e chance, accident
zu-fallen fall to
zufolge in consequence
der Zug =e feature, trait, draught
zugänglich accessible
zu-geben admit
zugebracht spent
zugegen present
das Zugehör appurtenance
der Zügel — rein

zugeschoben (schieben) pushed toward
zu-gestehen concede
sich zugetragen happened
zugleich concurrently
die Zugluft draught
zugrunde gehen be destroyed or ruined
zugunsten in favor of
der Zugvogel ≟ migratory bird
der Zuhörer auditor
zu-kommen be due
zu-lassen permit
zumal especially as
zunächst first of all, nearest, very close
die Zuneigung inclination
zu-nicken nod to
zurecht-legen straighten out
zu-reden urge
zürnen be angry
zurück-führen reduce
zurückgestrichen stroked back
zurückgewiesen (weisen) rejected
die Zurückhaltung self-control, restraint
zurück-legen cover
zusammen-fahren jump, start
zusammengeschoben (schieben) compressed
zusammengekauert crouching
zusammen-klingen a u harmonize
zusammen-laufen cooperate
zusammen-raffen snatch together
zusammen-richten fix up, prepare
zusammen-schmieden forge
zusammen-schrecken schrak o start, be startled
zusammen-sparen scrape together by saving
zusammen-treffen meet together
zusammen-zucken start
der Zusatz =e addition
der Zuschauer — spectator
zu-sehen look on
zusehends perceptibly
zu-setzen add
zu-sprechen admonish
der Zustand =e condition

*zu-stopfen* cork
*die Zutat* addition
*zuteil werden* receive, be granted, realize
*zu-trauen* grant, credit, trust, confide
*zuverlässig* trustworthy
*zuvorkommend* courteously
*zuwege bringen* produce
*der Zwang* force, compulsion

*zwanglos* naturally
*zweckdienlich* purposeful
*zweigleisig* with two ruts or tracks
*das Zwielicht* twilight
*der Zwischenakt* –e entr'acte
*die Zwischenpause* interval
*der Zwischenraum* =e interstice
*zwitschern* twitter